Instruction

STAMS

Strategies

To

Achieve

Mathematics

Success

CA101®
Online e-training
Use this product right away, the right way!
Online e-training at **CAtraining.com**

Curriculum Associates

Teacher Advisors

Anita Carter, Middle School Math Specialist
Fort Worth Independent School District
Fort Worth, Texas

Jennifer Chintala, Mathematics Specialist
East Rutherford School District
East Rutherford, New Jersey

Michelle Davis, Grade 5 Teacher
Washington Street School
Rockingham, North Carolina

Lisa B. Golub, Curriculum Resource Teacher
  and Math Coach
Millennia Elementary School
Orlando, Florida

Aggie Harrison, Grade 3 Teacher
Garden Elementary School
Sarasota County School District
Venice, Florida

Karen Kjar, Teacher Specialist
Carpenter Elementary School
Downey Unified School District
Downey, California

Scott Pearson, Special Education Math Trainer
6–12 Assessment Center Staff
Rosemount Independent School District 196
Rosemount, Minnesota

Janeen D. Shaw, Grade 4 Teacher
Daniel E. Morgan School
Cleveland Metropolitan School District
Cleveland, Ohio

Mary-Anne Sheppard, Math Coach
MS/HS 368-IN-Tech Academy
NYC District 10
Bronx, New York

Acknowledgments

Editorial Project Managers
Joan Krensky, Books C–D
Mary Ellen Osowski, Books E–F
Kathy Kellman, Books G–H

Designers
Cover: Matt Pollock
Book: Pat Lucas

Table of Contents

LESSON PLANS

Number and Operations

		CCSS

Fractions

Decimals

Algebra

ADDITIONAL LESSON PLANS

ADDITIONAL SCHOOL-HOME CONNECTIONS *(Reproducibles)*

The classroom math intervention program integrates assessment, data-driven instruction, and meaningful practice. The program focuses on the foundational math skills students must master in preparation for the Common Core State Standards. These are the critical math concepts and skills that students need to advance to the next grade level. *CAMS®*, *STAMS®*, and *STAMS® Solve® Series* work together effectively to ensure that your students gain a solid understanding of the key math concepts and skills. This knowledge will ultimately help them become independent problem solvers and succeed on high-stakes state tests.

Features

Data-driven instruction with a pretest, a post test, and benchmarks
(see page 8)

Emphasis on errors as opportunities for learning
(see pages 19 and 23)

Highly scaffolded lessons with gradual release of responsibility
(see pages 14–25)

Embedded professional development in supportive easy-to-use teacher guide
(see pages 14–25)

Interactive Whiteboard Lessons to enhance instruction
(see pages 11 and 15)

Books A–H
(Grades 1–8)

Assessment

Use the *CAMS® Assessment Series* to gather information for targeting instruction and measuring progress.

Books A–H
(Grades 1–8)

Instruction

Use the *STAMS® Instruction Series*, with Interactive Whiteboard Lessons, for in-depth teaching of the 16 concepts and skills to help students succeed at grade level.

Books C–H
(Grades 3–8)

Practice & Application

Use the *STAMS® Solve® Practice Series* for meaningful practice and application.

Assessment with CAMS® Series

Quickly identify which of the 16 foundational math concepts and skills your students find most difficult and use the results to monitor progress. These concepts and skills must be mastered for success with the Common Core State Standards.

- A pretest diagnoses students' strengths and weaknesses and guides their placement in the *STAMS® Instruction Series*.
- Four benchmarks assess class progress throughout the year.
- A post test assesses students' mastery of concepts and skills following instruction with the *STAMS® Series*.
- Tracking forms and charts facilitate data collection and student self-assessment encourages reflection.

Instruction with STAMS® Series

Provide struggling students with explicit instruction of the 16 foundational math concepts and skills—those topics identified as the most important instructional goals for each grade level.

- Five-part lessons are highly visual, engaging, and clearly presented.
- Three levels of scaffolding include:
  1. *Scaffolded student support* that gradually builds student independence
  2. *Scaffolded student accountability* that requires students to use increasing degrees of higher-level thinking to analyze and explain their answers to practice problems
  3. *Scaffolded problem-solving experience* with practice problems that increase in difficulty to build student proficiency and confidence.
- Step-by-step support helps teachers easily differentiate instruction and minimize planning time.
- Modeling helps teachers introduce each skill simply and confidently.
- Useful tips and embedded professional development guide instruction.

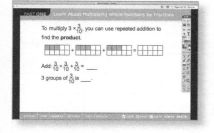

Interactive Whiteboard Lessons (Grades 3–8)

Preview lessons or review previous lessons from any level and use manipulable models to enhance instruction.

Practice and Application with STAMS® Solve® Series

Give students the practice they need to master the 16 foundational math concepts and skills. The *Solve® Practice Series* focuses on both conceptual understanding and computational fluency.

- A variety of multiple-choice, short-response, and extended-response problems.
- In each part, problems require increasing levels of higher-order thinking.
- Cumulative reviews tie related concepts together.
- Supportive teacher guides include answer analysis and make it easy to assign, correct, and review.

Implementing STAMS® with CAMS® and Solve®

Option 1: Data-Driven Instruction

1 Diagnose with CAMS® Pretest

- Use the *CAMS*® Pretest to place students in the *STAMS*® Series. Results identify which *STAMS*® lessons and corresponding *Solve*® practices students need.

2 Instruct with STAMS® Lessons

- Pinpoint a specific lesson in the *STAMS*® student book to remediate an area that needs improvement.

3 Reinforce with Solve® Practices

- Assign the corresponding practice in the *Solve*® student book to provide reinforcement for the *STAMS*® lesson you just taught. The practice has the same number and title as the lesson.

4 Monitor Progress with CAMS® Benchmarks

- Assess progress in all 16 foundational topics with the four 16-item *CAMS*® Benchmarks at four points during the year.

5 Assess Mastery with CAMS® Post Test

- Use the *CAMS*® Post Test to assess students' mastery of the 16 math concepts and skills following instruction with *STAMS*® and practice with *Solve*®.

Option 2: Comprehensive Instruction

For implementation of *CAMS*® and all 16 *STAMS*® lessons and the corresponding *Solve*® practices, follow this suggested pacing chart. Allocate 21 weeks, with each *STAMS*® lesson spanning 5 days and the related *Solve*® practice being completed simultaneously. (See the Week at a Glance on page 10 for more details.)

Suggested Pacing Chart

Day(s)	Lesson and Practice	STAMS® Instruction and Solve® Practice	CAMS® Assessment	Time (Minutes)
1–5		*CAMS*® Pretest		30–45/day
6–10	1	Multiply Whole Numbers by Fractions		30–45/day
11–15	2	Multiply Fractions		30–45/day
16–20	3	Divide Whole Numbers by Fractions		30–45/day
21–25	4	Divide Fractions by Fractions		30–45/day
26–27		*Solve*® Reviews 1–2		15/day
28			*CAMS*® Benchmark 1	30–45/day
29–33	5	Multiply and Divide by Powers of Ten		30–45/day
34–38	6	Multiply Decimals		30–45/day
39–43	7	Divide Decimals by Whole Numbers		30–45/day
44–48	8	Divide by Decimals		30–45/day
49–50		*Solve*® Reviews 3–4		15/day
51			*CAMS*® Benchmark 2	30–45/day
52–56	9	Understand Ratios		30–45/day
57–61	10	Understand Percent		30–45/day
62–66	11	Unit Rates		30–45/day
67–71	12	Ratios in Tables of Data		30–45/day
72–73		*Solve*® Reviews 5–6		15/day
74			*CAMS*® Benchmark 3	30–45/day
75–79	13	Solve Equations Using Number Sense		30–45/day
80–84	14	Solve Equations Using Inverse Operations		30–45/day
85–89	15	Use Formulas		30–45/day
90–94	16	Volume		30–45/day
95–96		*Solve*® Reviews 7–8		15/day
97			*CAMS*® Benchmark 4	30–45/day
98–102		*CAMS*® Post Test		30–45/day

Note: Allocate 15 minutes more per day if *STAMS*® additional activities are used in conjunction with each lesson and practice.

CAMS® and STAMS® *Grade-Level Foundational Skills*

All 16 concepts and skills covered in each level of the *STAMS® Series* align to NCTM Focal Points and Connections for that grade. Lesson topics have been carefully sequenced so students move from basic skills to more complex content within each grade and between grades as well. Building and reinforcing these foundational math skills will prepare students for the rigorous Common Core State Standards. (See Correlation Charts on page 31.)

Additional lessons included to address Common Core State Standards. *See Table of Contents.*

The focus of the *STAMS® Series* progresses from number sense and computational skills in early grades to pre-algebra in later grades.

Book A (Grade 1)
Understand Addition and Subtraction
Fact Families
Make Tens to Add and Subtract
Solve Word Problems
Add Three Numbers
Count to 120
Place Value
Compare Numbers
Add and Subtract Tens
Add 2-Digit Numbers
Subtract Tens
Shapes
Equal Parts
Length
Time
Data

Book B (Grade 2)
Counting Patterns
Place Value
Compare Numbers
Mental Math
Addition Strategies
Subtraction Strategies
Solve Word Problems
Add and Subtract to 1,000
Arrays
Equal Parts of Shapes
Length
Add and Subtract Length
Time
Money
Data and Line Plots
Graphs

Book C (Grade 3)
Place Value
Add and Subtract
Multiplication Concepts
Fact Strategies
More Fact Strategies
Division Concepts
Fact Families
Fraction Concepts
Model Equivalent Fractions
Benchmark Fractions
Compare Fractions
Fractions Greater Than 1
Plane Figures
Length
Perimeter
Pictographs and Bar Graphs

Book D (Grade 4)
Multiplication Properties
Multiply Mentally
Multiply by 1-Digit Numbers
Multiply by 2-Digit Numbers
Relate Division to Multiplication
Divide Without Regrouping
Divide with Regrouping
Equivalent Fractions
Simplify Fractions
Decimal Place Value
Compare and Order Decimals
Relate Decimals to Fractions
Angles
Understand Area
Area of Rectangles
Line Plots

Book E (Grade 5)
Multiply 3-Digit Numbers
Divide Mentally
Estimate Quotients
1-Digit Divisors
Zeros in the Quotient
2-Digit Divisors
Understand Mixed Numbers
Add and Subtract Like Fractions
Compare Unlike Fractions
Add and Subtract Unlike Fractions
Add and Subtract Mixed Numbers
Add and Subtract Decimals
Area
Surface Area
Understand Volume
Line Graphs

Book F (Grade 6)
Multiply Whole Numbers by Fractions
Multiply Fractions
Divide Whole Numbers by Fractions
Divide Fractions by Fractions
Multiply and Divide by Powers of Ten
Multiply Decimals
Divide Decimals by Whole Numbers
Divide by Decimals
Understand Ratios
Understand Percent
Unit Rates
Ratios in Tables of Data
Solve Equations Using Number Sense
Solve Equations Using Inverse Operations
Use Formulas
Volume

Book G (Grade 7)
Understand Integers
Add and Subtract Integers
Multiply and Divide Integers
Evaluate Expressions
Solve Linear Equations
Equations with Rational Numbers
Proportional Relationships
Solve Proportions
Rate Problems
Percent as a Ratio
Percent Problems
Similarity
Circles
Cylinders
Circle Graphs
Theoretical Probability

Book H (Grade 8)
Exponents
Square Roots
Solve Two-Step Equations
Two-Step Equations with Rational Numbers
Linear and Nonlinear Equations
Slope
Graph Linear Equations
Solve Systems Graphically
Solve Systems Algebraically
Special Pairs of Angles
Angle Sums
Triangle Similarity
Pythagorean Theorem
Distance Formula
Mean, Median, Range
Scatter Plots

STAMS® Instruction Overview

Each level of the *STAMS® Series* has 16 interrelated lessons designed to help students build mathematical competency. Emphasizing depth over breadth, each five-day, five-part lesson targets two closely-related aspects of a single concept or skill. Highly scaffolded lessons offer gradual release of responsibility from the teacher to the student. Part One and Part Two introduce the skill with modeled and guided instruction. Part Three and Part Four (modeled and guided practice) and Part Five (independent practice) have students work with growing accountability for their learning as they practice and apply the skills taught.

STAMS® lessons are optimally designed to be used in conjunction with the *CAMS®* assessments and *Solve®* practices, as described on page 9. However, teachers have found that the built-in flexibility also makes *STAMS®* lessons perfect for a variety of other uses.

Alternative Implementations

Other scenarios for using the *STAMS®* lessons with your class include the following:

Whole Group (at grade level)

State test review—Use the *STAMS®* lessons as a review for the entire class. The 16 weeks of lessons allow you to finish well before your state test date.

Small Group (at or below grade level)

Reteaching support—Use the *STAMS®* lessons with small groups to reteach skills that students are still struggling to master. See pages 12–13 for more information.

Individual (at or below grade level)

Tutoring or independent work—As you become aware of specific gaps in a student's background knowledge, assign the corresponding *STAMS®* lesson.

> **Tip:** *STAMS®* lessons are best used with teacher guidance, as students learn best when they are directed by knowledgeable, supportive teachers. However, the student book lessons are written to be inviting and accessible even to struggling students. If you do assign *STAMS®* lessons as independent class work, be sure to circulate and monitor students as they work.

Week at a Glance
Suggested Lesson Pacing

	Monday	Tuesday
	modeled and guided instruction	
	Part One	**Part Two**
Direct instruction	Introduce new skill with student book pages. **20 minutes**	Introduce new skill with student book pages. **20 minutes**
Interactive Whiteboard (IWB) *(optional)*	Use IWB Lesson in place of Part One in student book.	Use IWB Lesson in place of Part Two in student book.
Independent work Your Turn	Practice new skill. **10 minutes**	Practice new skill. **10 minutes**
Assessment ✓	Check *Your Turn* answer.	Check *Your Turn* answer.
Additional Activity *(optional)*	*Hands-on Activity* **15 minutes**	*Reteaching Activity* **15 minutes**

To download your
Interactive Whiteboard Lessons
and a User Guide, go to
CurriculumAssociates.com/STAMS/IWB.

Use the password STAMSIWB
to access your grade-level lessons.
Promethean software is required to present
these lessons. A free download of ActivInspire
Personal Edition is available at
http://support.prometheanplanet.com.

Wednesday	Thursday	Friday
modeled and guided practice		independent practice
Part Three	Part Four	Part Five
Model multiple-choice problem; analyze answers. **10 minutes** Review Parts One and Two as necessary.	Model extended-response problem. **10 minutes** Review Parts One and Two as necessary.	
Practice solving multiple-choice problems. **20 minutes**	Practice solving extended-response problem. **20 minutes**	Solve problems in test-prep format. **30 minutes**
Check *Your Turn* answers.	Check *Your Turn* answer.	Check *Your Turn* answers. Use *Assessment and Remediation.* **15 minutes**
Vocabulary Activity **15 minutes**	*Real-World Connection* plus *School-Home Connection* **15 minutes**	*Challenge Activity* **15 minutes**

Additional Instruction

Interactive Whiteboard (IWB) Lessons

Interactive Whiteboard Lessons are available for each lesson in Books C–H. The IWB Lessons offer students opportunities to question and explore mathematical concepts in greater depth.

- IWB Lessons can be used to supplement instruction in Part One and Part Two of each lesson.
- IWB Lessons can also recap and review previous lessons from any level before beginning instruction.
- Features, such as cloning and dragging objects, and whiteboard tools, such as highlighters, keep students actively engaged in learning.
- Teacher notes lead you through the modeled and guided instruction to maximize each lesson's instructional impact.
- For additional Interactive Whiteboard tips, see page 15.

Additional Common Core Lessons

The Common Core State Standards for Mathematics presents some math concepts and skills at different grade levels than the NCTM Focal Points and state standards have recommended. To address that discrepancy in grade-level content and anticipated differences in schools' timelines for implementing the Common Core State Standards (CCSS), the *STAMS® Series* offers Additional Lessons at the back of each book, C–G.

- Additional Lessons for CCSS are organized and labeled in the same topic groupings as the 16 foundational grade-level lessons.
- Refer to the Table of Contents for when to use each Additional Lesson. (Or you may wish to postpone those lessons until later in the year, after your state assessments are completed.)

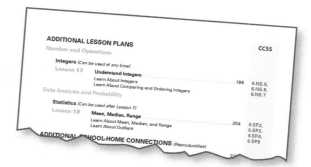

Using STAMS® Lesson Features for Differentiation

STAMS® lessons support several approaches to differentiated instruction. Work with small groups or individuals as needed by taking advantage of these lesson features.

For ELL students

- For any students who struggle with the language of math, preview math vocabulary (see page 15).

- Throughout the instruction, refer to *ELL Support* tips that alert you to potential language obstacles.

- Use the *Vocabulary Activity* to help students tie new math terms to words they already understand.

For struggling students

- Use the *Hands-on Activity, Reteaching Activity,* and *Real-World Connection* to give students other ways to access the skill.

- Review concepts visually with Interactive Whiteboard Lessons.

For confident students

- Provide students an opportunity to extend their understanding of the concepts in the lesson with the *Challenge Activity*.

Knowing how and when to differentiate

Effective differentiation is based on identifying where students are struggling. The ongoing assessment features help you stay informed about student progress.

- Observe student work with *Your Turn* on a daily basis to see which students are off track.

- Use *Error Alerts* to help recognize and correct common mistakes and misconceptions as soon as they surface.

- Use Assessment and Remediation to identify misconceptions or gaps in understanding at any point in the lesson. The activities listed can provide individual or small-group remediation (see page 23).

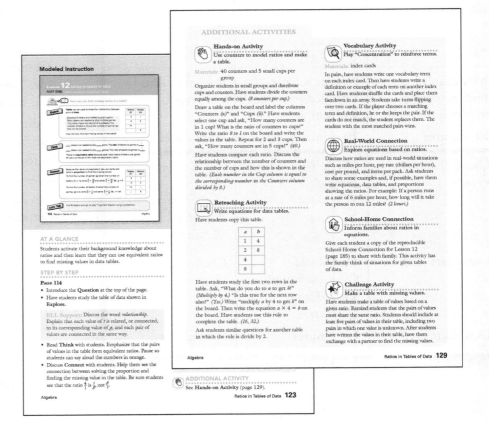

Using Related STAMS® Lessons to Remediate

STAMS® lessons are sequenced within each grade, and from grade to grade, to make instruction easy at the appropriate level. For any particular topic, use the Related *STAMS®* Lessons feature in the teacher guide to find a lesson, from the same grade level or from an earlier grade, that meets the student's needs.

Review within the grade level (Books A–H)

- If a student isn't succeeding with a lesson, your first resource is reviewing prerequisite skills in related lessons in the same book. In most cases these skills were taught in an earlier lesson.
- A careful review of Part One and Part Two of Related *STAMS®* Lessons can help a student quickly get back on track.

Review at a lower grade level (Books B–H)

- Sometimes lessons cover prerequisite skills from a previous grade's book.
- Again, a review of Part One and Part Two of Related *STAMS®* Lessons can help a student quickly get back on track.
- A student who frequently needs to review material from a previous level may need consistent instruction at that level before that student can succeed in the core program at grade level.
- Consider administering the *CAMS®* Pretest from the previous level. These results will help you place the student more appropriately.

> To review skills from related lessons, you might:
>
> - Use the corresponding Interactive Whiteboard Lessons and review only Part One and Part Two.
>
> - Use the appropriate student book lesson and work with the student through either Part One and Part Two, or all five parts.

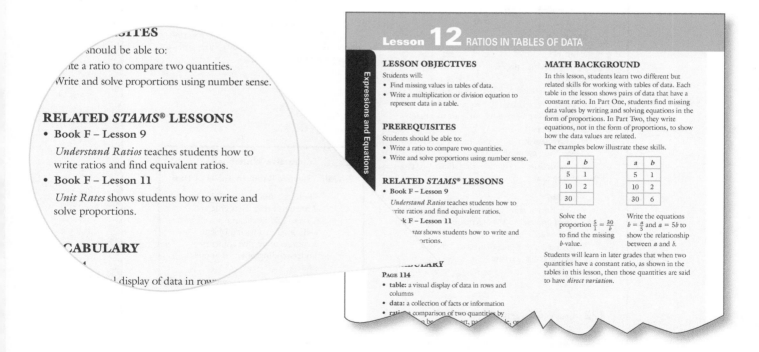

...ITES

...should be able to:
...te a ratio to compare two quantities.
...Write and solve proportions using number sense.

RELATED *STAMS®* LESSONS

- Book F – Lesson 9

  Understand Ratios teaches students how to write ratios and find equivalent ratios.
- Book F – Lesson 11

  Unit Rates shows students how to write and solve proportions.

...CABULARY

...l display of data in row...

Lesson 12 RATIOS IN TABLES OF DATA

Expressions and Equations

LESSON OBJECTIVES

Students will:
- Find missing values in tables of data.
- Write a multiplication or division equation to represent data in a table.

PREREQUISITES

Students should be able to:
- Write a ratio to compare two quantities.
- Write and solve proportions using number sense.

RELATED *STAMS®* LESSONS
- Book F – Lesson 9

  Understand Ratios teaches students how to write ratios and find equivalent ratios.

- ...k F – Lesson 11

  ...*tes* shows students how to write and ...ortions.

...ULARY

PAGE 114

- **table:** a visual display of data in rows and columns
- **data:** a collection of facts or information
- **rati...** a comparison of two quantities by...

MATH BACKGROUND

In this lesson, students learn two different but related skills for working with tables of data. Each table in the lesson shows pairs of data that have a constant ratio. In Part One, students find missing data values by writing and solving equations in the form of proportions. In Part Two, they write equations, not in the form of proportions, to show how the data values are related.

The examples below illustrate these skills.

a	b
5	1
10	2
30	

a	b
5	1
10	2
30	6

Solve the proportion $\frac{5}{1} = \frac{30}{b}$ to find the missing b-value.

Write the equations $b = \frac{a}{5}$ and $a = 5b$ to show the relationship between a and b.

Students will learn in later grades that when two quantities have a constant ratio, as shown in the tables in this lesson, then those quantities are said to have *direct variation*.

This 12-page section guides teachers through a sample lesson plan from the *STAMS®* teacher guide, which shows facsimiles of the student book lesson. Numbered boxes call out and describe the key features in both the teacher guide and student book.

INTRODUCTION

Lesson 12 RATIOS IN TABLES OF DATA

ssions and Equations

① LESSON OBJECTIVES

Students will:
- Find missing values in tables of data.
- Write a multiplication or division equation to represent data in a table.

② PREREQUISITES

Students should be able to:
- Write a ratio to compare two quantities.
- Write and solve proportions using number sense.

③ RELATED *STAMS®* LESSONS

- Book F – Lesson 9

  Understand Ratios teaches students how to write ratios and find equivalent ratios.
- Book F – Lesson 11

  Unit Rates shows students how to write and solve proportions.

④ VOCABULARY

PAGE 114

- **table:** a visual display of data in rows and columns
- **data:** a collection of facts or information
- **ratio:** a comparison of two quantities by division; can be part to part, part to whole, or whole to part
- **equivalent ratios:** two or more ratios that are equal to one another
- **proportion:** an equation that shows two ratios are equivalent

PAGE 116

- **equation:** a number sentence that contains an equal sign and shows two quantities have the same value
- **pattern:** a set of data values that share a common relationship

⑤ MATH BACKGROUND

In this lesson, students learn two different but related skills for working with tables of data. Each table in the lesson shows pairs of data that have a constant ratio. In Part One, students find missing data values by writing and solving equations in the form of proportions. In Part Two, they write equations, not in the form of proportions, to show how the data values are related.

The examples below illustrate these skills.

a	b
5	1
10	2
30	

a	b
5	1
10	2
30	6

Solve the proportion $\frac{5}{1} = \frac{30}{b}$ to find the missing b-value.

Write the equations $b = \frac{a}{5}$ and $a = 5b$ to show the relationship between a and b.

Students will learn in later grades that when two quantities have a constant ratio, as shown in the tables in this lesson, then those quantities are said to have *direct variation*.

⑥

Interactive Whiteboard

Visualize Ratios in Tables of Data

Go to the *Interactive Whiteboard Lessons* to bring Parts One and Two to life. Use features such as sliding screens with problem solutions to deepen students' understanding of ratios in tables of data.

122 Ratios in Tables of Data

Algebra

1 **Lesson Objectives:** Identifies skills-related goals for students.

2 **Prerequisites:** Lists critical concepts/skills required for success with the lesson.

3 **Related *STAMS*® Lessons:** Identifies precursor lessons that lay the foundation for the concepts/skills students are about to learn.

4 **Vocabulary:** Lists key math terms from the lesson, with definitions.

5 **Math Background:** Supports teacher understanding of why the lesson content is important for students to learn.

6 **Interactive Whiteboard:** Enhances instruction by turning the lesson into an engaging and visual experience.

Tips for using the Interactive Whiteboard Lessons:

- Click on and preview the teacher notes before teaching the lesson. Print out these notes for easy reference.

- Introduce the skills taught in Part One and Part Two with the Interactive Whiteboard Lessons. Have students follow along in their books so they will know where to find explanations and examples they may need to review later.

- Use the Interactive Whiteboard Lessons as a quick recap before Part Three and Part Four.

- Access Interactive Whiteboard Lessons from previous levels to quickly review topics in Related *STAMS*® Lessons.

- Encourage student participation. Allow plenty of time for students to use the interactive whiteboard features to work out problems.

- Rename, save, and print out the work done on the interactive whiteboard to share with students.

> To download the Interactive Whiteboard Lessons and a User Guide, go to *CurriculumAssociates.com/STAMS/IWB*. Use the password STAMSIWB.

Best Practices

Math Vocabulary

Knowledge of math terminology is critical to students' understanding of new concepts and skills. To master math vocabulary, students must see and use the words in context frequently, both orally and in writing.

- As students encounter new terms in text, model the correct pronunciation of each word and have students repeat the word.

- Model the correct use of math terms as you present each lesson.

- Suggest that students highlight or underline new vocabulary as they encounter it.

- Ask students to state or write the definition in their own words and/or use the word in context.

- Encourage students to use math terms whenever they are communicating their ideas about math.

Part One and Part Two have identical formats and features.

PART TWO

Modeled Instruction

Guided Instruction

1

Lesson 12 RATIOS IN TABLES OF DATA

PART ONE: Learn About Completing Tables

How can you find missing values in a table?

Explain | Tables can be used to show the relationship between pairs of data.

Suppose 4 tokens are needed to play a game. More tokens are needed to play multiple games. This table shows the relationship between the number of tokens (t) and the number of games (g) that can be played.

How can you find the missing values in the table?

Tokens (t)	Games (g)
4	1
8	2
16	
	6

2

Think | __4__ tokens are needed to play __1__ game. The ratio of tokens to games is $\frac{4}{1}$.
__8__ tokens are needed to play __2__ games. The ratio of tokens to games is $\frac{8}{2}$.

These are **equivalent ratios** because each ratio means 4 tokens per game. All pairs of values in this table are equivalent ratios.

Connect | Because the ratios are equivalent, you can write and solve **a proportion** to find the missing values.
To find the number of games (g) when the number of tokens (t) is 16, write $\frac{4}{1} = \frac{16}{g}$ and solve: $\frac{4}{1} = \frac{16}{g}$. So, g = 4.
To find the number of tokens (t) when the number of games (g) is 6, write $\frac{4}{1} = \frac{t}{6}$ and solve: $\frac{4}{1} = \frac{t}{6}$. So, t = 24.

Tokens (t)	Games (g)
4	1
8	2
16	4
24	6

3

Let's Talk | Are 40 tokens enough to play 11 games? Explain using a proportion.

114 Ratios in Tables of Data

Algebra

4

Think It Through

Fill in the blanks as you solve the problem.

Kayla is baking muffins for a bake sale. The table shows the relationship between the number of muffins (m) and the number of tins (t) she uses.

Kayla bakes 4 tins of muffins. Each tin holds the same number of muffins. How many muffins did Kayla bake?

Muffins (m)	Tins (t)
6	1
12	2
24	4
36	6

■ __6__ muffins are baked with 1 tin. The ratio of muffins to tins is $\frac{6}{1}$.

__12__ muffins are baked with 2 tins. The ratio of muffins to tins is $\frac{12}{2}$.

Each ratio means __6__ muffins per tin.

■ Find the number of muffins (m) when the number of tins (t) is 4. Write and solve a proportion.

$\frac{6}{1} = \frac{m}{4}$ $\frac{6}{1} = \frac{24}{4}$

So, m = __24__.

Solution: Kayla baked __24__ muffins in 4 tins.

Proportions can only be used when ratios are equivalent.

5

Your Turn | Now, use what you know to solve this problem.

1. A coach separates players into teams, each with the same number of players. Find the missing value in the table to find the number of teams if there are 30 players.

Teams (t)	Players (p)
1	5
3	15
4	20
6	30

$\frac{3}{15} = \frac{t}{30}$

When p = 30, t = __6__.

__6__ teams = 30 players

Algebra

Ratios in Tables of Data 115

---

6 **AT A GLANCE**

Students activate their background knowledge about ratios and then learn that they can use equivalent ratios to find missing values in data tables.

7 **STEP BY STEP**

PAGE 114

- Introduce the **Question** at the top of the page.
- Have students study the table of data shown in **Explore**.

ELL Support: Discuss the word *relationship*. Explain that each value of *t* is related, or connected, to its corresponding value of *g*, and each pair of values are connected in the same way.

8

- Read **Think** with students. Emphasize that the pairs of values in the table form equivalent ratios. Pause so students can say aloud the numbers in orange.
- Discuss **Connect** with students. Help them see the connection between solving the proportion and finding the missing value in the table. Be sure students see that the ratio $\frac{4}{1}$ is $\frac{t}{g}$, not $\frac{g}{t}$.

Algebra

9 **Tip:** Explain to students that not all tables show the same ratio in all rows. Give some examples and have students identify which show the same ratio.

- Organize students in pairs or groups for **Let's Talk** and monitor their discussions.
- Be sure students understand that 40 tokens is not enough because solving the proportion shows that for 11 games 44 tokens are needed.

PAGE 115

- Read the **Think It Through** problem with students.
- Guide students as they solve the problem. Help them write and solve a proportion to find the missing value.
- Show that multiplying the numerator and denominator by the same number results in an equivalent ratio.
- Monitor students as they complete **Your Turn**. Then discuss the correct answer.

10 **Error Alert:** Students who gave an answer of t = 5 wrote the number that each *t*-value is multiplied by.

ADDITIONAL ACTIVITY

See **Hands-on Activity** (page 129).

Ratios in Tables of Data **123**

Divide both sides of the equation by the same number to isolate the variable.
$a \div b \times 3$
$\frac{a}{3} = \frac{b \times 3}{3}$

	Bunches (b)
a	1
16	2
32	4
48	6

n Tables of Data 117

r **Let's Talk**

irs of values
hat students
nd which is

with students.
m. Pause as
iscuss each

write both

r Turn.

r × 8
ariables.

9).

124 Ratios in Tables of Data

Algebra

Features of a STAMS® Lesson

Student Book

1 **Focus Question:** Sets a purpose for student learning. Gets students thinking about the answer arrived at through Explore/Think/Connect.

2 **Explore/Think/Connect:** Provide students with a proven routine to apply to all math problems. **Explore** activates students' prior knowledge and introduces the concept/skill. **Think** presents leading questions or statements to get students thinking about the concept/skill. **Connect** answers the focus question.

3 **Let's Talk:** Develops students' ability to communicate effectively about math through an engaging peer-learning activity.

4 **Think It Through:** Walks students through the thinking process for solving an example problem.

5 **Your Turn:** Reinforces instruction with independent practice.

Teacher Guide

6 **At a Glance:** Sums up what students do in each lesson part.

7 **Step by Step:** Provides an explicit walk-through of the steps for guiding students through each lesson part.

8 **ELL Support:** Targets at point-of-use a language issue that may be affecting English language learners' ability to understand the math.

9 **Tip:** Provides on-the-spot information the teacher can use to build students' understanding of the concept/skill.

10 **Error Alert:** Addresses common errors or misconceptions that lead students to an incorrect answer.

Modeled & Guided Instruction

Teacher Led

After prompting students to tap into their prior knowledge, the teacher uses step-by-step examples to model the new concept/skill and guide instruction.

Best Practices

Think-Aloud

The ability to verbalize mathematical thinking and strategies to others strengthens conceptual understanding and problem-solving skills.

- To foster effective discussion, plan carefully when grouping students for Let's Talk. Consider skill levels, social skills, and English language proficiency.

- Circulate and provide tips or encouragement as students work together to discuss math ideas. Guide the discussion as needed.

- During Think It Through, allow students to work in pairs or groups and talk aloud as they follow the steps to solve the problem.

PART THREE

Modeled Practice   **Guided Practice**

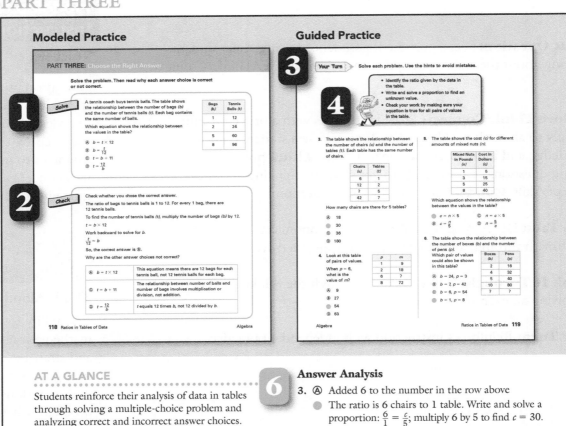

AT A GLANCE

Students reinforce their analysis of data in tables through solving a multiple-choice problem and analyzing correct and incorrect answer choices.

STEP BY STEP

PAGE 118

- Tell students that this page models finding the correct answer to a multiple-choice problem.
- Have students read the problem in **Solve** and choose the best answer. Remind students to check their math.
- Examine **Check** with students. Discuss the correct and incorrect choices.

PAGE 119

- Monitor students as they complete **Your Turn**.
- Organize students in pairs or small groups and have them discuss why each answer choice is correct or not and what errors may have been made.
- Review the answers with the class.

5 ADDITIONAL ACTIVITY

See **Vocabulary Activity** (page 129).

Algebra

6 Answer Analysis

3. Ⓐ Added 6 to the number in the row above

● The ratio is 6 chairs to 1 table. Write and solve a proportion: $\frac{6}{1} = \frac{c}{5}$; multiply 6 by 5 to find $c = 30$.

Ⓒ Subtracted 6 from the number in the row below

Ⓓ Set up the proportion incorrectly

4. Ⓐ Chose the number of mugs per pack

Ⓑ Added 9 to the number in the row above

● The ratio of p to m is 1 to 9. Write and solve a proportion: $\frac{1}{9} = \frac{6}{m}$; multiply 9 by 6 to find $m = 54$.

Ⓓ Subtracted 9 from the number in the row below

5. ● The cost per pound is $5. Multiply number of pounds by 5 to get the total cost.

Ⓑ Confused multiplication and division

Ⓒ Reversed the variables

Ⓓ Flipped the numerator and denominator

6. Ⓐ Reversed the variables

Ⓑ Thought values of b were multiplied by 6

Ⓒ Thought values of b were multiplied by 9

● The ratio of b to p is 1 to 8.

Ratios in Tables of Data **125**

Features of a *STAMS®* Lesson

Student Book

1 **Solve:** Presents a typical multiple-choice problem related to the concept/skill for students to solve.

2 **Check:** Explains the correct answer and analyzes the incorrect answers by pointing out common errors or misconceptions.

3 **Your Turn:** Provides four multiple-choice practice problems to be solved independently.

4 **Calculator Man:** Offers students helpful hints to avoid making common mistakes.

Teacher Guide

5 **Additional Activity:** References a specific activity, described in detail at the end of the lesson plan, that supports instruction.

6 **Answer Analysis:** Explains why an answer is correct and identifies the types of errors students commonly make in choosing incorrect answer choices.

Tips for using errors as opportunities for learning:

- Use the explanations for how students arrive at incorrect answers to understand why a concept might be difficult for a particular student and how to help.

- Have students cover the bottom half of the page with a sheet of paper before they try to solve the problem. Then have them uncover the page and self-check their answers.

- Challenge students to try to figure out why their answers might be incorrect without looking at the reasons listed.

- Encourage students to be reflective, to think about the error they made and understand why it led to an incorrect answer.

- Point out to students that they can use this same type of thinking whenever they have corrected math papers returned to them.

Modeled & Guided Practice

Teacher Supported

Students work through a sample multiple-choice problem. Then the teacher and students discuss and analyze both correct and incorrect answer choices.

Best Practices

Scaffolded Instruction

Scaffolded instruction provides the learning support struggling students need and gradually leads them toward independent learning.

- Let accuracy of student responses and your observations of student behavior guide your decisions about withdrawing instruction.

- Provide additional modeling and guidance for students who show they do not yet understand a math concept/skill.

- Provide immediate and specific feedback to each student response. Make sure students fully comprehend why an answer is correct and why the other answer choices are incorrect.

PART FOUR

Modeled Practice

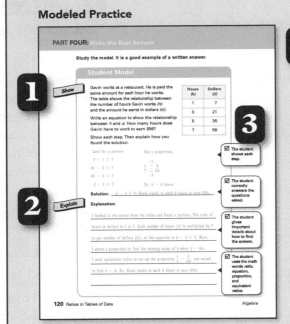

Guided Practice

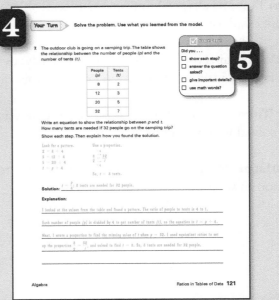

AT A GLANCE

Students study a model answer to an extended-response problem.

STEP BY STEP

PAGE 120

- Tell students that this page models building the solution to a problem one step at a time and writing explain the solution.

- Have students read the problem in **Show**. Discuss how the ratio of the data values and each mathematical step lead to the solution.

> **6** Tip: The problems in this lesson can all be solved by either using a proportion or by finding a pattern to write an equation. Suggest that students use both methods to check their work.

- Read **Explain** with students. Have students circle the math words in the explanation.

- Direct students' attention to the notes in the right margin. Tell students that this model would receive a high score for the reasons described in these notes.

126 Ratios in Tables of Data

Algebra

PAGE 121

- Monitor students as they complete **Your Turn**.
- Encourage students to follow the **Checklist** to write the best answer.
- Have students discuss their work with a partner. Then discuss the correct answer as a class.

7 **Answer and Explanation**

7. See the sample answer. This answer shows all of the steps taken to solve the problem, including writing an equation and setting up a proportion. The solution answers the question. The explanation provides important details about how the problem was solved and uses the math words *ratio*, *equation*, *proportion*, and *equivalent ratio*.

Also accept the equation $p = 4 \times t$ as a correct answer.

ADDITIONAL ACTIVITY
See **Real-World Connection** (page 129).

ADDITIONAL ACTIVITY
See **School-Home Connection** (page 129).

Student Book

1 **Show:** Models an exemplary response to an extended-response problem by showing each step leading to the solution.

2 **Explain:** Models an explanation of the process used to solve the problem.

3 **Sidebar Notes:** Point out the features of the response that make it a high-scoring answer.

4 **Your Turn:** Gives students practice expressing their mathematical thinking in writing.

5 **Checklist:** Provides students with an easy-to-use guide for writing the best response.

Teacher Guide

6 **Tip:** Explains an important feature of the student model in more detail.

7 **Answer and Explanation:** Provides a sample response for the extended-response problem and guidance about evaluating students' responses.

Tip for helping students with extended-response problems:

Provide students with your district or state rubric for extended-response problems so they can practice evaluating their own or one another's responses. Alternatively, use the following rubric:

4 points	The answer is correct, and all the steps are shown. The explanation uses math terms to describe all the steps for how to solve the problem and to tell why the solution is right.
3 points	The answer may have a small mistake, but most of the steps are shown. The explanation uses most math terms correctly. It explains most of how to solve the problem and a little bit of why the solution is right.
2 points	The answer is wrong, but some steps are right. Many math terms are used incorrectly, but some parts of the solution process are explained correctly.
1 point	There is an answer, but it is incorrect and it leaves out most of the steps or does not match the question in the problem. The explanation is not clear.
0 points	There is no answer and no explanation.

Modeled & Guided Practice

Teacher Supported

With teacher guidance, students read and analyze a model answer to a sample extended-response problem. Then students answer a similar problem using the model as a guide.

Best Practices

Differentiating Instruction for ELL Students

Support for English language learners is critical to students' success in mastering new mathematical concepts at the same time as they are acquiring a new language.

- Tap into students' background experiences and present mathematical concepts in the context of the students' home cultures or in contexts such as sports, entertainment, or games.

- As students learn new math vocabulary, encourage them to identify cognates from their own language, such as solution/solución.

- Use concrete materials, physical gestures, and visuals whenever possible to demonstrate concepts.

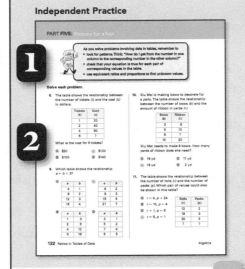

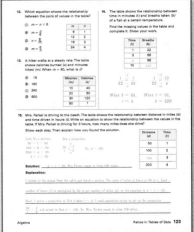

AT A GLANCE

Students practice using data in tables and ratios to solve problems that might appear on a mathematics test.

STEP BY STEP

find ... t = 10, write and ...
Multiply 22 by 10 to find *b* = 220.

Also accept the equation *t = n ÷ 50* as a correct answer.

Answers and Explanations

8. © The ratio of tickets to cost is 1 to 20. Write and solve a proportion: $\frac{1}{20} = \frac{6}{c}$; multiply 20 by 6 to find *c* = 120.

9. © For the table to have equation $a = b \times 3$, the ratio of *a* to *b* must be 3 to 1, for all pairs of ... and *b*. 6 to 2, 9 to 3, 15 to 5, and 21 to 7 are ... ratios equivalent to 3 to 1.

... he ratio of bows to ribbon is 3 to 6, or 1 to 2. ... rite and solve a proportion: $\frac{1}{2} = \frac{8}{r}$; multiply 2 ... 8 to find *r* = 16.

... he ratio of rolls to packs is 12 to 2, or 6 to 1. ... , *r* = 6 and *p* = 1 satisfies the relationship ... own in the table.

... he ratio of *m* to *n* is 6 to 1. So, to get *m* you ... multiply *n* by 6: $m = n \times 6$.

... he ratio of *c* to *m* is 40 to 10 or 4 to 1. Write ... d solve a proportion: $\frac{4}{1} = \frac{c}{60}$; multiply 4 by ... 0 to find *c* = 240.

(continued on page 128)

Ratios in Tables of Data **127**

✔ ASSESSMENT AND REMEDIATION

- Ask students to write an equation to show the relationship between the values in this table. Then have them find the missing value. ($d = t \times 7$ or $t = \frac{d}{7}$; 56)
- For students who are still struggling, use the chart below to guide remediation.
- After providing remediation, check students' understanding. Ask students to explain their thinking while writing an equation and finding the missing value for this table. ($f = 3 \times y$ or $y = \frac{f}{3}$; 30)
- If a student is still having difficulty, use *STAMS Book F*, Lesson 9, pages 84–93.

Distance (*d*)	Time (*t*)
7	1
21	3
28	4
?	8

Yards (*y*)	Feet (*f*)
1	3
2	6
4	12
10	?

If the error is ...	Students may ...	To remediate ...
writing an equation of $t = d \times 7$ or $d = \frac{t}{7}$	have reversed the variables.	Encourage students to describe the relationship in words before writing an equation. (Each value of *d* is 7 times the corresponding value of *t*.)
writing an equation of $d = t + 6$	have written an equation that only works for the first pair of data values	Encourage students to always get in the habit of checking their work. Here, they should substitute *all* given pairs of values from the table into their equation to verify that the equation is true.
a missing value of 32	have added 7 to the number in the row above it.	Explain that if the numbers in the second column were 1, 2, 3, and 4, students *could* simply find multiples of 7 for the first column. However, the numbers in the second column do *not* increase by 1, so you need to consider each pair independently of the others.
some other missing value	have difficulty with basic multiplication facts.	Have students review basic multiplication and division facts by drawing arrays, skip counting, or using flash cards with a partner.

⭐ ADDITIONAL ACTIVITY

For students who have mastered the skills in this lesson, see **Challenge Activity** (page 129).

128 Ratios in Tables of Data

Algebra

Student Book

1 **Calculator Man:** Presents hints for solving the kinds of problems related to the lesson concepts/skills that students are likely to encounter on tests.

2 **Test-Prep Practice:** Builds familiarity with the three types of problems commonly found on state and national tests: multiple-choice, short-response, and extended-response. Practice with these test-type problems will help put students at ease on test day.

Teacher Guide

1 **Answers and Explanations:** Gives brief explanations for correct answers as a starting point for discussion between the teacher and students.

2 **Assessment:** Provides a brief assessment of students' progress.

3 **Remediation:** Shows in chart form how to evaluate students' responses to the assessment and offer remediation.

Tips for using Assessment and Remediation:

- Use this assessment and remediation process at any point in the lesson after instruction of Part Two.

- Use with individual students, small groups, or the whole class. The fewer students you assess at one time, the more precisely you will be able to pinpoint misconceptions and the more effectively you will be able to redirect a student's thinking.

- To identify the source of student errors, look closely at their math work. For an even more accurate diagnosis, ask students to explain their thinking to you. Then use the suggested activities to remediate appropriately.

- Review one or more precursor lessons with students who continue to struggle. You might use the *STAMS®* Interactive Whiteboard Lesson for a quick and engaging recap, review the entire lesson in the student book, or refresh student understanding with the *Hands-on Activity* or *Reteaching Activity* from the lesson.

Independent Practice

Independent Work

Scaffolding is removed. Students work independently to answer a variety of problems, including multiple-choice, short-response, and extended-response.

Best Practices

Metacognition

Thinking about what strategies or skills they need to solve specific problems, especially word problems, enhances students' performance and deepens conceptual understanding.

- Allow students to discuss problems with one another to evaluate which strategies or skills they will apply. Encourage students to explore different ways to solve a problem.

- Emphasize that students need to decide if their answers make sense.

- Request step-by-step oral explanations of the process students use to solve problems.

ADDITIONAL ACTIVITIES

These resources are for optional use if there is time after completing each 30-minute part of the student book lesson.

ADDITIONAL ACTIVITIES

1 **Hands-on Activity**
Use counters to model ratios and make a table.

Materials: 40 counters and 5 small cups per group

Organize students in small groups and distribute cups and counters. Have students divide the counters equally among the cups. *(8 counters per cup.)*

Draw a table on the board and label the columns "Counters *(a)*" and "Cups *(b)*." Have students select one cup and ask, "How many counters are in 1 cup? What is the ratio of counters to cups?" Write the ratio *8 to 1* on the board and write the values in the table. Repeat for 2 and 3 cups. Then ask, "How many counters are in 5 cups?" *(40.)*

Have students compare each ratio. Discuss the relationship between the number of counters and the number of cups and how this is shown in the table. *(Each number in the Cup column is equal to the corresponding number in the Counters column divided by 8.)*

2 **Reteaching Activity**
Write equations for data tables.

Have students copy this table.

a	b
1	4
2	8
4	
8	

Have students study the first two rows in the table. Ask, "What do you do to *a* to get *b*?" *(Multiply by 4.)* "Is this true for the next row also?" *(Yes.)* Write "multiply *a* by 4 to get *b*" on the board. Then write the equation $a \times 4 = b$ on the board. Have students use this rule to complete the table. *(16, 32.)*

Ask students similar questions for another table in which the rule is divide by 2.

3 **Vocabulary Activity**
Play "Concentration" to reinforce terms.

Materials: index cards

In pairs, have students write one vocabulary term on each index card. Then have students write a definition or example of each term on another index card. Have students shuffle the cards and place them facedown in an array. Students take turns flipping over two cards. If the player chooses a matching term and definition, he or she keeps the pair. If the cards do not match, the student replaces them. The student with the most matched pairs wins.

4 **Real-World Connection**
Explore equations based on ratios.

Discuss how ratios are used in real-world situations such as miles per hour, pay rate (dollars per hour), cost per pound, and items per pack. Ask students to share some examples and, if possible, have them write equations, data tables, and proportions showing the ratios. For example: If a person runs at a rate of 6 miles per hour, how long will it take the person to run 12 miles? *(2 hours.)*

5 **School-Home Connection**
Inform families about ratios in equations.

Give each student a copy of the reproducible School-Home Connection for Lesson 12 (page 185) to share with family. This activity has the family think of situations for given tables of data.

6 **Challenge Activity**
Make a table with missing values.

Have students make a table of values based on a given ratio. Remind students that the pairs of values must share the same ratio. Students should include at least five pairs of values in their table, including two pairs in which one value is unknown. After students have written the values in their table, have them exchange with a partner to find the missing values.

Algebra

Ratios in Tables of Data **129**

Teacher Guide

1 **Hands-on Activity:** Provides concrete examples of math concepts and procedures for students who can benefit from using manipulatives to enhance their understanding.

2 **Reteaching Activity:** Offers another instructional approach for students still struggling with the concepts/skills.

3 **Vocabulary Activity:** Provides additional practice with the lesson vocabulary to connect words and meanings.

4 **Real-World Connection:** Helps students relate the concepts/skills they are learning to their world.

5 **School-Home Connection:** Enables the family to become active participants in their child's learning. A letter informing the family about the content of the child's math lesson is accompanied by a fun activity to do with the child at home.

6 **Challenge Activity:** Provides enrichment for those students who have a solid understanding of the concepts/skills and are ready to move to the next level.

Tips for using Additional Activities:

- Note that all Additional Activities are optional. Each of the five activities is designed to support one part of the lesson, but you may use them in any way that best addresses students' needs and available time.

- Plan to spend about 15 minutes on each Additional Activity.

- Manipulatives for these activities were carefully chosen to be commonly available materials, such as base-ten blocks and fraction circles. If necessary, replace the actual manipulatives with paper substitutes.

- Search for virtual manipulatives that are available with interactive whiteboard software or can be downloaded from various websites.

Best Practices

Family Involvement

Family involvement contributes significantly to student success in school. Schools must reach out to parents so they feel that they are respected and needed.

- Communicate regularly with parents by sending them the *School-Home Connection* (available in English and Spanish) for each lesson.

- Acknowledge that parents may have limited time to spend; encourage but do not require that students complete the activity with parents.

- Occasionally, write a brief note of appreciation to parents on the *School-Home Connection* letter before photocopying, or write a personal note after photocopying.

- Remind parents that although math may not have been their favorite subject, it is important for them to consistently express enthusiasm for and confidence in their child's math work.

- Initiate contact with parents early and often; create multiple ways for parents to communicate with you.

COMPONENTS OF MATH INSTRUCTION

Math Strategies	Examples in *STAMS®* Series	Research Says
Computational Fluency Computational fluency is having recall of number facts and knowledge, and the ability to apply multiple computational methods.	**Student Book** Problems in each lesson part reinforce grade appropriate methods for computing.	"Efficient, accurate computational fluency is key to students' success in higher-level mathematics necessary for the workplace." — *National Research Council, 2001*
Conceptual Understanding Conceptual understanding is the knowledge of why math processes and rules work.	**Student Book** Students develop conceptual understanding in Part One and Part Two and demonstrate their knowledge in Part Three, Part Four, and Part Five.	"Students with conceptual understanding know more than isolated facts and methods. They understand why a mathematical idea is important and the kinds of context problem-solving in which it is useful." — *National Research Council, 2001*
Error Analysis Error analysis is an explanation of the patterns of mistakes students make. It allows teachers to provide targeted instruction that will help correct the errors.	**Student Book** • Part Three: Check **Teacher Guide** • Part One and Part Two: Error Alert feature • Part Three: Answer Analysis • Assessment and Remediation chart	"Research has shown that building upon students' prior knowledge and directly addressing misconceptions can lead to increased learning." — *Swan, 2002; Askew, 2002*
Math Vocabulary Math vocabulary is the group of content-area words, or Tier 3 words, that are most often specific to math text and used rarely in other contexts. **Controlled Vocabulary** Controlled vocabulary is the use of words at a lower reading level. It allows students to learn new concepts without struggling with reading issues.	**Student Book** • Students must use math language in their explanations for solving the extended-response problems in Part Four and Part Five. • Math vocabulary words are boldfaced. • Key terms are defined explicitly. • The Let's Talk activities in Part One and Part Two provide opportunities for students to use math language in context. • Each lesson uses controlled vocabulary to make new math knowledge more accessible and understandable. **Teacher Guide** • Vocabulary Activity • Definitions of key math terms are provided for each lesson.	"Tier Three words should be taught at point of contact, or as they occur in text." — *Beck, McKeown, & Kagan, 2002* "Without a basic knowledge of these terms, students will have difficulty understanding information they read or hear. Knowledge of important terms is critical to understanding any subject." — *Marzano & Pickering, 2005* "Research has demonstrated that vocabulary learning occurs most successfully through instructional environments that are language-rich, actively involve students in using language, require that students both understand spoken or written words and also express that understanding orally and in writing, and require students to use words in multiple ways over extended periods of time." — *CCSSO/NGA, 2010*

For a full report and bibliography, go to *CurriculumAssociates.com/STAMS/research.*

Math Strategies	Examples in *STAMS® Series*	Research Says
Meaningful Practice Meaningful practice is problem solving that requires students to apply learned concepts and skills.	Student Book • Part One through Part Four: Your Turn • Part Five: Independent practice	"Meaningful practice: to gain deeper understanding of topic — practice that focuses on building conceptual understanding related to skills and procedures." — *Marzano et al, 2000*
Multiple Representations Multiple representations are the ways in which a teacher or student represents a math idea, including spoken, written, symbolic, and concrete formats.	Student Book Symbolic, pictorial, spoken, and written methods are used throughout each lesson part to instruct students.	"Each of the different types of representation adds a new layer or a new dimension to the understanding of the concept being represented. Some students find some representations easier to understand than others." — *Mendieta, 2006*
Procedural Knowledge Procedural knowledge is the understanding of when and how to use mathematical procedures effectively. It aids in automatic recall of facts, allowing for further study of new math concepts and skills.	Student Book Through scaffolding, students develop procedural knowledge in Part One through Part Four. By Part Five they become independent problem solvers.	"Students need to be efficient and accurate in performing basic computation with whole numbers without having to rely on tables or other aids. They also need to know reasonably efficient and accurate ways to add, subtract, multiply, and divide multi-digit numbers, both mentally and with pencil and paper." — *National Research Council, 2001*

ASSESSMENT AND INTERVENTION

Strategies and Features	Examples in *CAMS®* and *STAMS® Series*	Research Says
Data-driven Instruction Data-driven instruction is the use of instructional decisions based on the systematic collection of data that reflects students' understanding.	*CAMS®* • 1 Pretest • 4 Benchmarks • 1 Post Test	"Districts and schools that are improving generally show a commitment to the use of student assessment data to diagnose weaknesses and guide improvement efforts." — *U.S. Department of Education, 2010*
Progress Monitoring Progress monitoring is a strategy that involves frequent, in-classroom progress checks of students' understanding and mastery of math concepts and skills.	Student Book • Part One through Part Four: Your Turn • Part Five: Independent practice *CAMS®* • 1 Pretest • 4 Benchmarks • 1 Post Test	"Teachers' regular use of formative assessments improves their students' learning, especially if teachers have additional guidance on using the assessment results to design and individualize instruction." — *NMAP, 2008*

Process Standards	Examples in *STAMS® Series*	Research Says
Communication Students use the language of math to accurately express their mathematical ideas to others, and analyze and evaluate the mathematical thinking and strategies of others.	**Student Book** • Part One and Part Two: Let's Talk • Part Three: Check • Part Four and Part Five: Explanation of solution **Teacher Guide** • ELL Support • School-Home Connection • Vocabulary Activity	"Encouraging math talk so that students can clarify their strategies to themselves and others, and compare the benefits and limitations of alternate approaches to problem solving." — *National Research Council, 2001*
Connections Students recognize and use connections among mathematical ideas, such as linking knowledge of the subtraction of whole numbers to the subtraction of decimals or fractions. Students also connect math concepts to their daily lives, and to other subjects, such as science.	**Student Book** • Part One and Part Two: Explore, Think, and Connect **Teacher Guide** • Math Background • Real-World Connection	"Connections are most useful when they link related concepts and methods in appropriate ways. Appropriate ways include methods of extending the understanding of one math concept to another (using multiple representations). Rote memorization does not lead to understanding and building connections." — *National Research Council, 2001*
Problem Solving Students build new math knowledge through problem solving and use various strategies to solve problems in math and in other contexts.	**Student Book** • Part One, Part Two, Part Three, Part Four: Your Turn • Part Five: Independent practice	"Problem solving is an integral part of all mathematics learning. In everyday life and in the workplace, being able to solve problems can lead to great advantages." — *NCTM, 2000*
Reasoning and Proof Students recognize, use, and evaluate various types of reasoning and methods of proof. Reasoning enables students to make sense of new mathematical ideas. Proofs build a logical argument based on known facts.	**Student Book** • Part One and Part Two: Let's Talk and Think It Through • Part Three: Solve and Check • Part Four and Part Five: Explanation of solution **Teacher Guide** Many teacher tips show how to help students reason through a problem.	"Knowing particular mathematical ideas and procedures as mere fact or routine is insufficient for using those ideas flexibly in diverse cases. Making mathematics reasonable means making it reasoned and, therefore, known in useful and usable ways." — *NCTM, 2003*
Representations Students communicate, clarify, or extend mathematical ideas through concrete or visual models. A representation may be a number sentence, manipulatives, diagrams or graphs and/or symbols.	**Student Book** • Part One and Part Two: Use of visual models • Part Four and Part Five: Show	"Intervention materials should include opportunities for students to work with visual representations of mathematical ideas and interventionists should be proficient in the use of visual representations of mathematical ideas." — *Gersten et al, 2009*

The chart below shows how instruction of key math concepts/skills tracks across the different levels of the *STAMS® Series,* Books C–H. For Books A and B, go to: www.CurriculumAssociates.com.

Number and Operations		Book C	Book D	Book E	Book F	Book G	Book H
Place Value							
	Understand place value	✔					
Addition							
	Add with regrouping	✔					
Subtraction							
	Subtract with regrouping	✔					
Multiplication							
	Understand multiplication	✔					
	Fact strategies	✔					
	Fact families	✔					
	Multiplication properties		✔				
	Multiply mentally		✔				
	Multiply by 1- and 2-digit numbers		✔				
	Multiply by 3-digit numbers				✔		
Division							
	Understand division	✔					
	Relate division to multiplication	✔	✔				
	Fact families	✔					
	Divide with and without regrouping		✔				
	Divide mentally			✔			
	Estimate quotients			✔			
	1- and 2-digit divisors			✔			
	Zeros in the quotient			✔			
Fractions							
	Understand fraction concepts	✔					
	Equivalent fractions	✔	✔				
	Simplify fractions		✔				
	Benchmark fractions	✔					
	Compare fractions	✔					
	Understand improper fractions and mixed numbers	✔		✔			
	Add and subtract like fractions			✔			
	Compare unlike fractions			✔			
	Add and subtract unlike fractions			✔			
	Add and subtract mixed numbers			✔			
	Multiply and divide whole numbers by fractions				✔		
	Multiply and divide fractions by fractions				✔		
Decimals							
	Understand decimal place value		✔				
	Compare and order decimals		✔				
	Relate decimals to fractions		✔				
	Add and subtract decimals			✔			
	Multiply and divide decimals by powers of 10				✔		
	Multiply and divide decimals by whole numbers				✔		
	Multiply and divide decimals by decimals				✔		
Integers							
	Understand Integers					✔	
	Add and subtract integers					✔	
	Multiply and divide integers					✔	

Algebra

	Book C	Book D	Book E	Book F	Book G	Book H
Operations and Algebraic Thinking						
Solve word problems	✔	✔	✔	✔	✔	✔
Understand inverse operations	✔	✔	✔	✔	✔	✔
Ratios and Proportional Relationships						
Understand ratios				✔		
Percent as a ratio				✔	✔	
Solve equations with ratios				✔		
Solve percent problems				✔	✔	
Understand rates and solve rate problems				✔	✔	
Understand proportional relationships				✔	✔	
Solve proportions				✔	✔	
Expressions and Equations						
Evaluate expressions					✔	
Exponents						✔
Square roots						✔
Solve equations using number sense				✔		
Solve equations using inverse operations				✔	✔	✔
Use formulas	✔	✔	✔	✔	✔	✔
Equations with rational numbers					✔	
Nonlinear equations						✔
Solve two-step equations						✔
Slope						✔
Graph linear equations						✔
Solve systems graphically						✔
Solve systems algebraically						✔

Geometry and Measurement

	Book C	Book D	Book E	Book F	Book G	Book H
Plane Geometry						
Plane shapes	✔					
Angles		✔				
Special angle pairs						✔
Angle sums						✔
Similarity concepts					✔	
Triangle similarity						✔
Linear Measurement and Area						
Length	✔					
Perimeter	✔					
Area concepts		✔				
Area of rectangles		✔				
Area formulas		✔	✔			
Circumference and area of circles					✔	
Pythagorean Theorem						✔
Distance formula						✔
Surface Area and Volume						
Surface area of rectangular prisms				✔		
Volume concepts				✔		
Volume of rectangular prisms				✔		
Surface area and volume of cylinders					✔	

Data Analysis and Probability

	Book C	Book D	Book E	Book F	Book G	Book H
Graphs						
Picture graphs	✔					
Bar graphs	✔					
Line plots		✔				
Line graphs			✔			
Circle graphs					✔	
Scatter plots						✔
Statistics						
Mean, median, range						✔
Probability						
Theoretical probability					✔	

Correlations Charts

NCTM Focal Points and Connections The chart below indicates the lessons in *STAMS® Book F* that provide instruction for the NCTM Focal Points and related Connections for grade 6. (For correlations between the NCTM Process Standards and the *STAMS® Series*, see page 28 of the teacher guide.)

NCTM Focal Points and Connections for Grade 6	STAMS® Book F Lesson(s)
FOCAL POINTS	
Number and Operations: Students develop fluency with multiplication and division of fractions and decimals.	1, 2, 3, 4, 5, 6, 7, 8
Number and Operations: Students develop understanding of ratio and rate and relate them to multiplication and division.	9, 10, 11, 12
Algebra: Students write, interpret, and use mathematical expressions and equations.	12, 13, 14, 15, 16
CONNECTIONS	
Measurement and Geometry: Students solve problems involving area and volume.	15, 16

Common Core State Standards The chart below correlates the lessons in *STAMS® Book F* with Common Core State Standards for grade 6 mathematics. (For correlations between the Common Core Standards for Mathematical Practice and the *STAMS® Series*, see page 33 of the teacher guide.)

CCSS	Description	STAMS® Book F Lesson(s)
Ratios and Proportional Relationships		
6.RP.1	Understand the concept of a ratio and use ratio language to describe a ratio relationship between two quantities. *For example, "The ratio of wings to beaks in the bird house at the zoo was 2:1, because for every 2 wings there was 1 beak." "For every vote candidate A received, candidate C received nearly three votes."*	9
6.RP.2	Understand the concept of a unit rate a/b associated with a ratio $a:b$ with $b \neq 0$, and use rate language in the context of a ratio relationship. *For example, "This recipe has a ratio of 3 cups of flour to 4 cups of sugar, so there is 3/4 cup of flour for each cup of sugar." "We paid $75 for 15 hamburgers, which is a rate of $5 per hamburger."*	11, 12
6.RP.3	Use ratio and rate reasoning to solve real-world and mathematical problems, e.g., by reasoning about tables of equivalent ratios, tape diagrams, double number line diagrams, or equations.	10, 11, 12
The Number System		
6.NS.1	Interpret and compute quotients of fractions, and solve word problems involving division of fractions by fractions, e.g., by using visual fraction models and equations to represent the problem. *For example, create a story context for (2/3) ÷ (3/4) and use a visual fraction model to show the quotient; use the relationship between multiplication and division to explain that (2/3) ÷ (3/4) = 8/9 because 3/4 of 8/9 is 2/3. (In general, (a/b) ÷ (c/d) = ad/bc.) How much chocolate will each person get if 3 people share 1/2 lb of chocolate equally? How many 3/4-cup servings are in 2/3 of a cup of yogurt? How wide is a rectangular strip of land with length 3/4 mi and area 1/2 square mi?*	4
6.NS.3	Fluently add, subtract, multiply, and divide multi-digit decimals using the standard algorithm for each operation.	6, 7, 8
6.NS.5	Understand that positive and negative numbers are used together to describe quantities having opposite directions or values (e.g., temperature above/below zero, elevation above/below sea level, credits/debits, positive/negative electric charge); use positive and negative numbers to represent quantities in real-world contexts, explaining the meaning of 0 in each situation.	17
6.NS.6	Understand a rational number as a point on the number line. Extend number line diagrams and coordinate axes familiar from previous grades to represent points on the line and in the plane with negative number coordinates.	17
6.NS.7	Understand ordering and absolute value of rational numbers.	17

Correlations Charts

31

Common Core State Standards for Grade 6 Mathematics

CCSS	Description	*STAMS® Book F* Lesson(s)
Expressions and Equations		
6.EE.2	Write, read, and evaluate expressions in which letters stand for numbers.	13, 14, 15
6.EE.5	Understand solving an equation or inequality as a process of answering a question: which values from a specified set, if any, make the equation or inequality true? Use substitution to determine whether a given number in a specified set makes an equation or inequality true.	13, 14
6.EE.6	Use variables to represent numbers and write expressions when solving a real-world or mathematical problem; understand that a variable can represent an unknown number, or, depending on the purpose at hand, any number in a specified set.	13, 14, 15
6.EE.7	Solve real-world and mathematical problems by writing and solving equations of the form $x + p = q$ and $px = q$ for cases in which p, q and x are all nonnegative rational numbers.	13, 14, 15
6.EE.9	Use variables to represent two quantities in a real-world problem that change in relationship to one another; write an equation to express one quantity, thought of as the dependent variable, in terms of the other quantity, thought of as the independent variable. Analyze the relationship between the dependent and independent variables using graphs and tables, and relate these to the equation. *For example, in a problem involving motion at constant speed, list and graph ordered pairs of distances and times, and write the equation $d = 65t$ to represent the relationship between distance and time.*	12, 15
Geometry		
6.G.2	Find the volume of a right rectangular prism with fractional edge lengths by packing it with unit cubes of the appropriate unit fraction edge lengths, and show that the volume is the same as would be found by multiplying the edge lengths of the prism. Apply the formulas $V = l\,w\,h$ and $V = b\,h$ to find volumes of right rectangular prisms with fractional edge lengths in the context of solving real-world and mathematical problems.	16
Statistics and Probability		
6.SP.2	Understand that a set of data collected to answer a statistical question has a distribution which can be described by its center, spread, and overall shape.	18
6.SP.3	Recognize that a measure of center for a numerical data set summarizes all of its values with a single number, while a measure of variation describes how its values vary with a single number.	18
6.SP.4	Display numerical data in plots on a number line, including dot plots, histograms, and box plots.	18
6.SP.5	Summarize numerical data sets in relation to their context, such as by: a. Reporting the number of observations. b. Describing the nature of the attribute under investigation, including how it was measured and its units of measurement. c. Giving quantitative measures of center (median and/or mean) and variability (interquartile range and/or mean absolute deviation), as well as describing any overall pattern and any striking deviations from the overall pattern with reference to the context in which the data were gathered. d. Relating the choice of measures of center and variability to the shape of the data distribution and the context in which the data were gathered.	18
Common Core State Standards for Grade 5 Mathematics		
Number and Operations in Base Ten		
5.NBT.1	Recognize that in a multi-digit number, a digit in one place represents 10 times as much as it represents in the place to its right and 1/10 of what it represents in the place to its left.	5
5.NBT.2	Explain patterns in the number of zeros of the product when multiplying a number by powers of 10, and explain patterns in the placement of the decimal point when a decimal is multiplied or divided by a power of 10. Use whole-number exponents to denote powers of 10.	5
Number and Operations—Fractions		
5.NF.4	Apply and extend previous understandings of multiplication to multiply a fraction or whole number by a fraction.	1, 2
5.NF.6	Solve real world problems involving multiplication of fractions and mixed numbers, e.g., by using visual fraction models or equations to represent the problem.	1, 2
5.NF.7	Apply and extend previous understandings of division to divide unit fractions by whole numbers and whole numbers by unit fractions.	3

Features of a *STAMS®* Lesson

Common Core Standards for Mathematical Practice

Standard	Examples in *STAMS*® Series	
1. Make sense of problems and persevere in solving them.	**Student Book** • Part One and Part Two Focus Question • Part One, Part Two, Part Three, Part Four: Your Turn • Part Five: Independent Practice	**Teacher Guide** • Part Three: Answer Analysis • Challenge Activity
2. Reason abstractly and quantitatively.	**Student Book** • Part One and Part Two: Let's Talk and Think It Through • Part Three: Solve and Check • Part Four and Part Five: Explanation of solution	**Teacher Guide** • Many teacher tips show how to help students reason through a problem.
3. Construct viable arguments and critique the reasoning of others.	**Student Book** • Part One and Part Two: Let's Talk • Part Three: Check • Part Four and Part Five: Explain your answer	**Teacher Guide** • Assessment and Remediation
4. Model with mathematics.	**Student Book** • Part One and Part Two: Your Turn • Part Four and Part Five: Explain your answer	**Teacher Guide** • Many "Step by Step" Tips help students develop models for solving a problem. • Hands-on Activity
5. Use appropriate tools strategically.	**Student Book** • Part Three and Part Four: Your Turn	**Teacher Guide** • Hands-on Activity • Reteaching Activity • Real-World Connection
6. Attend to precision.	**Student Book** • Part One and Part Two: Let's Talk • Part Four: Explain your answer	**Teacher Guide** • Vocabulary in lesson introduction • Vocabulary Activity
7. Look for and make use of structure.	**Student Book** • Lessons 1–15	**Teacher Guide** • Math Background for Lessons 1–15
8. Look for and express regularity in repeated reasoning.	**Student Book** • All lessons	**Teacher Guide** • Tips • Challenge Activity

LESSON OBJECTIVES

Students will:

- Use repeated addition to find the product of a whole number and a fraction.
- Multiply a whole number by a fraction using a standard algorithm.

PREREQUISITES

Students should be able to:

- Add like fractions.
- Simplify fractions.
- Rewrite improper fractions as whole numbers and mixed numbers.

RELATED *STAMS*® LESSONS

- **Book D – Lesson 9**

  Simplify Fractions introduces simplifying fractions by dividing by a common factor.

- **Book E – Lesson 7**

  Understand Mixed Numbers introduces renaming improper fractions.

- **Book E – Lesson 8**

  Add and Subtract Like Fractions introduces adding and subtracting fractions with common denominators.

VOCABULARY

PAGE 4

- **multiplication:** an operation used to find the total number of items in equal-sized groups
- **repeated addition:** addition of the same number a particular number of times
- **factor:** a number multiplied by another number
- **product:** the answer to a multiplication problem

PAGE 5

- **numerator:** the top number in a fraction that tells the number of equal parts described by the fraction.
- **denominator:** the bottom number in a fraction that tells the total number of equal parts in a whole.
- **improper fraction:** a fraction whose numerator is greater than or equal to its denominator

MATH BACKGROUND

Rectangle models can be used to multiply a whole number and a fraction. For example, when you multiply 3 and $\frac{2}{5}$, the whole number 3 tells how many whole rectangles there are. The denominator of the fraction tells how many parts are in each rectangle. The numerator tells how many sections of each rectangle to shade. Shade 2 fifths of each of the 3 rectangles. To multiply, count the number of shaded rectangles. There are 6 fifths shaded, so the product is $\frac{6}{5} = 1\frac{1}{5}$.

When you shade 2 fifths of each rectangle, you are displaying how multiplying $3 \times \frac{2}{5}$ is the same as adding $\frac{2}{5} + \frac{2}{5} + \frac{2}{5}$. Students learn about this method in Part One. In Part Two, students learn a standard algorithm.

Interactive Whiteboard

Visualize Multiplying Whole Numbers by Fractions

Go to the *Interactive Whiteboard Lessons* to bring Parts One and Two to life. Use features such as interactive fraction models to deepen students' understanding of multiplying whole numbers by fractions.

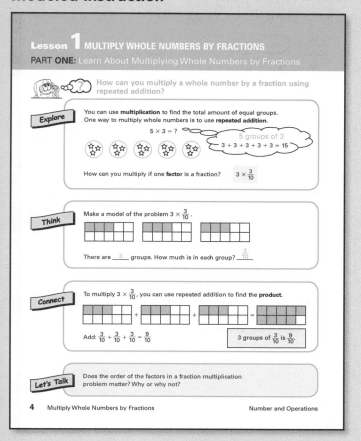

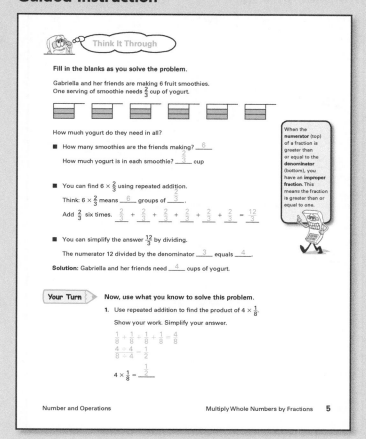

AT A GLANCE

Students activate their background knowledge about repeated addition and its connection to multiplication. Then they use models and repeated addition to find equal groups of a fractional amount.

STEP BY STEP

PAGE 4

- Introduce the **Question** at the top of the page.
- Have students study the groups shown in **Explore** and connect the picture to the equation.
- Read **Think** with students. Emphasize that the groups all show the same fractional amount.

ELL Support: Emphasize the correct way to read a fraction. The numerator is read as a counting number. The denominator is read as an ordinal number, with the exception of 2 (halves) and 1 (wholes). So the fraction in this example is read "three-tenths."

- Discuss **Connect** with students. Make sure they understand why the numerators are added and the denominator remains the same in the sum.

- Organize students in pairs or groups for **Let's Talk** and monitor their discussions.
- Be sure students understand that changing the order of the factors in any multiplication problem does not change the product. (Commutative Property)

PAGE 5

- Read the **Think It Through** problem with students.
- Make sure students see the connection between the factors in the multiplication equation and the addends in the repeated addition equation. Review rewriting improper fractions as mixed numbers.

Tip: Draw a model of the answer, showing 4 full measuring cups, each divided into thirds.

- Monitor students as they complete **Your Turn**. Then discuss the correct answer. If necessary, review simplifying fractions.

Error Alert: Students who got $\frac{4}{32}$ (before simplifying) are also adding the denominators.

 ADDITIONAL ACTIVITY

See **Hands-on Activity** (page 41).

Modeled Instruction

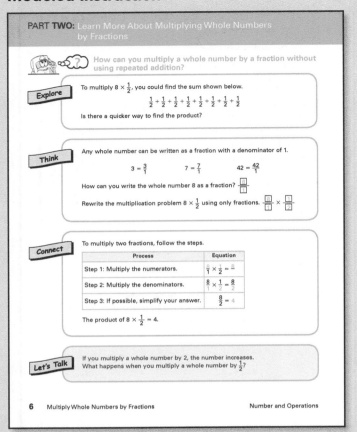

Guided Instruction

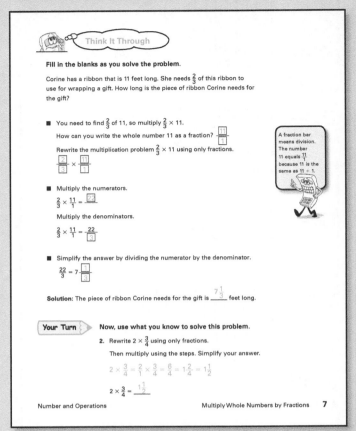

AT A GLANCE

Students learn to multiply a whole number by a fraction using standard fraction multiplication steps.

STEP BY STEP

PAGE 6

- Introduce the **Question** at the top of the page.
- Read **Explore** with students. Have students find the sum of the repeated addition problem $\left(\frac{8}{2} = 4\right)$.

> **ELL Support:** Clear up any confusion about the word *sum* and its homonym *some*.

- Read **Think** with students. Remind students that a denominator of 1 indicates a whole, so for example $\frac{3}{1}$ means *3 wholes*. Pause so students can read aloud the numbers in orange.
- Read and discuss the multiplication steps in **Connect**.

> **Tip:** Compare the answer here to the one found in **Explore**. Help students understand that they are the same because with the repeated addition,

the numerator 1 was added *8 times*, and the denominator 2 was added *0 times* (kept the same).

- Organize students in pairs or groups for **Let's Talk** and monitor their discussions.
- Be sure students realize that the product of a whole number and $\frac{1}{2}$ will be less than the whole number. This is because it takes two halves to equal one whole.

PAGE 7

- Read the **Think It Through** problem with students.
- Guide students as they solve the problem. Pause for students to fill in missing information. Then discuss each response. Show how to rewrite the improper fraction as a mixed number on the board.
- Monitor students as they complete **Your Turn**. Then discuss the correct answer.

> **Error Alert:** Students who got the incorrect answer of $\frac{3}{4}$ may have multiplied the numerator by 2 and the denominator by 2, and then simplified $\frac{6}{8}$ to $\frac{3}{4}$.

 ADDITIONAL ACTIVITY

See **Reteaching Activity** (page 41).

Modeled Practice

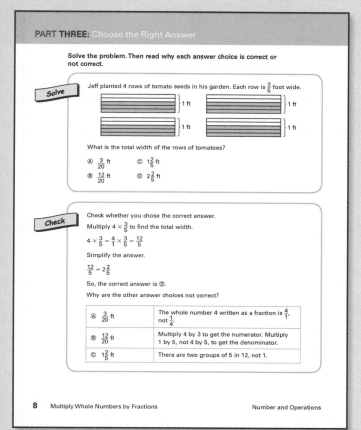

Guided Practice

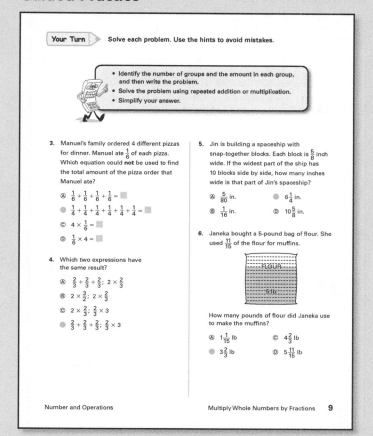

AT A GLANCE

Students reinforce their understanding of fraction multiplication through solving a multiple-choice problem and analyzing correct and incorrect answer choices.

STEP BY STEP

PAGE 8

- Tell students that this page models finding the correct answer to a multiple-choice problem.
- Have students read the problem in **Solve** and choose the best answer. Remind students to check their math.
- Examine **Check** with students. Discuss the correct and incorrect choices.

PAGE 9

- Monitor students as they complete **Your Turn**.
- Organize students in pairs or small groups and have them discuss why each answer choice is correct or not and what errors may have been made.
- Review the answers with the class.

 ADDITIONAL ACTIVITY

See **Vocabulary Activity** (page 41).

Answer Analysis

3. Ⓐ This shows 4 groups of $\frac{1}{6}$ as addition.

   ● This shows 6 groups of $\frac{1}{4}$.

   Ⓒ This shows 4 groups of $\frac{1}{6}$ as multiplication.

   Ⓓ This shows reversed order of factors.

4. Ⓐ Used numerator as number of groups in second expression

   Ⓑ Considered reciprocal of fraction as same fraction

   Ⓒ Changed value of whole number in addition to changing order of factors

   ● Both expressions represent 3 groups of $\frac{2}{3}$.

5. Ⓐ Multiplied denominator by 10 and kept numerator

   Ⓑ Before multiplying, wrote 10 as $\frac{1}{10}$ instead of $\frac{10}{1}$

   ● $10 \times \frac{5}{8} = \frac{10}{1} \times \frac{5}{8} = \frac{50}{8} = 6\frac{2}{8} = 6\frac{1}{4}$

   Ⓓ Added instead of multiplying

6. Ⓐ Added whole number to numerator

   ● $5 \times \frac{11}{15} = \frac{5}{1} \times \frac{11}{15} = \frac{55}{15} = 3\frac{10}{15} = 3\frac{2}{3}$

   Ⓒ Simplified incorrectly

   Ⓓ Added instead of multiplying

Modeled Practice

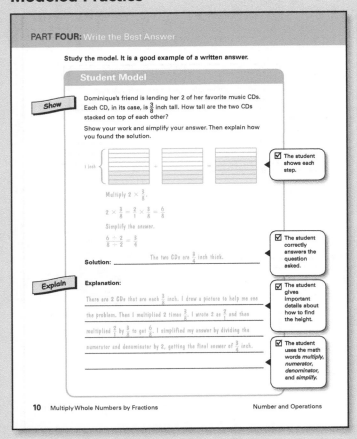

Guided Practice

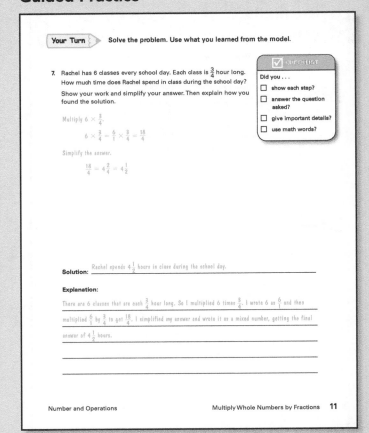

AT A GLANCE
. . . .

Students study a model answer to an extended-response problem.

STEP BY STEP
. . . .

PAGE 10

- Tell students that this page models building the solution to a problem one step at a time and writing to explain the solution.

- Have students read the problem in **Show**. Discuss how the drawing and each mathematical step lead to the solution.

> Tip: Make sure students don't mistake each group as a stack of 8 CDs. Each group represents a single CD. The parts represent an inch divided into eighths.

- Read **Explain** with students. Have students circle the math words in the explanation.

- Direct students' attention to the notes in the right margin. Tell students that this model would receive a high score for the reasons described in these notes.

PAGE 11

- Monitor students as they complete **Your Turn**.
- Encourage students to follow the **Checklist** to write the best answer.
- Have students discuss their work with a partner. Then discuss the correct answer as a class.

Answer and Explanation

7. See the sample answer. This answer shows all of the steps taken to solve the problem. The solution answers the question. The explanation provides important details about how the problem was solved and uses the math words *multiply, mixed number,* and *simplify.*

 ADDITIONAL ACTIVITY
. . . .
See **Real-World Connection** (page 41).

 ADDITIONAL ACTIVITY
. . . .
See **School-Home Connection** (page 41).

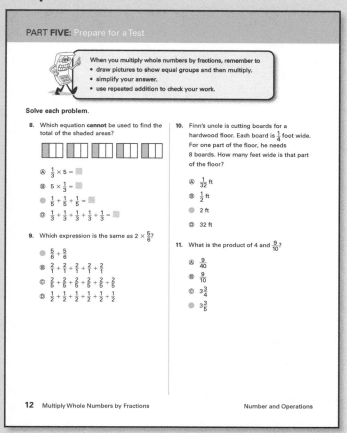

PART FIVE: Prepare for a Test

When you multiply whole numbers by fractions, remember to
• draw pictures to show equal groups and then multiply.
• simplify your answer.
• use repeated addition to check your work.

Solve each problem.

8. Which equation **cannot** be used to find the total of the shaded areas?

Ⓐ $\frac{1}{3} \times 5 = $ ▦

Ⓑ $5 \times \frac{1}{3} = $ ▦

● $\frac{1}{5} + \frac{1}{5} + \frac{1}{5} = $ ▦

Ⓓ $\frac{1}{3} + \frac{1}{3} + \frac{1}{3} + \frac{1}{3} + \frac{1}{3} = $ ▦

9. Which expression is the same as $2 \times \frac{5}{6}$?

● $\frac{5}{6} + \frac{5}{6}$

Ⓑ $\frac{2}{1} + \frac{2}{1} + \frac{2}{1} + \frac{2}{1} + \frac{2}{1}$

Ⓒ $\frac{2}{6} + \frac{2}{6} + \frac{2}{6} + \frac{2}{6} + \frac{2}{6}$

Ⓓ $\frac{1}{2} + \frac{1}{2} + \frac{1}{2} + \frac{1}{2} + \frac{1}{2} + \frac{1}{2}$

10. Finn's uncle is cutting boards for a hardwood floor. Each board is $\frac{1}{4}$ foot wide. For one part of the floor, he needs 8 boards. How many feet wide is that part of the floor?

Ⓐ $\frac{1}{32}$ ft

Ⓑ $\frac{1}{2}$ ft

● 2 ft

Ⓓ 32 ft

11. What is the product of 4 and $\frac{9}{10}$?

Ⓐ $\frac{9}{40}$

Ⓑ $\frac{9}{10}$

Ⓒ $3\frac{3}{4}$

● $3\frac{3}{5}$

12 Multiply Whole Numbers by Fractions   Number and Operations

---

12. Ava planted a flower bulb in a pot. The flower grew $\frac{4}{5}$ inch each week during 6 weeks in the spring. How many inches did Ava's flower grow during those weeks?

Ⓐ $\frac{2}{15}$ in.

Ⓑ $1\frac{2}{3}$ in.

Ⓒ 2 in.

● $4\frac{4}{5}$ in.

13. Solve. $9 \times \frac{2}{3} = $ ▦

Ⓐ $\frac{2}{27}$

Ⓑ $\frac{1}{6}$

Ⓒ $3\frac{2}{3}$

● 6

14. Lacy's hair grows $\frac{2}{5}$ inch every month. She let it grow for 3 months between haircuts. How many inches did Lacy's hair grow in that time?

Write an addition equation and a multiplication equation that show the amount of hair growth.

Addition equation:
$\frac{2}{5} + \frac{2}{5} + \frac{2}{5} = \frac{6}{5} = 1\frac{1}{5}$

Multiplication equation:
$3 \times \frac{2}{5} = \frac{3}{1} \times \frac{2}{5} = \frac{6}{5} = 1\frac{1}{5}$

15. Benjamin and his friends are making homemade slime. The recipe needs $\frac{3}{4}$ cup glue for each batch of slime. If Benjamin plans to make 7 batches of slime, how much glue does he need?

Show your work and simplify your answer. Then explain how you found the solution.

Multiply. $7 \times \frac{3}{4} = \frac{7}{1} \times \frac{3}{4} = \frac{21}{4}$

Simplify. $\frac{21}{4} = 5\frac{1}{4}$

Check. $\frac{3}{4} + \frac{3}{4} + \frac{3}{4} + \frac{3}{4} + \frac{3}{4} + \frac{3}{4} + \frac{3}{4} = \frac{21}{4} = 5\frac{1}{4}$

Solution: Benjamin needs $5\frac{1}{4}$ cups of glue.

Explanation:
There are 7 batches that each need $\frac{3}{4}$ cup glue. I multiplied $\frac{7}{1}$ by $\frac{3}{4}$ to get $\frac{21}{4}$. I simplified my answer and wrote it as a mixed number, getting the final answer of $5\frac{1}{4}$ cups. I used repeated addition $\frac{3}{4} + \frac{3}{4} + \frac{3}{4} + \frac{3}{4} + \frac{3}{4} + \frac{3}{4} + \frac{3}{4}$ to check my answer.

Number and Operations   Multiply Whole Numbers by Fractions 13

AT A GLANCE

Students practice solving problems involving the multiplication of whole numbers and fractions that might appear on a mathematics test.

STEP BY STEP

PAGES 12–13

• Tell students that they will practice solving multiplication problems using repeated addition and/or multiplication.

• Point out the tips at the top of page 12. Explain to students that these tips will help them answer the problems correctly.

• You may wish to have students review the hints for avoiding mistakes on page 9 as well.

• Tell students to complete problems 8–15 on pages 12 and 13. Encourage students to check their answers.

• Discuss the correct responses as a class.

Answers and Explanations

8. Ⓒ This equation represents three groups of one-fifth, not five groups of one-third.

9. Ⓐ This expression represents two groups of five-sixths.

10. Ⓒ $8 \times \frac{1}{4} = \frac{8}{1} \times \frac{1}{4} = \frac{8}{4} = 2$

11. Ⓓ $4 \times \frac{9}{10} = \frac{4}{1} \times \frac{9}{10} = \frac{36}{10} = 3\frac{6}{10} = 3\frac{3}{5}$

12. Ⓓ $6 \times \frac{4}{5} = \frac{6}{1} \times \frac{4}{5} = \frac{24}{5} = 4\frac{4}{5}$

13. Ⓓ $9 \times \frac{2}{3} = \frac{9}{1} \times \frac{2}{3} = \frac{18}{3} = 6$

(continued on page 40)

(continued from page 39)

14. The 3 months are the groups. Each group has $\frac{2}{5}$ inch of growth. To find the total of 3 groups of $\frac{2}{5}$, add $\frac{2}{5}$ three times or multiply $3 \times \frac{2}{5}$.

15. See the sample answer. This answer shows all of the steps the student took to solve the problem and check the solution, using multiplication and repeated addition, respectively. The solution answers the question. The explanation provides important details about how the student solved the problem and uses the math words *multiply*, *simplify*, and *repeated addition*.

 ## ASSESSMENT AND REMEDIATION

- Ask students to solve the problem $5 \times \frac{1}{10}$. $\left(\frac{5}{10} = \frac{1}{2}\right)$
- For students who are still struggling, use the chart below to guide remediation.
- After providing remediation, check students' understanding. Ask students to explain their steps while solving the problem $6 \times \frac{1}{3}$. $\left(\frac{6}{3} = 2\right)$
- If a student is still having difficulty, use *STAMS Book D*, Lesson 9, pages 84–93, and *Book E*, Lessons 7 and 8, pages 64–83.

If the error is . . .	Students may . . .	To remediate . . .
$\frac{5}{50} = \frac{1}{10}$	have used repeated addition, but added denominators as well as numerators, *or*	Encourage students to draw a picture, reinforcing the concept of a denominator as the number of equal parts into which a whole is divided, which remains the same when adding like fractions.
	have multiplied the whole number 5 by both numerator and denominator of the fraction.	Have student use grid paper to write each numeral in the numerator and the denominator of the two fractions in the problem in just one grid space, putting a 1 in the available space under the whole number to write it as a fraction.
$\frac{6}{11}$	have correctly written the multiplication expression $\frac{5}{1} \times \frac{1}{10}$, but then added the corresponding parts of the fraction.	Remind students that a whole number times a fraction can be solved using repeated addition or multiplication, but these methods cannot be combined. Have students circle the operation sign(s) in their solution method of choice.
$\frac{1}{50}$	have written the multiplication problem as $\frac{1}{5} \times \frac{1}{10}$.	Use fraction circles to reinforce the conceptual difference between $\frac{1}{5}$ and $\frac{5}{1}$, showing that only $\frac{5}{1}$ is equivalent to 5 wholes.

 ## ADDITIONAL ACTIVITY

For students who have mastered the skills in this lesson, see **Challenge Activity** (page 41).

ADDITIONAL ACTIVITIES

Hands-on Activity
Use fraction circles to model a whole number times a fraction as repeated addition.

Materials: 3 sets of fraction circles per group

Organize students in small groups and distribute fraction circles. Tell students that they can use repeated addition to understand $3 \times \frac{4}{6}$. Write the phrase ___ *groups of* ___ on the board. Have students fill in the missing numbers. $\left(3, \frac{4}{6}\right)$ Then have students model $3 \times \frac{4}{6}$ by showing 3 groups with 4 sixths pieces in each group. Have students count the sixths. Ask, "How many sixths are there in all?" *(12)* Point out that the model shows that $3 \times \frac{4}{6} = \frac{12}{6}$.

To simplify, have students rearrange the sixths to create as many wholes, or circles with 6 sixths, as possible. Ask, "How many whole circles can you make?" *(2)* Explain that the model shows that $\frac{12}{6} = 2$ so $3 \times \frac{4}{6} = 2$.

Reteaching Activity
Use grid paper to align factors.

Materials: grid paper with large squares

Distribute paper to each student. Tell students to write the problem $4 \times \frac{2}{9}$, where each digit of the problem must be in a grid square.

Ask students, "Where does the 4 go, in relation to the 2 and 9?" *(It aligns horizontally with the 2)* "Does anything line up with the 9?" *(1, writing 4 as the fraction $\frac{4}{1}$)* "Why is it important to line up the whole number with the numerator of the fraction?" *(So the correct numbers get multiplied.)*

Vocabulary Activity
Play "Concentration" to reinforce terms.

Materials: index cards

In pairs, have students write one vocabulary term on each index card. Then have students write a definition or example of each term on another index card. Have students shuffle the cards and place them face down in an array. Students take turns flipping over two cards. If the player chooses a matching term and definition, he keeps the pair. If the cards do not match, he replaces them. The student with the most matched pairs wins.

Real-World Connection
Solve whole number times fraction problems using recipes.

Bring in copies of a recipe that include several ingredients with fractional quantities. Tell students that you want to triple the recipe to serve to a large group of people. Have them calculate the needed amount of each ingredient by finding the product of *3 × [quantity]* and write the modified ingredients list.

School-Home Connection
Inform families about multiplying whole numbers by fractions.

Give each student a copy of the reproducible School-Home Connection for Lesson 1 (page 163) to share with the family. The activity included in the letter has the family examine a recipe to multiply a whole number by a fraction.

Challenge Activity
Write word problems involving whole numbers multiplied by fractions.

Have students write a whole number times a fraction word problem. Remind students that the problem should involve finding the total of groups of the same fractional size. Students should use one-digit numbers for the number of groups. After students have written their problem, have them exchange it with a partner to solve.

Fractions

LESSON OBJECTIVES

Students will:

- Understand that fraction multiplication is a way to find a fraction *of* a fraction.
- Multiply a fraction by a fraction using a model to understand a standard algorithm.
- Multiply a fraction by a mixed number using a standard algorithm.

PREREQUISITES

Students should be able to:

- Simplify fractions and improper fractions.
- Write improper fractions as mixed numbers.
- Write mixed numbers as improper fractions.

RELATED *STAMS®* LESSONS

- **Book F – Lesson 1**

  Multiply Whole Numbers by Fractions introduces how to multiply a whole number by a fraction.

- **Book E – Lesson 7**

  Understand Mixed Numbers shows how to rename improper fractions and mixed numbers

VOCABULARY

PAGE 14

- **multiply:** to find the total number of items in equal-sized groups
- **fraction:** a number that compares a part, the numerator, to a whole, the denominator
- **numerator:** the top number in a fraction that tells the number of equal parts described by the fraction
- **denominator:** the bottom number in a fraction that tells the total number of equal parts in a whole
- **product:** the result of multiplication

PAGE 16

- **mixed number:** a number containing whole and fraction parts
- **improper fraction:** a fraction whose numerator is greater than the denominator
- **cross-simplify:** simplify numerator/denominator pairs in the factors of a multiplication problem
- **greatest common factor (GCF):** the greatest positive integer that is a common factor of two or more numbers

MATH BACKGROUND

In this lesson, students first multiply a fraction by a fraction using models. This helps them see why the algorithm for multiplying fractions works. Then, students multiply a fraction by a mixed number using an algorithm. The next step will be for them to multiply a mixed number by a mixed number. After students learn how to multiply fractions and mixed numbers, they then learn how to use those multiplication concepts to divide fractions and mixed numbers.

Interactive Whiteboard
Visualize Multiplying Fractions

Go to the *Interactive Whiteboard Lessons* to bring Parts One and Two to life. Have students use features such as the pen tool to shade fraction models to help deepen their understanding of multiplying fractions.

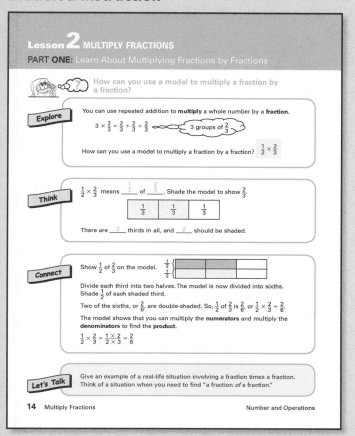

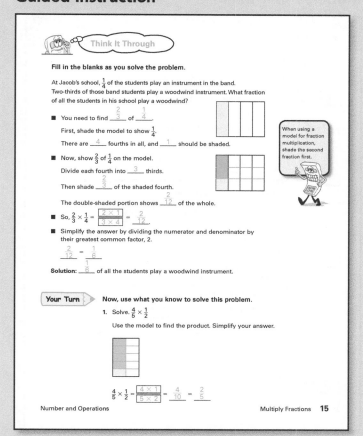

AT A GLANCE

Students activate their background knowledge about a whole number times a fraction, then build on the idea that a fraction *times* a fraction means a fraction *of* a fraction to model fraction multiplication.

STEP BY STEP

PAGE 14

- Introduce the **Question** at the top of the page.
- Have students study the math sentence in **Explore** and emphasize that × means "of."
- Read **Think** with students. Point out that the shading here represents the second fraction in the problem. Pause so students can say aloud the numbers in range.
- Discuss **Connect** with students. Make sure they understand how and why to shade one-half of two-thirds and that the double-shaded region represents the product.

> **Tip:** Use the model to show that $\frac{1}{2}$ of $\frac{2}{3}$ is the same as $\frac{1}{2}$ of $\frac{1}{3}$ plus $\frac{1}{2}$ of $\frac{1}{3}$, or $\frac{1}{6} + \frac{1}{6}$, which is $\frac{2}{6}$.

- Organize students in pairs or groups for **Let's Talk** and monitor their discussions.

- If students have trouble thinking of real-life situations, have them first consider the second factor. This is their "whole."

PAGE 15

- Read the **Think It Through** problem with students.
- Guide students as they solve the problem. Make clear that it doesn't matter how many students are in the school, because they are finding a portion of the whole.

> **ELL Support:** Review the correct way to read a fraction. The denominator is read as an ordinal number (halves, thirds, fourths, etc.) and indicates the number of equal parts a whole is divided into.

- Monitor students as they complete **Your Turn**. Then discuss the correct answer.

> **Error Alert:** Students who got the incorrect answer of $\frac{8}{10} = \frac{4}{5}$ may have shaded four-fifths of *both* halves instead of the just the previously shaded *one*-half.

 ADDITIONAL ACTIVITY

See **Hands-on Activity** (page 49).

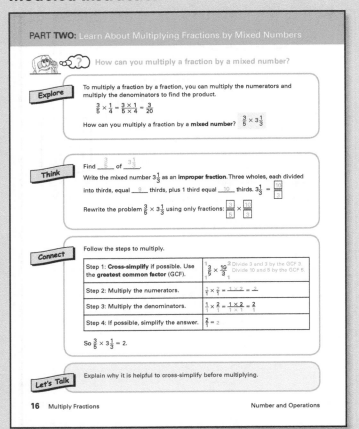

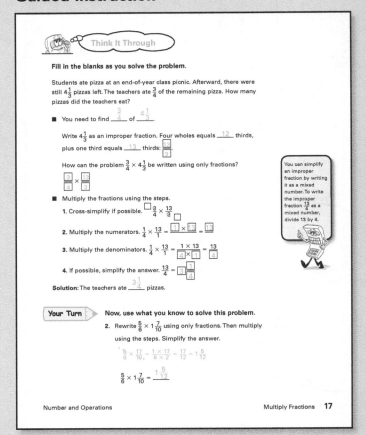

AT A GLANCE

Students learn to multiply a fraction by a mixed number by rewriting the mixed number as an improper fraction, and then using the standard fraction multiplication steps.

STEP BY STEP

PAGE 16

- Introduce the **Question** at the top of the page.
- Read **Explore** with students. Make sure they understand that a mixed number is made up of a whole number and a fraction.

ELL Support: Clear up confusion about the multiple meanings of the word *product*. In math, a product is the result of multiplication.

- Read **Think** with students. Show the steps for changing the mixed number to an improper fraction. Pause so students can read aloud the numbers in orange.
- Read through the multiplication steps in **Connect**.

Tip: Rewrite $\frac{3}{5} \times \frac{10}{3}$ as $\frac{3 \times 10}{5 \times 3}$. This will help students to see that the numerator and denominator can be simplified.

- Organize students in pairs or groups for **Let's Talk** and monitor their discussions.
- Be sure students realize that they can simplify before or after multiplying fractions, but the advantage of cross-simplifying is working with smaller numbers.

PAGE 17

- Read the **Think It Through** problem with students.
- Guide students as they solve the problem. Pause for students to fill in missing information. Then discuss each response. Show students how to simplify the improper fraction by writing it as a mixed number.
- Monitor students as they complete **Your Turn**. Then discuss the correct answer.

Error Alert: Students who got an incorrect answer because of difficulty simplifying the answer may not be cross-simplifying the factors first. Encourage cross-simplifying before multiplying.

 ADDITIONAL ACTIVITY

See **Reteaching Activity** (page 49).

Modeled Practice

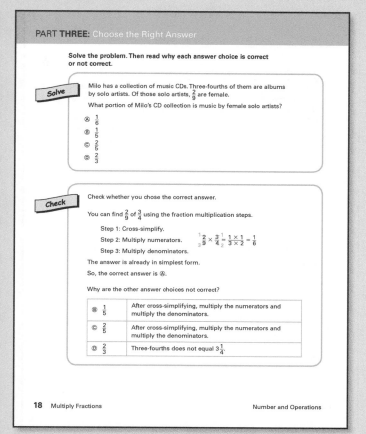

Guided Practice

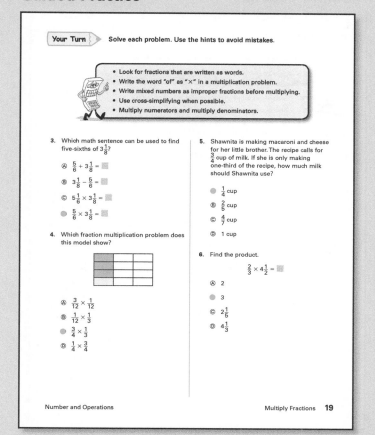

AT A GLANCE

Students reinforce their understanding of fraction multiplication concepts through solving a multiple-choice problem and analyzing correct and incorrect answer choices.

STEP BY STEP

Page 18

- Tell students that this page models finding the correct answer to a multiple-choice problem that involves multiplying fractions.

- Have students read the problem in **Solve** and choose the best answer. Remind students to check their math.

- Examine **Check** with students. Discuss the correct and incorrect choices.

Page 19

- Monitor students as they complete **Your Turn**.

- Organize students in pairs or small groups and have them discuss each answer choice.

- Review the answers with the class.

ADDITIONAL ACTIVITY

See **Vocabulary Activity** (page 49).

Answer Analysis

3. Ⓐ Translated "of" as + (addition)

   Ⓑ Translated "of" as − (subtraction)

   Ⓒ Wrote "five-sixths" as $5\frac{1}{6}$

   ● This multiplication expression represents $\frac{5}{6}$ of $3\frac{1}{8}$.

4. Ⓐ Saw $\frac{3}{12}$ and $\frac{1}{12}$ shaded individually instead of their union.

   Ⓑ Considered the $\frac{1}{12}$ independent of the $\frac{1}{3}$

   ● The double-shaded region represents $\frac{3}{4}$ of $\frac{1}{3}$.

   Ⓓ Looked only at shaded $\frac{1}{3}$ and saw $\frac{1}{4}$ and $\frac{3}{4}$

5. ● $\frac{1}{3}$ of $\frac{3}{4}$ is $\frac{1}{\cancel{3}_1} \times \frac{\cancel{3}^1}{4} = \frac{1}{4}$.

   Ⓑ Added numerators and added denominators after cross-simplifying

   Ⓒ Added numerators and added denominators

   Ⓓ Wrote "one-third" as $1\frac{1}{3}$

6. Ⓐ Cross-simplified 3 and 9 to 1 and 2

   ● $\frac{2}{3} \times 4\frac{1}{2} = \frac{\cancel{2}^1}{\cancel{3}_1} \times \frac{\cancel{9}^3}{\cancel{2}_1} = \frac{3}{1} = 3$

   Ⓒ Added numerators and added denominators

   Ⓓ Failed to write mixed number as improper fraction, and just multiplied fraction parts

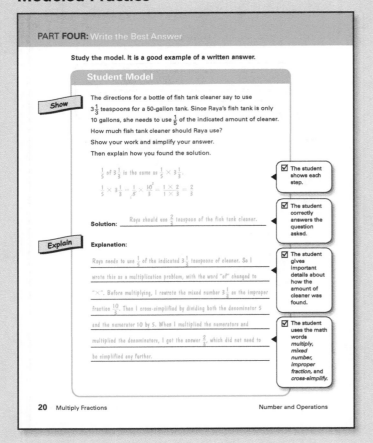

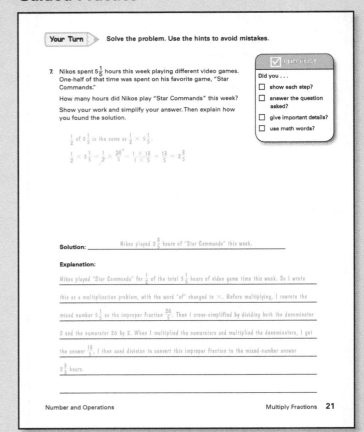

AT A GLANCE

Students study a model answer to an extended-response problem.

STEP BY STEP

PAGE 20

- Tell students that this page models building the solution to a problem one step at a time and writing to explain the solution.

- Have students read the problem in **Show**. Discuss how each mathematical step leads to the solution.

Tip: Make sure students don't get hung up on the numbers 10 and 50 in the given word problem. These are relevant to the situation but not needed as part of the mathematical solution. Have students cross out 50 and 10.

- Read **Explain** with students. Have students circle the math words in the explanation.

- Direct students' attention to the notes in the right margin. Tell students that this model would receive a high score for the reasons described in these notes.

PAGE 21

- Monitor students as they complete **Your Turn**.

- Encourage students to follow the **Checklist** to write the best answer.

- Have students discuss their work with a partner. Then discuss the correct answer as a class.

Answer and Explanation

7. See the sample answer. This answer shows all of the steps taken to solve the problem, by rewriting the mixed number as an improper fraction, and then using fraction multiplication steps. The solution answers the question. The explanation provides important details about how the problem was solved and uses the math words *multiply*, *mixed number*, *improper fraction*, and *cross-simplify*.

 ADDITIONAL ACTIVITY

See **Real-World Connection** (page 49).

 ADDITIONAL ACTIVITY

See **School-Home Connection** (page 49).

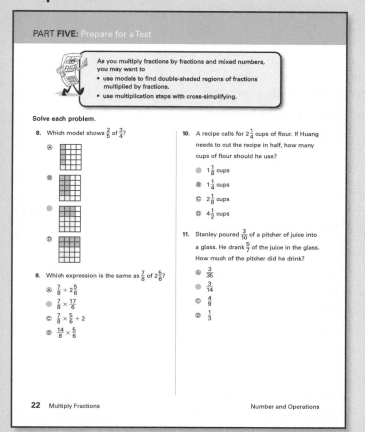

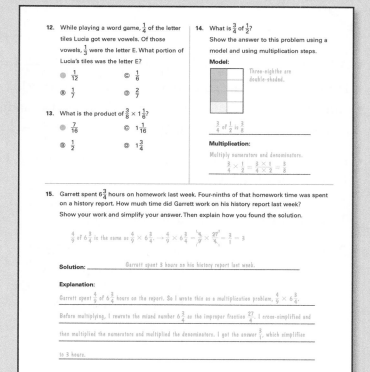

AT A GLANCE

Students practice solving fraction and mixed-number multiplication problems that might appear on a mathematics test.

STEP BY STEP

PAGES 22–23

- Tell students they will practice multiplying fractions by fractions, and fractions by mixed numbers. They will use models and multiplication steps to solve problems.
- Point out the tips at the top of page 22. Explain to students that these tips will help them answer the problems correctly.
- You may wish to have students review the hints for avoiding mistakes on page 19 as well.
- Tell students to complete problems 8–15 on pages 22 and 23. Encourage students to check their answers.
- Discuss the correct responses as a class.

Answers and Explanations

8. © This model shows that $\frac{3}{4}$ of the whole was shaded, and then $\frac{2}{5}$ of $\frac{3}{4}$ was double-shaded.

9. ® This expression shows "of" as multiplication, with the mixed number changed to an improper fraction.

10. ® $\frac{1}{2} \times 2\frac{1}{4} = \frac{1}{2} \times \frac{9}{4} = \frac{1 \times 9}{2 \times 4} = \frac{9}{8} = 1\frac{1}{8}$

11. ® $\frac{5}{7} \times \frac{3}{10_2} = \frac{1 \times 3}{7 \times 2} = \frac{3}{14}$

12. ® $\frac{1}{3} \times \frac{1}{4} = \frac{1 \times 1}{3 \times 4} = \frac{1}{12}$

13. ® $\frac{3}{8} \times 1\frac{1}{6} = \frac{3}{8} \times \frac{7}{6_2} = \frac{1 \times 7}{8 \times 2} = \frac{7}{16}$

14. The model shows $\frac{1}{2}$ shaded and $\frac{3}{4}$ of $\frac{1}{2}$ double-shaded. There is no simplification needed in the multiplication steps.

15. See the sample answer. This answer shows all of the steps taken to solve the problem using fraction multiplication. The solution answers the question. The explanation provides important details and uses the math words *multiply*, *mixed number*, *improper fraction*, and *cross-simplify*.

ASSESSMENT AND REMEDIATION

- Ask students to find $\frac{1}{6}$ of $2\frac{2}{3}$. $\left(\frac{1}{6} \times 2\frac{2}{3} = \frac{1}{\cancel{6}_{3}} \times \frac{\cancel{8}^{4}}{3} = \frac{1 \times 4}{3 \times 3} = \frac{4}{9}\right)$

- For students who are still struggling, use the chart below to guide remediation.

- After providing remediation, check students' understanding. Ask students to explain their steps while finding $\frac{2}{3}$ of $1\frac{5}{6}$. $\left(\frac{2}{3} \times 1\frac{5}{6} = \frac{\cancel{2}^{1}}{3} \times \frac{11}{\cancel{6}_{3}} = \frac{1 \times 11}{3 \times 3} = \frac{11}{9} = 1\frac{2}{9}\right)$

- If a student is still having difficulty, use *STAMS Book F*, Lesson 1, pages 4–15 and *Book E*, Lesson 7, pages 64–73.

If the error is . . .	Students may . . .	To remediate . . .
$2\frac{2}{18} = 2\frac{1}{9}$	not be seeing the mixed number as a single factor, and thus multiplied only the fraction portion of the mixed number by the first fraction.	Encourage students to put a box around the two factors in the problem. This will include the entire mixed number, whole and fraction parts. Remind students that the steps for multiplying fractions include numerators and denominators only. Thus, the mixed number must be changed to an improper fraction before applying the multiplication steps.
$2\frac{5}{6}$	have written this problem as an addition problem.	Reinforce the idea that the word "of" in a problem indicates multiplication. Have students get in the habit of putting a big X (for multiplication sign) over the word "of" in a problem.
4	have incorrectly cross-simplified, by dividing both denominators by 3.	Remind students that the simplification process, whether before or after multiplying, involves a numerator/denominator pair. Rewrite $\frac{1}{6} \times \frac{8}{3}$ as $\frac{1 \times 8}{6 \times 3}$ and explain that, like any fraction, the numerator and denominator can be divided by the same number (in this case $\frac{2}{2}$), since that is equivalent to dividing the whole fraction by 1.

 ADDITIONAL ACTIVITY

For students who have mastered the skills in this lesson, see **Challenge Activity** (page 49).

ADDITIONAL ACTIVITIES

Hands-on Activity
Use paper folding/shading to model a fraction of a fraction.

Materials: 1 sheet of plain paper and 2 different colored pencils or crayons per person

Have students model $\frac{1}{2}$ of $\frac{3}{4}$ by folding and shading a rectangular piece of paper. First, model the fraction $\frac{3}{4}$. Have students fold their rectangular paper into 4 parts, representing the fourths in the denominator. It is very important that the folding occurs in only one direction, either horizontally or vertically. Ask, "How can you show three-fourths?" Students should open the paper and shade 3 of the 4 parts with one color.

Next, model $\frac{1}{2}$ of $\frac{3}{4}$. Have students fold their rectangular paper into 2 parts, going in the *other direction*, representing the halves in the denominator of the first fraction. When they open the paper, ask "Do you still see the shaded part? What does it look like now?" There should now be 6 out of 8 parts shaded $\left(\frac{3}{4} = \frac{6}{8}\right)$. Ask, "How can you shade one-half of the shaded parts?" Students should shade 3 of the now 6 shaded parts in the other color. This will give 3 double-shaded parts out of a total 8 parts on the paper. So $\frac{1}{2}$ of $\frac{3}{4}$ is $\frac{3}{8}$.

Reteaching Activity
Cross-simplify using GCF lists.

Reinforce that cross-simplifying follows the same rules as any simplifying, but with crisscross pairs.

Using the problem in Part Two, ask students, "If you make an X through the four numbers in the multiplication problem, which numbers form pairs?" Students should identify 3, 3 and 5, 10. Have students list all the factors of each number and identify the greatest common factor (GCF) of each pair. Remind them that this is the number by which you divide. So 3 and 3 divided by the GCF 3 gives 1 and 1, and 5 and 10 divided by the GCF 5 gives 1 and 2.

Vocabulary Activity
Label a fraction multiplication problem using vocabulary terms.

Materials: a set of index cards

Write each of the vocabulary terms for this lesson on an index card. Put adhesive on the back of each card. Distribute the cards to students. Write the following problem on the board:
$\frac{4}{5} \times 7\frac{1}{2} = \frac{\cancel{4}^{2}}{\cancel{5}_{1}} \times \frac{\cancel{15}^{3}}{\cancel{2}_{1}} = \frac{6}{1} = 6.$

Have students come to the board and place their vocabulary terms around the problem as labels to the components of the fraction multiplication problem. Note: Some terms could correctly label more than one item in the problem.

Real-World Connection
Solve fraction multiplication problems using building plans.

Bring in copies of woodworking plans (such as building a birdhouse) that include several fractional and mixed-number measurements. Tell students that you want to make the object half the size. Have them calculate the new measurements of the materials by finding $\frac{1}{2}$ *of [measurement]*.

School-Home Connection
Inform families about multiplication.

Give each student a copy of the reproducible School-Home Connection for Lesson 2 (page 165) to share with family. The activity in the letter has the family use a recipe to multiply a mixed number by a fraction.

Challenge Activity
Multiply mixed number by mixed number.

Have students apply skills from the lesson to find the product of two mixed numbers. Example:
$4\frac{1}{5} \times 3\frac{1}{3} = \boxed{}$ $\left(\frac{\cancel{21}^{7}}{\cancel{5}_{1}} \times \frac{\cancel{10}^{2}}{\cancel{3}_{1}} = \frac{14}{1} = 14\right)$

Fractions

LESSON OBJECTIVES

Students will:

- Use a model to divide a whole number by a unit fraction.
- Divide a whole number by a fraction using a standard algorithm.

PREREQUISITES

Students should be able to:

- Multiply whole numbers by fractions.
- Model fractions.
- Simplify fractions.

RELATED *STAMS*® LESSONS

- **Book F – Lesson 1**

  Multiply Whole Numbers By Fractions shows how to multiply a whole number by a fraction.

- **Book F – Lesson 2**

  Multiply Fractions shows how to multiply fractions by fractions and mixed numbers.

VOCABULARY

PAGE 24

- **fraction:** a number that compares a part, the numerator, to a whole, the denominator
- **unit fraction:** a fraction with a numerator of 1
- **dividend:** in a division sentence, the number being divided
- **divisor:** in a division sentence, the number to divide by

PAGE 25

- **quotient:** the result of division

PAGE 26

- **reciprocal:** the multiplicative inverse of a number; a fraction with the numerator and denominator switched
- **numerator:** the top number of a fraction; tells the number of equal parts described by the fraction
- **denominator:** the bottom number of a fraction; tells the total number of equal parts in a whole

MATH BACKGROUND

When you divide a whole number by a fraction, the result will always be greater than that whole number. Help students understand how the models in Part One of this lesson demonstrate this concept. The models show a given number of wholes, which is the dividend. To divide by a fraction means to divide those wholes into parts. If each whole is separated into multiple parts, the number of parts will be greater than the number of wholes.

To find the quotient, students can count the number of divisor groups. Since each whole has multiple parts, students are counting the total of some equal groups, which models multiplication. The algorithm for dividing by a fraction is to multiply by its reciprocal, or multiplicative inverse. To find the reciprocal of a fraction, simply switch the numerator and denominator. Dividing by a fraction is the same as multiplying by its reciprocal because division and multiplication are inverse operations.

Interactive Whiteboard

Visualize Dividing Whole Numbers by Fractions

Go to the *Interactive Whiteboard Lessons* to bring Parts One and Two to life. Use features such as interactive fraction models to deepen students' understanding of dividing whole numbers by fractions.

Modeled Instruction

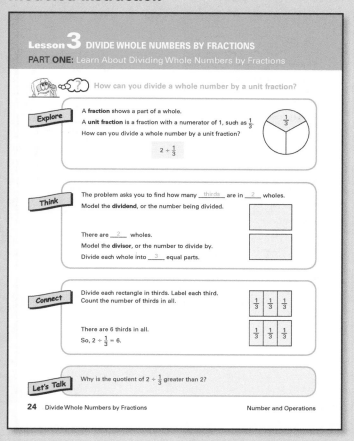

Guided Instruction

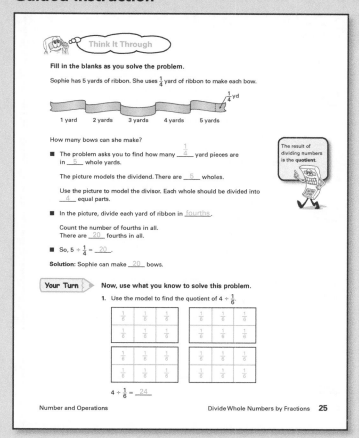

AT A GLANCE

Students activate their background knowledge about fractions and then learn how to use a model to divide a whole number by a unit fraction.

STEP BY STEP

PAGE 24

- Introduce the **Question** at the top of the page.
- Have students study the expression shown in **Explore** and connect the image to the unit fraction.
- Read **Think** with students. Emphasize that the two wholes are being divided into thirds. Pause so students can say aloud the responses in orange.
- Discuss **Connect** with students. Help students see the connection between the model and the division sentence.

Tip: Write three other division sentences that involve a whole number divided by a unit fraction on the board. Have students draw a model for each.

- Organize students in pairs or groups for **Let's Talk** and monitor their discussions.

- Be sure students understand that division of a whole number by a unit fraction results in a whole number greater than the dividend.

PAGE 25

- Read the **Think It Through** problem with students.
- Guide students as they solve the problem. Help them determine that they can use division in this problem because each bow uses $\frac{1}{4}$ yard of ribbon.
- Help students see that they should model 5 wholes and then divide each whole into fourths. The number of fourths is the answer, or quotient.
- Monitor students as they complete **Your Turn**. Then discuss the correct answer.

Error Alert: Students who gave an answer of $\frac{4}{6}$, or $\frac{2}{3}$, found one-sixth of 4 instead of how many sixths are in 4.

ADDITIONAL ACTIVITY

See **Hands-on Activity** (page 57).

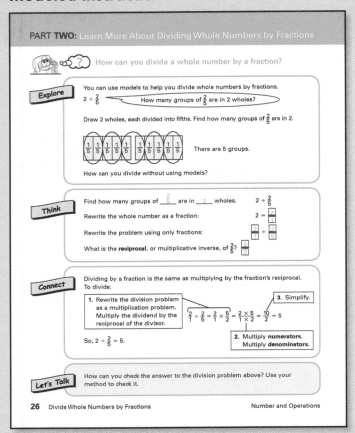

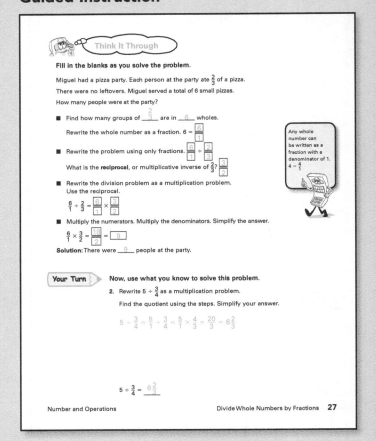

AT A GLANCE

Students learn that dividing by a fraction is the same as multiplying by the fraction's reciprocal.

STEP BY STEP

PAGE 26

- Introduce the **Question** at the top of the page.
- Read **Explore** with students. Reinforce how the model shows the quotient by having students count how many $\frac{2}{5}$ are in 2 wholes.

ELL Support: Check if students understand the given division problem: *2 divided by two-fifths*. Point out that 2 is the starting amount, or dividend, and it is being separated into groups of two-fifths.

- Read **Think** with students. Pause so students can read aloud the numbers in orange.
- Tell students to study the number sentence in **Connect**. Test their understanding by asking why $\frac{2}{1}$ is the first factor and $\frac{5}{2}$ is the second factor. Explain that dividing by a fraction is the same as multiplying by its reciprocal because division and multiplication are inverse operations.

- Organize students in pairs or groups for **Let's Talk** and monitor their discussions.
- Be sure students know that a division problem can be checked by multiplying the quotient by the divisor. The product should equal the dividend.

PAGE 27

- Read the **Think It Through** problem with students.
- Guide students as they solve the problem. Pause for students to fill in missing information. Then discuss each response.

Tip: Have students practice finding the reciprocal of various fractions.

- Monitor students as they complete **Your Turn**. Then discuss the correct answer.

Error Alert: Students who found an incorrect quotient may not have used the reciprocal of the divisor in the multiplication sentence.

 ADDITIONAL ACTIVITY

See **Reteaching Activity** (page 57).

Modeled Practice

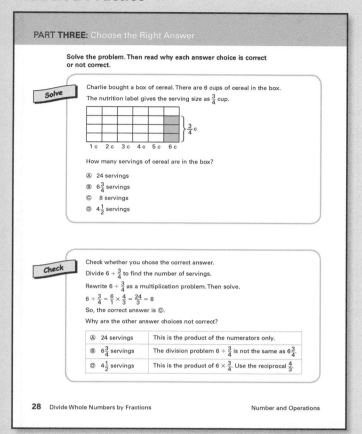

Guided Practice

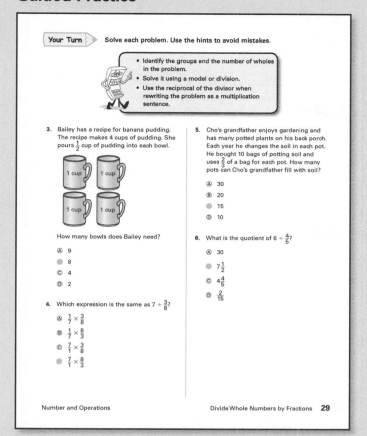

AT A GLANCE

Students reinforce their understanding of dividing by fractions through solving a multiple-choice problem and analyzing correct and incorrect answer choices.

STEP BY STEP

PAGE 28

- Tell students that this page models finding the correct answer to a multiple-choice problem.
- Have students read the problem in **Solve** and choose the best answer. Remind students to check their math.
- Examine **Check** with students. Discuss the correct and incorrect choices.

PAGE 29

- Monitor students as they complete **Your Turn**.
- Organize students in pairs or small groups and have them discuss why each answer choice is correct or not and what errors may have been made.
- Review the answers with the class.

 **ADDITIONAL ACTIVITY**

See **Vocabulary Activity** (page 57).

Answer Analysis

3. Ⓐ Multiplied 4 times 2 and added the numerator
   - ● The picture shows 4 wholes; $4 \div \frac{1}{2} = 8$.
   - Ⓒ Used the number of cups the recipe makes
   - Ⓓ Multiplied instead of divided

4. Ⓐ Multiplied the reciprocal of the dividend and the divisor
   - Ⓑ Multiplied the reciprocal of the dividend and the reciprocal of divisor
   - Ⓒ Did not use the reciprocal
   - ● Dividing by a fraction is the same as multiplying by the fraction's reciprocal.

5. Ⓐ Found the product of the numerators
   - Ⓑ Multiplied 10 times 2
   - ● $10 \div \frac{2}{3} = \frac{10}{1} \times \frac{3}{2} = \frac{30}{2} = 15$
   - Ⓓ Used the number of bags

6. Ⓐ This is the product of the numerators.
   - ● $6 \div \frac{4}{5} = \frac{6}{1} \times \frac{5}{4} = \frac{30}{4} = 7\frac{2}{4} = 7\frac{1}{2}$
   - Ⓒ Found $6 \times \frac{4}{5}$
   - Ⓓ Multiplied the reciprocal of the dividend and the divisor

Modeled Practice

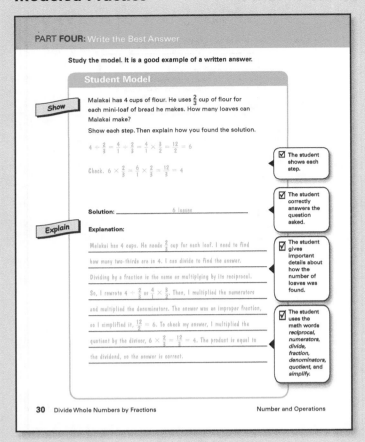

Guided Practice

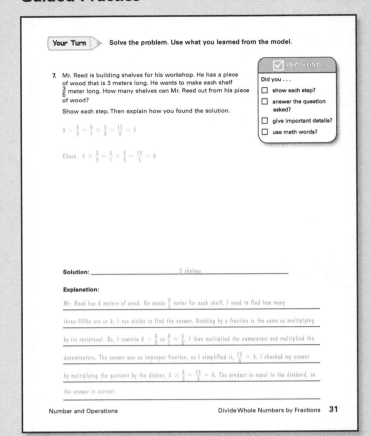

AT A GLANCE

Students study a model answer to an extended-response problem.

STEP BY STEP

PAGE 30

- Tell students that this page models building the solution to a problem one step at a time and writing to explain the solution.

- Have students read the problem in **Show**. Discuss how the expression and each mathematical step lead to the solution.

> **Tip:** Suggest students draw a model to help them visualize the problem. They can draw 4 rectangles, divide them into thirds, and circle groups of two-thirds.

- Read **Explain** with students. Have students circle the math words in the explanation.

- Direct students' attention to the notes in the right margin. Tell students that this model would receive a high score for the reasons described in these notes.

PAGE 31

- Monitor students as they complete **Your Turn**.
- Encourage students to follow the **Checklist** to write the best answer.
- Have students discuss their work with a partner. Then discuss the correct answer as a class.

Answer and Explanation

7. See the sample answer. This answer shows all of the steps taken to solve the problem, including writing a number sentence. The solution answers the question. The explanation provides important details about how the problem was solved and uses the math words *reciprocal*, *divisor*, and *quotient*. (If student draws a correct model to find the solution and explains the response fully, accept that answer.)

 ADDITIONAL ACTIVITY

See **Real-World Connection** (page 57).

 ADDITIONAL ACTIVITY

See **School-Home Connection** (page 57).

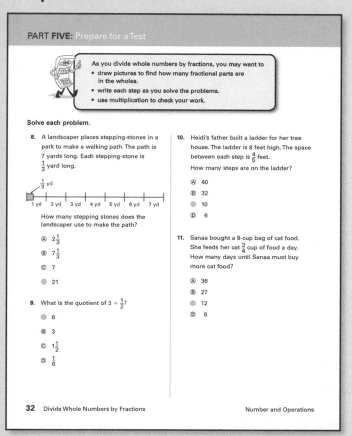

12. How many $\frac{1}{4}$ hours are in 5 hours?

- (A) 1
- (B) 2
- (C) 9
- ● 20

13. Which expression is the same as $9 \div \frac{2}{3}$?

- (A) $\frac{2}{27}$
- (B) 6
- ● $13\frac{1}{2}$
- (D) 27

14. For dessert, Tamara served blueberry parfaits. She put $\frac{3}{8}$ cup of blueberries in each bowl. She used a total of 3 cups of blueberries. How many bowls did she fill?

Write a division problem and solve to show the number of bowls.

Division problem:

$3 \div \frac{3}{8} = \frac{3}{1} \times \frac{8}{3} = \frac{24}{3} = 8$

Solution:

_____ 8 bowls

15. Reece works at a bakery. Today he is baking carrot nut muffins. The recipe calls for $\frac{3}{4}$ cup of chopped walnuts for each batch. Reece has a total of 6 cups of walnuts. How many batches of carrot muffins can Reece bake?

Show each step. Then explain how you found the solution.

$6 \div \frac{3}{4} = \frac{6}{1} \div \frac{3}{4} = \frac{6}{1} \times \frac{4}{3} = \frac{24}{3} = 8$

Check. $8 \times \frac{3}{4} = \frac{8}{1} \times \frac{3}{4} = \frac{24}{4} = 6$

Solution: _____ 8 batches

Explanation:

To find how many three-fourths are in 6, I can divide. Dividing by a fraction is the same as multiplying by its reciprocal. So, I rewrote $6 \div \frac{3}{4}$ as $\frac{6}{1} \times \frac{4}{3}$. Then, I multiplied numerators and multiplied denominators. The answer was an improper fraction, so I simplified it, $\frac{24}{3} = 8$. To check my answer, I multiplied the quotient by the divisor, $8 \times \frac{3}{4} = \frac{24}{4} = 6$. The product is equal to the dividend, so the answer is correct.

Number and Operations   Divide Whole Numbers by Fractions **33**

AT A GLANCE

Students practice using division of whole numbers by fractions to solve problems that might appear on a mathematics test.

STEP BY STEP

PAGES 32–33

- Tell students they will practice solving division problems that involve whole numbers divided by fractions.
- Point out the tips at the top of page 32. Explain to students that these tips will help them answer the problems correctly.
- You may wish to have students review the hints for avoiding mistakes on page 29 as well.
- Tell students to complete problems 8–15 on pages 32 and 33. Encourage students to check their answers.
- Discuss the correct responses as a class.

Answers and Explanations

8. (D) Find how many $\frac{1}{3}$s are in 7. Divide.

$$7 \div \frac{1}{3} = \frac{7}{1} \times \frac{3}{1} = \frac{21}{1} = 21$$

9. (A) Find how many $\frac{1}{2}$s are in 3.

$$3 \div \frac{1}{2} = \frac{3}{1} \times \frac{2}{1} = \frac{6}{1} = 6$$

10. (C) Find how many groups of $\frac{4}{5}$ are in 8. Divide.

$$8 \div \frac{4}{5} = \frac{8}{1} \times \frac{5}{4} = \frac{40}{4} = 10$$

11. (C) Find how many groups of $\frac{3}{4}$ are in 9. Divide.

$$9 \div \frac{3}{4} = \frac{9}{1} \times \frac{4}{3} = \frac{36}{3} = 12$$

12. (D) Find how many $\frac{1}{4}$s are in 5. Divide.

$$5 \div \frac{1}{4} = \frac{5}{1} \times \frac{4}{1} = \frac{20}{1} = 20$$

13. (C) $9 \div \frac{2}{3} = \frac{9}{1} \times \frac{3}{2} = \frac{27}{2} = 13\frac{1}{2}$

(continued on page 56)

(continued from page 55)

14. Find how many groups of $\frac{3}{8}$ are in 3. Divide.
$$3 \div \frac{3}{8} = \frac{3}{1} \times \frac{8}{3} = \frac{24}{3} = 8$$

15. See the sample answer. This answer shows all of the steps the student took to solve the problem. The solution answers the question. The explanation provides important details about how the student solved the problem and uses the math words *divide, reciprocal, fraction, multiply, numerators, denominators, improper fraction,* and *quotient*.

(If student draws a correct model to find the solution and explains the response fully, accept that answer.)

 ASSESSMENT AND REMEDIATION

- Ask students to solve the problem $2 \div \frac{1}{8}$. *(16)*
- For students who are still struggling, use the chart below to guide remediation.
- After providing remediation, check students' understanding. Ask students to explain their steps while solving the problem $6 \div \frac{2}{3}$. *(9)*
- If a student is still having difficulty, use *STAMS Book F*, Lesson 2, pages 14–23.

If the error is . . .	Students may . . .	To remediate . . .
$\frac{1}{4}$	have not used the reciprocal of the divisor when rewriting the expression as a multiplication problem.	Stress that division and multiplication are inverse operations. Review that dividing by a fraction is the same as multiplying by the reciprocal, or its multiplicative inverse. Show a model of 2 rectangles divided into 8 equal parts. Show that there are 16 one-eighths in 2 wholes, or 16 equal parts.
$\frac{1}{16}$	have used the reciprocal of the dividend instead of the divisor when writing the division as a multiplication sentence.	Label the parts of the division sentence. Circle the divisor. Have student practice rewriting three other division sentences as multiplication sentences using the reciprocal of the divisor.
4	have rewritten the division problem as $\frac{1}{2} \times \frac{8}{1} = \frac{8}{2} = 4$.	Have students model both the division sentence and the multiplication sentence to demonstrate that they are not equal. Demonstrate that using only the reciprocal of the divisor creates two equal equations.

 ADDITIONAL ACTIVITY

For students who have mastered the skills in this lesson, see **Challenge Activity** (page 57).

ADDITIONAL ACTIVITIES

Hands-on Activity
Use fraction circles to model dividing a whole number by a fraction.

Materials: 3 sets of fraction bars per group

Organize students in small groups and distribute fraction circles. Have students model $3 \div \frac{1}{6}$. Write the sentence *There are _____ sixths in 3 wholes* on the board. Students model this by using the $\frac{1}{6}$ fraction pieces to show 3 wholes. Establish that each whole is made with 6 pieces, for a total of 18 pieces. There are 18 sixths in 3 wholes. So, the quotient of $3 \div \frac{1}{6}$ is 18.

Repeat with other division problems involving a whole number divided by a unit fraction.

Reteaching Activity
Practice rewriting division problems as multiplication problems.

Materials: index cards, craft sticks

Distribute five index cards and craft sticks to each pair of students. Explain to students that the sticks will be used as fraction bars. On an index card, tell students to write a division sign on one side and a multiplication sign on the other.

Have students write digits on the index cards and place them to show $\frac{3}{1} \div \frac{3}{5}$. Ask, "Which number is the divisor?" $\left(\frac{3}{5}\right)$ Tell students that dividing by a fraction is the same as multiplying by its reciprocal because division and multiplication are inverse, or opposite, operations. Guide students to show the reciprocal of the divisor by switching the numerator and denominator cards. "What is the reciprocal of $\frac{3}{5}$?" $\left(\frac{5}{3}\right)$ Have students flip the division sign card to show the multiplication sign. "What multiplication sentence is the same as $\frac{3}{1} \div \frac{3}{5}$?" $\left(\frac{3}{1} \times \frac{5}{3}\right)$

Repeat with other division expressions.

Vocabulary Activity
Play bingo to reinforce terms.

Materials: blank sheets of paper, counters

Have each student create a grid by folding a sheet of paper in thirds horizontally and then in thirds vertically. Display the vocabulary words. Then tell students to write BINGO in the center box and the vocabulary words in the other boxes.

Read a definition and have students cover the corresponding word on their grid with a counter. The winner for each round is the first student to cover 3 spaces vertically, horizontally, or diagonally.

Real-World Connection
Solve whole number divided by fraction problems using recipes.

Bring in copies of a recipe that includes several ingredients with fractional quantities. Tell students that you have a certain whole-number amount of an ingredient. For that ingredient, have them use division to calculate how many batches of the recipe you could make.

School-Home Connection
Inform families about dividing by fractions.

Give each student a copy of the reproducible School-Home Connection for Lesson 3 (page 167) to share with family. The activity in the letter has the family plan a project by dividing a whole number by a fraction.

Challenge Activity
Brainstorm fraction division situations.

Have students brainstorm situations that involve the division of whole numbers by fractions. Have students describe a specific situation, and provide a division problem that models the situation. Students should solve the problem.

Fractions

LESSON OBJECTIVES

Students will:

- Divide a fraction by a fraction using a model.
- Understand and apply the concept that dividing by a fraction is the same as multiplying by the reciprocal.

PREREQUISITES

Students should be able to:

- Multiply fractions.
- Rewrite improper fractions as mixed numbers.
- Cross-simplify factors and simplify answers.

RELATED *STAMS*® LESSONS

- **Book F – Lesson 2**

  Multiply Fractions by Fractions shows students how to multiply fractions and mixed numbers.

- **Book F – Lesson 3**

  Divide Whole Numbers by Fractions illustrates how a fraction division problem means the separation of equal groups.

VOCABULARY

PAGE 34

- **division:** the process by which a number is separated into equal-sized groups
- **fraction:** a number that compares a part, the numerator, to a whole, the denominator
- **dividend:** in a division problem, the number being divided
- **divisor:** in a division problem, the number being divided by
- **quotient:** the result of division

PAGE 36

- **reciprocal:** the multiplicative inverse of a number; with fractions, the numerator and denominator are switched
- **greatest common factor (GCF):** the greatest positive integer that is a common factor of two or more numbers

MATH BACKGROUND

In Part One of this lesson, students divide fractions by modeling. Because it is easier to understand, the example has fractions with the same denominator. Using a model to divide fractions reinforces the division concept of separating an amount into equal groups.

In Part Two, students learn an algorithm for fraction division. They learn that to multiply two fractions, they can simply multiply the first fraction by the reciprocal (multiplicative inverse) of the second fraction. For example, $\frac{4}{1} \div \frac{1}{2}$ is the same as $\frac{4}{1} \times \frac{2}{1}$. This makes sense because to find the number of halves in 4 wholes, count 2 halves for each whole, or multiply 2 halves times 4 wholes.

Interactive Whiteboard

Visualize Dividing Fractions by Fractions

Go to the *Interactive Whiteboard Lessons* to bring Parts One and Two to life. Use features such as interactive fraction models to deepen students' understanding of dividing fractions by fractions.

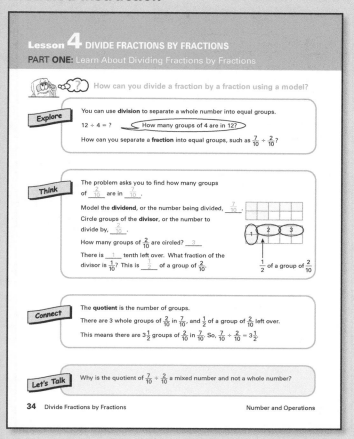

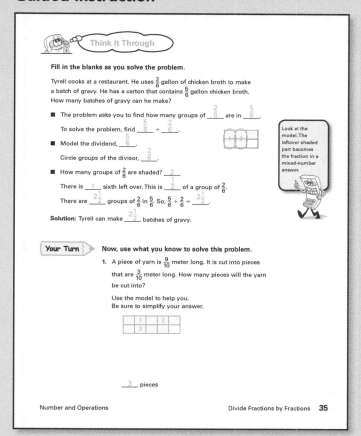

AT A GLANCE

Students activate their background knowledge about division as a way to separate a number into equal groups, and then apply the concept to fraction division using models.

STEP BY STEP

PAGE 34

- Introduce the **Question** at the top of the page.
- Have students read the **Explore** section.

Tip: Ask students how they could model $12 \div 4$ using counters. *(Separate 12 counters into 3 equal groups of 4.)* It's very important that students have a clear conceptual understanding of division with whole numbers before moving on to fractions.

- Read **Think** with students. Reinforce the fact that, although the one shaded square remaining is $\frac{1}{10}$ of the whole, it is $\frac{1}{2}$ of a *group*. A quotient reflects the number of equal-sized *groups*. Pause so students can say aloud the numbers in orange.
- Discuss **Connect** with students.

- Organize students in pairs or groups for **Let's Talk** and monitor their discussions.
- Make sure they understand that the quotient is a mixed number and not a whole number, because $\frac{7}{10}$ cannot be divided "evenly" into groups of $\frac{2}{10}$.

PAGE 35

- Read the **Think It Through** problem with students.
- Guide students as they solve the problem.

ELL Support: To help students remember which part is the dividend and which is the divisor, share that *divisor* is the same word form as *mentor* or *counselor*. The suffix *-or* means one who does something. The divisor does something to (separates) the dividend.

- Monitor students as they complete **Your Turn**. Then discuss the correct answer.

Error Alert: Students who answered $\frac{6}{10} = \frac{3}{5}$ may have circled $\frac{3}{10}$ of the whole and identified how many shaded parts were left over (subtraction).

 ADDITIONAL ACTIVITY

See **Hands-on Activity** (page 65).

Modeled Instruction

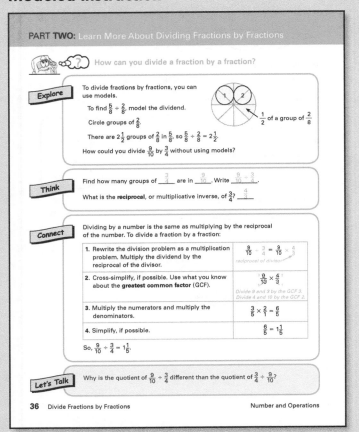

Guided Instruction

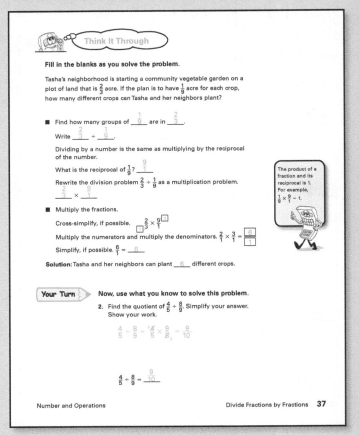

AT A GLANCE

Students learn to divide a fraction by a fraction by rewriting the problem as multiplication by the reciprocal.

STEP BY STEP

PAGE 36

- Introduce the **Question** at the top of the page.
- Read **Explore** with students. Ask what makes the problem $\frac{9}{10} \div \frac{2}{3}$ difficult to solve by modeling. (*different denominators*)

ELL Support: Explain the meaning of *reciprocal* to students. Have them multiply $\frac{3}{4} \times \frac{4}{3}$ to get 1. Then have them multiply $\frac{5}{8} \times \frac{8}{5}$ to get 1. What pattern do they notice? (*A fraction times its reciprocal equals 1.*)

- Read **Think** with students. Pause so students can read aloud the numbers in orange.
- Read through the solution steps in **Connect,** making sure students understand each step.

Tip: Point out the cross-simplification. Emphasize that if a numerator in one fraction is divided by a number, the denominator in the other fraction must also be divided by that same number. Review GCF if necessary.

- Organize students in pairs or groups for **Let's Talk** and monitor their discussions.
- Point out that order matters for division. The problems $3 \div 6$ and $6 \div 3$ represent different situations. The first indicates 3 wholes divided into 6 parts, and the second indicates 6 wholes divided into 3 parts.

PAGE 37

- Solve the **Think It Through** problem with students.
- Have students check the answer by multiplying $\frac{1}{9}$ acre by 6, getting $\frac{6}{9} = \frac{2}{3}$ acre.
- Monitor students as they complete **Your Turn**. Then discuss the correct answer.

Error Alert: Students who answered $\frac{10}{9} = 1\frac{1}{9}$ may have used the reciprocal of the dividend.

 ADDITIONAL ACTIVITY

See **Reteaching Activity** (page 65).

Modeled Practice

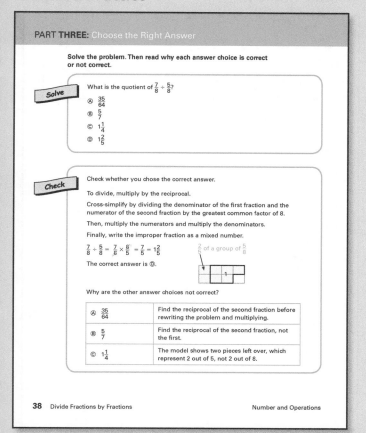

Guided Practice

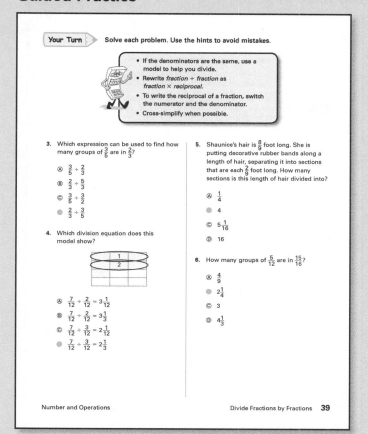

AT A GLANCE
. . . .

Students reinforce their understanding of fraction division through solving a multiple-choice problem and analyzing correct and incorrect answer choices.

STEP BY STEP
. . . .

PAGE 38

- Tell students that this page models finding the correct answer to a multiple-choice problem.
- Have students read the problem in **Solve** and choose the best answer. Remind students to check their math.
- Examine **Check** with students. Discuss the correct and incorrect choices.

PAGE 39

- Monitor students as they complete **Your Turn**.
- Organize students in pairs or small groups and have them discuss why each answer choice is correct or not and what errors may have been made.
- Review the answers with the class.

ADDITIONAL ACTIVITY
. . . .

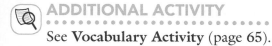

See **Vocabulary Activity** (page 65).

Answer Analysis

3. Ⓐ Switched dividend and divisor
   Ⓑ Used reciprocal but kept division sign
   Ⓒ Switched dividend and divisor; used reciprocal
   ● This shows $\frac{2}{3}$ separated into groups of $\frac{3}{5}$.

4. Ⓐ Wrote number of parts in a group as the whole-number part of quotient
   Ⓑ Wrote number of parts in a group as the whole-number part of quotient
   Ⓒ Wrote remaining shaded part as $\frac{1}{12}$ instead of $\frac{1}{3}$
   ● This reflects the model: $2\frac{1}{3}$ groups of $\frac{3}{12}$ in $\frac{7}{12}$.

5. Ⓐ Multiplied with reciprocal of first fraction
   ● $\frac{8}{9} \div \frac{2}{9} = \frac{4\,\cancel{8}}{\cancel{9}_{1}} \times \frac{\cancel{9}^{1}}{\cancel{2}_{1}} = \frac{4}{1} = 4$
   Ⓒ Multiplied with reciprocal of both fractions
   Ⓓ Multiplied numerators and divided denominators

6. Ⓐ Multiplied with reciprocal of first fraction
   ● $\frac{15}{16} \div \frac{5}{12} = \frac{3\,\cancel{15}}{4\,\cancel{16}} \times \frac{\cancel{12}^{3}}{\cancel{5}_{1}} = \frac{9}{4} = 2\frac{1}{4}$
   Ⓒ Cross-simplified by dividing 12 by 3 and 16 by 4
   Ⓓ Divided numerators, divided denominators, combined results into a mixed number

Modeled Practice

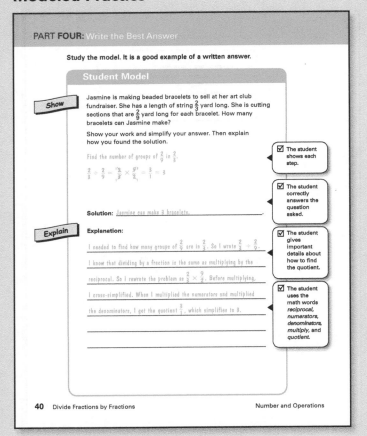

Guided Practice

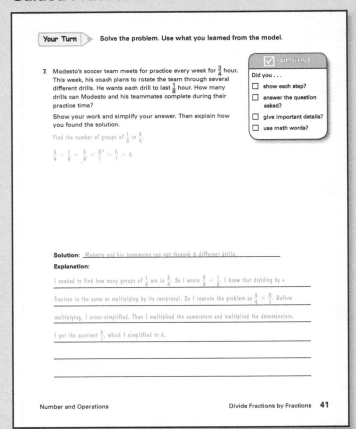

Students study a model answer to an extended-response problem.

STEP BY STEP

PAGE 40

- Tell students that this page models building the solution to a problem one step at a time and writing to explain the solution.

- Have students read the problem in **Show**. Discuss how each mathematical step leads to the solution.

> Tip: Help students identify the dividend and divisor by making a sketch. Draw a line representing the string, which is labeled $\frac{2}{3}$ yard. This will get $\frac{2}{3}$ set in their minds as the starting value (dividend), which is then separated (divided) into groups (divisor), each $\frac{2}{9}$ yard long.

- Read **Explain** with students. Have students circle the math words in the explanation.

- Direct students' attention to the notes in the right margin. Tell students that this model would receive a high score for the reasons described in these notes.

PAGE 41

- Monitor students as they complete **Your Turn**.

- Encourage students to follow the **Checklist** to write the best answer.

- Have students discuss their work with a partner. Then discuss the correct answer as a class.

Answer and Explanation

7. See the sample answer. This answer shows all of the steps taken to solve the problem, by setting up a fraction division problem, rewriting it as multiplication by the reciprocal, and then using fraction multiplication steps. The solution answers the question. The explanation provides important details about how the problem was solved and uses the math words *reciprocal*, *numerators*, *denominators*, *multiply*, and *quotient*.

 ADDITIONAL ACTIVITY

See **Real-World Connection** (page 65).

 ADDITIONAL ACTIVITY

See **School-Home Connection** (page 65).

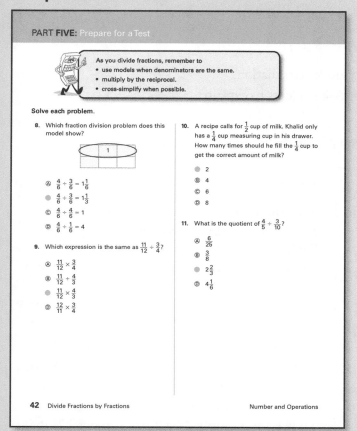

Independent Practice

Independent Practice

PART **FIVE**: Prepare for a Test

As you divide fractions, remember to
- use models when denominators are the same.
- multiply by the reciprocal.
- cross-simplify when possible.

Solve each problem.

8. Which fraction division problem does this model show?

⬭ 1

Ⓐ $\frac{4}{6} \div \frac{3}{2} = 1\frac{1}{6}$

⬤ $\frac{4}{6} \div \frac{3}{6} = 1\frac{1}{3}$

Ⓒ $\frac{4}{6} \div \frac{4}{6} = 1$

Ⓓ $\frac{4}{6} \div \frac{1}{6} = 4$

9. Which expression is the same as $\frac{11}{12} \div \frac{3}{4}$?

Ⓐ $\frac{11}{12} \times \frac{3}{4}$

Ⓑ $\frac{11}{12} \div \frac{4}{3}$

⬤ $\frac{11}{12} \times \frac{4}{3}$

Ⓓ $\frac{12}{11} \times \frac{3}{4}$

10. A recipe calls for $\frac{1}{2}$ cup of milk. Khalid only has a $\frac{1}{4}$ cup measuring cup in his drawer. How many times should he fill the $\frac{1}{4}$ cup to get the correct amount of milk?

⬤ 2

Ⓑ 4

Ⓒ 6

Ⓓ 8

11. What is the quotient of $\frac{4}{5} \div \frac{3}{10}$?

Ⓐ $\frac{6}{25}$

Ⓑ $\frac{3}{8}$

⬤ $2\frac{2}{3}$

Ⓓ $4\frac{1}{6}$

42   Divide Fractions by Fractions   Number and Operations

---

12. Which expression can be used to find how many groups of $\frac{2}{7}$ are in $\frac{5}{8}$?

Ⓐ $\frac{2}{7} \div \frac{5}{8}$

Ⓑ $\frac{2}{7} \times \frac{5}{8}$

⬤ $\frac{5}{8} \div \frac{2}{7}$

Ⓓ $\frac{5}{8} \times \frac{2}{7}$

13. Vivian has $\frac{2}{3}$ box of crackers. She packs a snack bag with $\frac{1}{4}$ box. How many bags can she fill?

Ⓐ $\frac{1}{6}$

Ⓑ $\frac{3}{8}$

⬤ $2\frac{2}{3}$

Ⓓ 6

14. Henry has $\frac{9}{10}$ sheet of stickers. He uses $\frac{4}{10}$ sheet for each art project. How many projects can Henry create?

Show the answer to this problem using a model and using the steps for division.

Model:

$\frac{1}{4}$ of a group of $\frac{4}{10}$

$\frac{9}{10}$ divided into groups of $\frac{4}{10}$

is $2\frac{1}{4}$ groups.

Division:

$\frac{9}{10} \div \frac{4}{10} = \frac{9}{10} \times \frac{10^1}{4} = \frac{9}{4} = 2\frac{1}{4}$

15. Avia and her aunt are canning peaches. They have $\frac{11}{12}$ crate of peaches. They want to put $\frac{1}{6}$ crate in each jar. How many jars can they fill?

Show your work and simplify your answer. Then explain how you found the solution.

$\frac{11}{12} \div \frac{1}{6} = \frac{11}{{}_2\cancel{12}} \times \frac{\cancel{6}^1}{1} = \frac{11}{2} = 5\frac{1}{2}$

Solution: Avia and her aunt can fill $5\frac{1}{2}$ jars.

Explanation:

I needed to find how many groups of $\frac{1}{6}$ are in $\frac{11}{12}$. So I wrote $\frac{11}{12} \div \frac{1}{6}$. I found the reciprocal of $\frac{1}{6}$ and rewrote the problem as $\frac{11}{12} \times \frac{6}{1}$. Next, I cross-simplified. Then, I multiplied the numerators and the denominators. I got the quotient $\frac{11}{2}$, which I simplified to $5\frac{1}{2}$.

Number and Operations   Divide Fractions by Fractions   43

AT A GLANCE

Students practice solving fraction division problems that might appear on a mathematics test.

STEP BY STEP

Pages 42–43

- Tell students that they will practice solving fraction division problems. They may use models when appropriate but should be encouraged to rely on the standard fraction division steps.
- Point out the tips at the top of page 42. Explain to students that these tips will help them answer the problems correctly.
- You may wish to have students review the hints for avoiding mistakes on page 39 as well.
- Tell students to complete problems 8–15 on pages 42 and 43. Encourage students to check their answers to see if they are reasonable.
- Discuss the correct responses as a class.

Answers and Explanations

8. Ⓑ This reflects the model: $1\frac{1}{3}$ groups of $\frac{3}{6}$ in $\frac{4}{6}$.

9. Ⓒ This expression shows division of the fraction rewritten as multiplication by the reciprocal.

10. Ⓐ $\frac{1}{2} \div \frac{1}{4} = \frac{1}{2} \times \frac{4}{1} = \frac{4}{2} = 2$

11. Ⓒ $\frac{4}{5} \div \frac{3}{10} = \frac{4}{\cancel{5}_1} \times \frac{\cancel{10}^2}{3} = \frac{8}{3} = 2\frac{2}{3}$

12. Ⓒ This expression is $\frac{5}{8}$ separated into groups of $\frac{2}{7}$.

13. Ⓒ $\frac{2}{3} \div \frac{1}{4} = \frac{2}{3} \times \frac{4}{1} = \frac{8}{3} = 2\frac{2}{3}$

14. The model should show $\frac{9}{10}$ shaded and $2\frac{1}{4}$ groups of $\frac{4}{10}$ circled. The division steps should show multiplication of the reciprocal, with the answer $2\frac{1}{4}$.

15. See the sample answer. This answer shows all of the steps taken to solve the problem using fraction multiplication. The solution answers the question. The explanation provides important details and uses the math words *reciprocal*, *multiply*, *numerators*, *denominators*, and *quotient*.

ASSESSMENT AND REMEDIATION

- Ask students to find the quotient of $\frac{5}{6} \div \frac{2}{3}$. $\left(\frac{5}{6} \div \frac{2}{3} = \frac{5}{{}_2\cancel{6}} \times \frac{\cancel{3}^{1}}{2} = \frac{5}{4} = 1\frac{1}{4} \right)$

- For students who are still struggling, use the chart below to guide remediation.

- After providing remediation, check students' understanding. Ask students to explain their steps while finding the quotient of $\frac{8}{9} \div \frac{3}{4}$. $\left(\frac{8}{9} \div \frac{3}{4} = \frac{8}{9} \times \frac{4}{3} = \frac{32}{27} = 1\frac{5}{27} \right)$

- If a student is still having difficulty, use *STAMS Book F*, Lesson 3, pages 24–33.

If the error is . . .	Students may . . .	To remediate . . .
$4\frac{1}{2}$	have divided numerators ($2\frac{1}{2}$) and divided denominators (2), and then added results.	Reiterate that division of a fraction is always rewritten as multiplication by the reciprocal. Explain why this works by giving a whole-number example: $6 \div 2$ is like finding *half* of 6, which is $6 \times \frac{1}{2}$.
$\frac{5}{9}$	have multiplied the fractions without finding the reciprocal of the divisor.	Use the simpler problem $6 \div \frac{1}{2}$ to show why multiplying by a reciprocal works. To model this problem, draw 6 wholes. Show that to divide by $\frac{1}{2}$, each whole is split into two parts. So 6 wholes are multiplied by 2 parts to get 12. Point out that 6×2 is the same as 6 multiplied by the reciprocal of $\frac{1}{2}$.
$\frac{12}{15} = \frac{4}{5}$	have written the reciprocal of the first fraction (dividend) instead of the second fraction (divisor).	
$\frac{9}{5} = 1\frac{4}{5}$	have written the reciprocal of both the first and second fractions before multiplying.	
5	have incorrectly cross-simplified, by dividing both denominators in the problem by 2.	Remind students that the simplification process, whether before or after multiplying, involves a numerator/denominator pair. Rewrite $\frac{5}{6} \times \frac{3}{2}$ as $\frac{5 \times 3}{6 \times 2}$ and explain that, like any fraction, a numerator and denominator (in this case $\frac{3}{6}$) can be divided by the same number (in this case $\frac{3}{3}$), because that is equivalent to dividing the whole fraction by 1.

 ADDITIONAL ACTIVITY

For students who have mastered the skills in this lesson, see **Challenge Activity** (page 65).

ADDITIONAL ACTIVITIES

Hands-on Activity
Use fraction circles to model fraction division.

Materials: one set of fraction circles per student/group

Have students model $\frac{11}{12} \div \frac{2}{12} = 5\frac{1}{2}$ using fraction-circle pieces. Write the division problem (without the answer) on the board. Have students start with a whole circle and layer pieces on top.

First, have students model the dividend $\frac{11}{12}$. They should lay eleven $\frac{1}{12}$ pieces on top of the whole. Ask, "How can you make groups of $\frac{2}{12}$ out of the $\frac{11}{12}$ using another color (size) piece?" Students should find another piece that is equivalent to $\frac{2}{12}$. (This is the $\frac{1}{6}$ piece. But to avoid confusion, do not identify it that way.) Ask, "How many of these $\frac{2}{12}$ pieces can you lay on top of the $\frac{11}{12}$ to form groups?" *(5)* Students should lay 5 of the $\frac{2}{12}$ pieces on top, covering $\frac{10}{12}$. Ask, "With these 5 groups, have you completely covered the $\frac{11}{12}$?" *(No)* Ask, "This remaining uncovered piece forms what portion of another group?" $\left(\frac{1}{2}\right)$ So you can make 5 and $\frac{1}{2}$ groups of $\frac{2}{12}$ out of $\frac{11}{12}$. Write the answer $5\frac{1}{2}$ on the board.

Reteaching Activity
Draw a division model.

Have students draw a model for $\frac{7}{8}$. Tell them they will use the model to divide $\frac{7}{8}$ by $\frac{3}{8}$. Ask students to find a group of $\frac{3}{8}$ and circle the group. Then have students circle another group of $\frac{3}{8}$. Show that one part is left over. Show that this part makes up a third of a circled group, so this part can be called $\frac{1}{3}$.

Vocabulary Activity
Make a crossword puzzle.

Materials: grid paper

Have each student use the vocabulary words to make a puzzle where the words share common letters.

Sample:

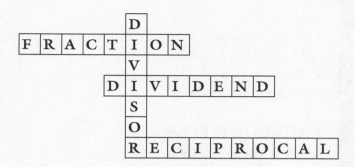

To help students check that their puzzles are complete, read a definition and have them check that they have used the corresponding word in their puzzle. Have them finalize the puzzles with numbers for each vertical and horizontal word and numbered, written definitions. Finally, have pairs exchange and complete each other's puzzle.

Real-World Connection
Discuss measurement.

Have students think about measurement. Many real-world objects are not a whole number of feet or meters long. Explain that knowing how to work with fractions can help to work with measurements. For example, if a rope that is $\frac{9}{10}$ meter long is cut into pieces that are $\frac{2}{10}$ meter, this models the division problem $\frac{9}{10} \div \frac{2}{10}$.

School-Home Connection
Inform families about fractions.

Give each student a copy of the reproducible School-Home Connection for Lesson 4 (page 169) to share with family. This activity has the family solve a division problem about planting seeds.

Challenge Activity
Divide mixed numbers by fractions.

Challenge students to draw a model to find the quotient of $3\frac{2}{3} \div \frac{2}{3}$. $\left(5\frac{1}{2}\right)$ Then have students multiply by the reciprocal to find the quotient. Ask students to think of a word problem that this problem could model.

Decimals

LESSON OBJECTIVES

Students will:

- Use patterns to multiply decimal numbers by 10, 100, and 1,000.
- Use patterns to divide decimal numbers by 10, 100, and 1,000.

PREREQUISITES

Students should be able to:

- Understand multiplication and division.
- Recognize multiples of 10.

RELATED *STAMS®* LESSON

- **Book E – Lesson 2**

  Divide Mentally shows students how to mentally divide multiples of 10 and 100.

VOCABULARY

PAGE 44

- **power of ten:** 10 raised to some power, such as 10^1, 10^2, 10^3, and so on
- **decimal number:** a number containing a decimal point that separates a whole from fractional place values (tenths, hundredths, thousandths, and so on)
- **decimal point:** a point that separates the ones from the tenths, or the whole-number part from the fractional part in a decimal number
- **product:** the result of multiplication

PAGE 45

- **exponent:** the number in a power that tells how many times to use the base as a factor
- **base (of a power):** the bottom number; the factor that is multiplied by itself

MATH BACKGROUND

A power of ten is the number 10 raised to a power. This is not to be confused with a multiple of ten, which is the product of ten and any whole number.

When powers of ten are written with exponents, the exponent is the number of zeros in the power of ten: $10^1 = 10$; $10^2 = 100$; $10^3 = 1,000$; and so on. So, when you multiply or divide by a power of ten, the exponent tells you how many places to move the decimal point. When you multiply by a power of ten, the decimal moves right, and the value of the number increases. When you divide by a power of ten, the decimal moves left, which decreases the value of the number.

In this lesson, students study examples of multiplying and dividing by powers of ten to find patterns. They discover the "rule" of moving the decimal point, and then apply it to solve problems.

Interactive Whiteboard

Visualize Multiplying and Dividing by Powers of Ten

Go to the *Interactive Whiteboard Lessons* to bring Parts One and Two to life. Use features such as movable decimal points to deepen students' understanding of multiplying and dividing by powers of ten.

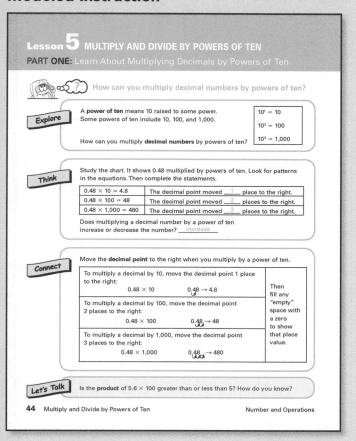

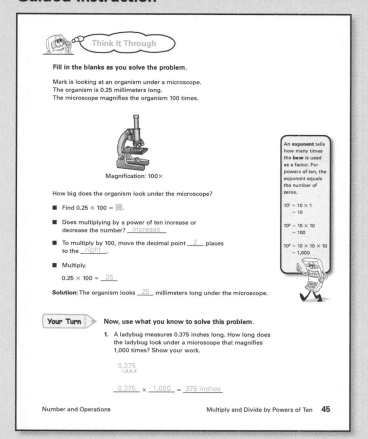

AT A GLANCE

Students activate their background knowledge about powers of ten and then learn to use a pattern to multiply decimal numbers by powers of ten.

STEP BY STEP

PAGE 44

- Introduce the **Question** at the top of the page.

- Have students read about powers of ten in **Explore** and study the examples. Discuss the examples to ensure students understand exponents.

- Read **Think** with students. Emphasize that the equations involve multiplication of decimal numbers by a power of ten. Pause so students can say aloud the numbers and words in orange.

- Discuss **Connect** with students. Help students correlate the number of zeros in the power of ten to the number of places the decimal point is moved.

Tip: Write other multiplication expressions involving decimal numbers and powers of ten on the board. Have students mentally find each product.

- Organize students in pairs or groups for **Let's Talk** and monitor their discussions.

- Be sure students understand that the product will be greater because multiplying a decimal number by a power of ten always increases the value of the number.

PAGE 45

- Read the **Think It Through** problem with students.

- Guide students as they solve the problem. Help them determine how many places to move the decimal point and in what direction.

- Help students see that they can use patterns to mentally multiply decimal numbers by powers of ten.

ELL Support: Have students draw arrows to show the direction words *right* and *left* or say the directions aloud in their native language.

- Monitor students as they complete **Your Turn**. Then discuss the correct answer.

Error Alert: Students who wrote an answer of 3.75, 37.5, or 3,750 placed the decimal point incorrectly.

ADDITIONAL ACTIVITY

See **Hands-on Activity** (page 73).

Modeled Instruction

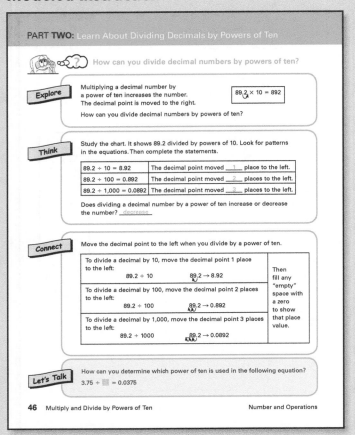

AT A GLANCE

Students learn how to use patterns to divide decimal numbers by powers of ten.

STEP BY STEP

PAGE 46

- Introduce the **Question** at the top of the page.
- Read **Explore** with students. Reinforce that multiplying by a power of ten moves the decimal point to the right and increases the value of the number. Note: This is only true for positive numbers.

ELL Support: Demonstrate the words *increase* and *decrease* by showing examples such as a series of numbers or pictures of different sizes.

- Read **Think** with students. Pause so students can read aloud the numbers and words in orange.
- Tell students to study the division sentences in **Connect**. Test their understanding by asking why the decimal point is moved 2 places to the left when dividing by 100. Have them identify which quotients have additional zeros and why (to account for place value).

- Organize students in pairs or groups for **Let's Talk** and monitor their discussions.
- Be sure students grasp that the quotient is a result of the decimal number being divided by a power of ten.

Tip: Guide students to determine if the divisor was 10, 100, or 1,000, based on how many places the decimal point moved and the value of the quotient. Have them write each division sentence to find which gives a quotient of 0.0375.

PAGE 47

- Read the **Think It Through** problem with students.
- Guide students as they solve the problem. Pause for students to fill in missing information. Then discuss each response.
- Monitor students as they complete **Your Turn**. Then discuss the correct answer.

Error Alert: Students who gave an answer of 950 moved the decimal point to the right.

 ADDITIONAL ACTIVITY

See **Reteaching Activity** (page 73).

Modeled Practice

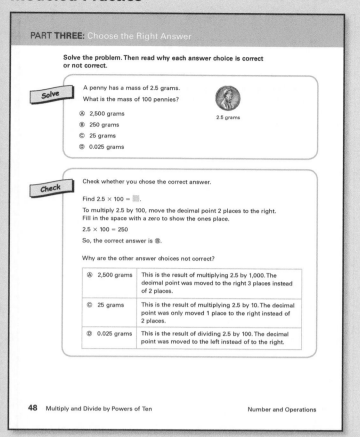

Guided Practice

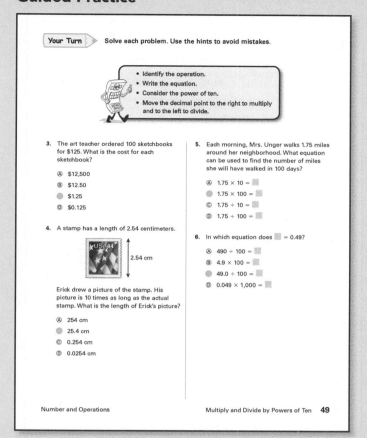

AT A GLANCE

Students reinforce their understanding of multiplying and dividing by powers of ten through solving a multiple-choice problem and analyzing correct and incorrect answer choices.

STEP BY STEP

Page 48

- Tell students that this page models finding the correct answer to a multiple-choice problem.
- Have students read the problem in **Solve** and choose the best answer. Remind students to check their math.
- Examine **Check** with students. Discuss the correct and incorrect choices.

Page 49

- Monitor students as they complete **Your Turn**.
- Organize students in pairs or small groups and have them discuss each problem.
- Review the answers with the class.

 ADDITIONAL ACTIVITY

See **Vocabulary Activity** (page 73).

Answer Analysis

3. Ⓐ Multiplied instead of divided; moved the decimal point to the right
   Ⓑ Moved the decimal point only 1 place
   ● $\$125 \div 100 = \$1.25$
   Ⓓ Moved the decimal point 3 places

4. Ⓐ Moved the decimal point 2 places
   ● $2.54 \times 10 = 25.4$
   Ⓒ Divided instead of multiplied; moved the decimal point to the left
   Ⓓ Divided instead of multiplied; moved the decimal point to the left

5. Ⓐ Multiplied by 10^1
   ● Multiplied by 10^2
   Ⓒ Divided by 10^1
   Ⓓ Divided by 10^2

6. Ⓐ $490 \div 100 = 4.9$
   Ⓑ $4.9 \times 100 = 490$
   ● $49.0 \div 100 = 0.49$
   Ⓓ $0.049 \times 1,000 = 49$

Modeled Practice

Guided Practice

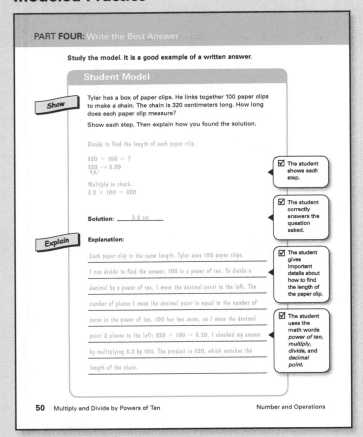

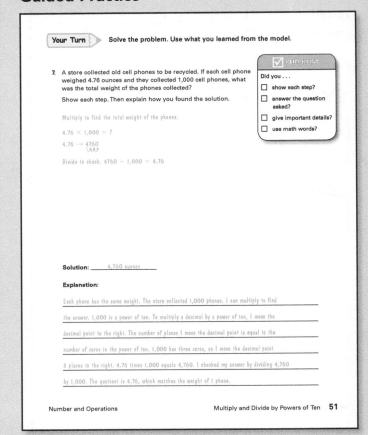

AT A GLANCE

Students study a model answer to an extended-response problem.

STEP BY STEP

PAGE 50

- Tell students that this page models building the solution to a problem one step at a time and writing to explain the solution.

- Have students read the problem in **Show**. Discuss how the expression and each mathematical step lead to the solution.

> **Tip:** Suggest students use arrows to show moving the decimal point to each place. Reinforce that multiplication moves the decimal point to the right because the number increases and division moves it to the left because the number decreases.

- Read **Explain** with students. Have students circle the math words in the explanation.

- Direct students' attention to the notes in the right margin. Tell students that this model would

receive a high score for the reasons described in these notes.

PAGE 51

- Monitor students as they complete **Your Turn**.

- Encourage students to follow the **Checklist** to write the best answer.

- Have students discuss their work with a partner. Then discuss the correct answer as a class.

Answer and Explanation

7. See the sample answer. This answer shows all of the steps taken to solve the problem, including writing an equation and showing the pattern. The solution answers the question. The explanation provides important details about how the problem was solved and uses the math words *power of ten*, *multiply*, *divide*, *decimal point*, and *quotient*.

 ADDITIONAL ACTIVITY

See **Real-World Connection** (page 73).

 ADDITIONAL ACTIVITY

See **School-Home Connection** (page 73).

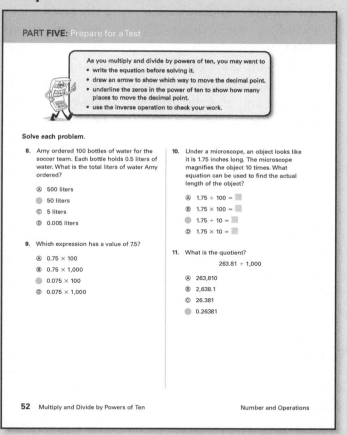

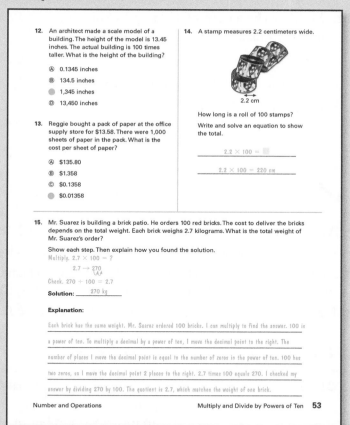

AT A GLANCE

Students practice using patterns to multiply and divide decimals by powers of ten to solve problems that might appear on a mathematics test.

STEP BY STEP

PAGES 52–53

- Tell students that they will practice solving multiplication and division problems that involve decimal numbers and powers of ten.

- Point out the tips at the top of page 52. Explain to students that these tips will help them answer the problems correctly.

- You may wish to have students review the hints for avoiding mistakes on page 49 as well.

- Tell students to complete problems 8–15 on pages 52 and 53. Encourage students to check their answers.

- Discuss the correct responses as a class.

Answers and Explanations

8. Ⓑ Multiply to find the total liters of water. Move the decimal point 2 places to the right. $0.5 \times 100 = 50$

9. Ⓒ $0.075 \times 100 = 7.5$

10. Ⓒ Divide 1.75 by 10, which is 10^1.

11. Ⓓ Move the decimal point 3 places to the left. $263.81 \div 1{,}000 = 0.26381$

12. Ⓒ Multiply to find the height of the building. Move the decimal point 2 places to the right. $13.45 \times 100 = 1{,}345$ inches

13. Ⓓ Divide the total cost by the number of sheets to find the cost per sheet. Move the decimal point 3 places to the left. $\$13.58 \div 1{,}000 = \$0.01358$

(continued on page 72)

(continued from page 71)

14. Multiply the length of 1 stamp by the total number of stamps. Write the equation.

$2.2 \times 100 = $

Move the decimal point 2 places to the right.

$2.2 \times 100 = 220$ cm

15. See the sample answer. This answer shows all of the steps the student took to solve the problem, including an equation and an example with arrows that shows student's use of a pattern. The solution answers the question. The explanation provides important details about how the student solved the problem and uses the math words *multiply*, *power of ten*, *decimal point*, *divide*, and *quotient*.

✔ ASSESSMENT AND REMEDIATION

- Ask students to use a pattern to find the product of 2.184×100. *(218.4)*
- For students who are still struggling, use the chart below to guide remediation.
- After providing remediation, check students' understanding. Ask students to explain their thinking while finding the quotient of $41.62 \div 100$. *(0.4162)*
- If a student is still having difficulty, use *STAMS Book E*, Lesson 2, pages 14–23.

If the error is . . .	Students may . . .	To remediate . . .
21.84	have moved the decimal point to the right but an incorrect number of places.	Reinforce the pattern by having students show multiplying by each power of ten. For example: $2.184 \times 10 = 21.84$ $2.184 \times 100 = 218.4$ $2.184 \times 1,000 = 2,184$
2,184	have mentally moved the decimal point too many places.	Encourage students to underline the zeros in the power of ten and then draw arrows to show moving the decimal the number of places equal to the number of zeros in the power of ten.
0.02184	be confusing multiplication and division.	Clarify that multiplication moves the decimal point to the right and that the product is greater than the decimal number factor. Demonstrate this with several examples.
0.2184	not understand the pattern that can be used to multiply and divide by powers of ten.	Review with students the concepts on pages 44 and 45. Have students practice identifying which direction to move the decimal point and how many places. Help students understand why the patterns work.

ADDITIONAL ACTIVITY

For students who have mastered the skills in this lesson, see **Challenge Activity** (page 73).

ADDITIONAL ACTIVITIES

Hands-on Activity
Act out multiplying a decimal number by a power of ten.

Materials: 4 index cards, markers, and a counter per pair of students

Write 0.48×10 on the board.

Organize students in pairs and distribute index cards, markers, and counters. Have students write the digits 0, 4, and 8 on the index cards and arrange the cards to show the number 0.48, using the counter for the decimal point.

Point to the multiplication expression. Then ask students, "In which direction do we move the decimal point to multiply by a power of ten?" *(right)* "How many places do we move to multiply by ten?" *(1)*

Have students model this by moving the counter one place to the right. Have a volunteer record the answer on the board. Repeat for multiplying 0.48 by 100 and 1,000.

Reteaching Activity
Have students determine the missing power of ten.

Review multiplying and dividing by powers of ten by giving students the initial and final numbers. Ask students to determine the power of ten.

Write $163.4 \rightarrow 1.634$ on the board. Ask: "Was the decimal point moved left or right? *(left)* "Was 163.4 multiplied or divided?" *(divided)* "How many places did the decimal point move?" *(2)* "What power of ten was 163.4 divided by?" *(100)* "What is the division sentence?" *(163.4 ÷ 100 = 1.634)*

Repeat this activity with the example $3.005 \rightarrow 3,005$. *(3.005 × 1,000 = 3,005)*

Vocabulary Activity
Play "Bingo" to reinforce terms.

Materials: blank sheets of paper, counters

Have each student create a grid by folding a sheet of paper in thirds horizontally and then in thirds vertically. Display the vocabulary words, include additional multiplication and division terms such as *multiply*, *divide*, *factor*, *divisor*, and *quotient*. Then tell students to write BINGO in the center box and the vocabulary words in the other boxes. Read a definition and have students cover the corresponding word on their grid with a counter. The winner for each round is the first student to cover three spaces vertically, horizontally, or diagonally.

Real-World Connection
Identify everyday examples of powers of ten.

Discuss everyday examples of multiplying or dividing by powers of ten, such as scale models, enlarging or shrinking a picture, converting within the metric system, and items packaged in groups of 10, 100, or 1,000. Then have students name other real-life examples and, if reasonable, write a multiplication or division sentence for each.

School-Home Connection
Inform families about multiplication.

Give each student a copy of the reproducible School-Home Connection for Lesson 5 (page 171) to share with family. This activity has the family play a game involving multiplication and division by powers of ten.

Challenge Activity
Extend patterns of powers of ten.

Have students write a multiplication expression that involves finding the product of a decimal number and a power of ten greater than 1,000. Write power of tens on the board for students to reference: 10,000, 100,000, and 1,000,000. After students have written their problem, have them exchange it with a partner to solve. Repeat with division expressions.

LESSON OBJECTIVES

Students will:

- Use rounding to estimate the product of decimal numbers.
- Find the exact product of decimal numbers.

PREREQUISITES

Students should be able to:

- Multiply 3-digit whole numbers by 2-digit whole numbers.
- Round numbers to the nearest whole number and the nearest ten.

RELATED *STAMS®* LESSONS

- **Book E – Lesson 1**

  Multiply 3-Digit Numbers shows students how to multiply 3-digit numbers by 1-digit and 2-digit numbers.

- **Book F – Lesson 5**

  Multiply and Divide by Powers of 10 shows students how to mentally multiply decimal numbers by powers of 10.

VOCABULARY

PAGE 54

- **multiplication:** an operation used to find the total number of items in equal-sized groups
- **product:** the result of multiplication
- **estimate:** an answer that is close to the exact answer
- **decimal number:** a number containing a decimal point that separates a whole from fractional place values (tenths, hundredths, thousandths, and so on)

PAGE 55

- **overestimate:** an estimate that is greater than the actual answer
- **underestimate:** an estimate that is less than the actual answer

PAGE 56

- **factor:** a number that is multiplied by another number
- **decimal point:** a dot that separates the whole number from the fractional part in a decimal number

MATH BACKGROUND

In this lesson, students find estimated and actual products of decimal numbers. In Part One, students learn how to estimate. If the decimal numbers are greater than 1, they are to first round each number to the nearest whole. If this does not result in numbers that are easy to multiply, they are encouraged to round numbers to the nearest ten before multiplying. If a factor is a decimal less than 1, it should not be rounded to zero, because this would always result in a product of zero. Instead, students can round numbers less than 0.5 to 0.5, and numbers between 0.5 and 1 to 1.

Students then determine the actual products in Part Two. They can organize the multiplication problems in the same way that they organize whole-number multiplication problems. Students are encouraged to use estimation and place value when placing the decimal point in the product. For example, the product of 3.7×4.1 must be 15.17, not 1.517 or 151.7, because 3.7 is about 4, and 4.1 is about 4. Because $4 \times 4 = 16$, the product must be close in value to 16.

Interactive Whiteboard
Visualize Multiplying Decimals

Go to the *Interactive Whiteboard Lessons* to bring Parts One and Two to life. Use features such as sliding screens with problem hints to deepen students' understanding of multiplying decimals.

Modeled Instruction

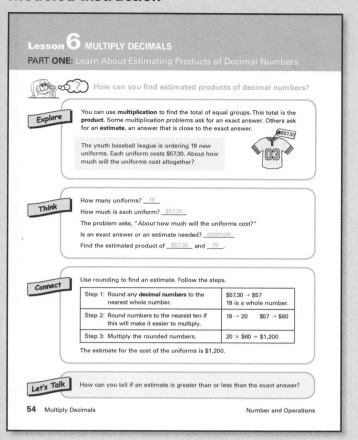

How can you find estimated products of decimal numbers?

Explore

You can use **multiplication** to find the total of equal groups. This total is the **product**. Some multiplication problems ask for an exact answer. Others ask for an **estimate**, an answer that is close to the exact answer.

The youth baseball league is ordering 19 new uniforms. Each uniform costs $57.30. About how much will the uniforms cost altogether?

$57.30
03

Think

How many uniforms? __19__

How much is each uniform? __$57.30__

The problem asks, "*About* how much will the uniforms cost?"

Is an exact answer or an estimate needed? __estimate__

Find the estimated product of __$57.30__ and __19__.

Connect

Use rounding to find an estimate. Follow the steps.

Step 1: Round any **decimal numbers** to the nearest whole number.	$57.30 → $57 19 is a whole number.
Step 2: Round numbers to the nearest ten if this will make it easier to multiply.	19 → 20 $57 → $60
Step 3: Multiply the rounded numbers.	20 × $60 = $1,200

The estimate for the cost of the uniforms is $1,200.

Let's Talk

How can you tell if an estimate is greater than or less than the exact answer?

54   Multiply Decimals   Number and Operations

Guided Instruction

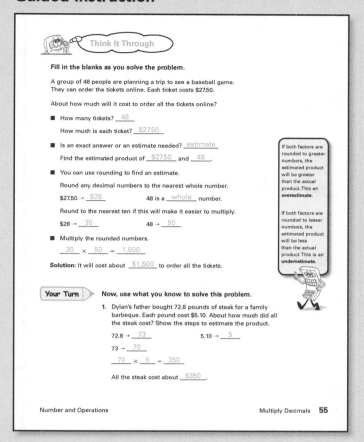

Think It Through

Fill in the blanks as you solve the problem.

A group of 48 people are planning a trip to see a baseball game. They can order the tickets online. Each ticket costs $27.50.

About how much will it cost to order all the tickets online?

■ How many tickets? __48__

How much is each ticket? __$27.50__

■ Is an exact answer or an estimate needed? __estimate__

Find the estimated product of __$27.50__ and __48__.

■ You can use rounding to find an estimate.

Round any decimal numbers to the nearest whole number.

$27.50 → __$28__   48 is a __whole__ number.

Round to the nearest ten if this will make it easier to multiply.

$28 → __30__   48 → __50__

■ Multiply the rounded numbers.

__30__ × __50__ = __1,500__

Solution: It will cost about __$1,500__ to order all the tickets.

> If both factors are rounded to greater numbers, the estimated product will be greater than the actual product. This an **overestimate**.
>
> If both factors are rounded to lesser numbers, the estimated product will be less than the actual product. This is an **underestimate**.

Your Turn

Now, use what you know to solve this problem.

1. Dylan's father bought 72.8 pounds of steak for a family barbeque. Each pound cost $5.10. About how much did all the steak cost? Show the steps to estimate the product.

72.8 → __73__   5.10 → __5__

73 → __70__

__70__ × __5__ = __350__

All the steak cost about __$350__.

Number and Operations   Multiply Decimals   55

AT A GLANCE

Students activate their background knowledge about multiplication and then learn how to find estimated products of decimal numbers.

STEP BY STEP

PAGE 54

- Introduce the **Question** at the top of the page.
- Have students read the word problem in **Explore** and notice the word *about*.
- Read **Think** with students. Emphasize that the groups are the number of uniforms and the cost is the amount in each group. Pause so students can say aloud the responses in orange.
- Discuss **Connect** with students. Help students see the how rounding the factors allows one to mentally find a product that is close to the exact answer.
- Organize students in pairs or groups for **Let's Talk** and monitor their discussions.
- Be sure students understand that how the factors are rounded will determine if the estimate is greater than or less than the exact answer.

Tip: Encourage students to round both numbers up or both numbers down whenever possible so they can judge whether an estimate is an *overestimate* or an *underestimate*.

PAGE 55

- Read the **Think It Through** problem with students.
- Guide students as they solve the problem. Help them determine that they can estimate the product (*about*).
- Help students see that both factors are rounded up, so the estimate will be greater than the exact answer.

ELL Support: Use a number line to clarify the word *nearest*. Point to a decimal number and identify the nearest whole number and then the nearest ten.

- Monitor students as they complete **Your Turn**. Then discuss the correct answer.

Error Alert: Students who got an answer of 35 did not include the zero when multiplying.

 ## ADDITIONAL ACTIVITY

See **Hands-on Activity** (page 81).

Modeled Instruction

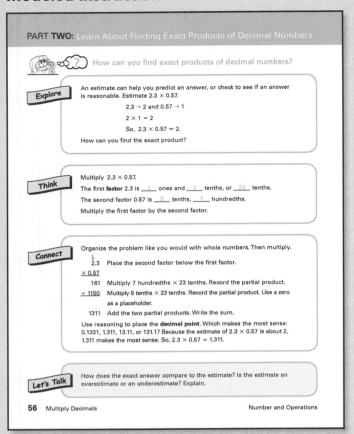

Guided Instruction

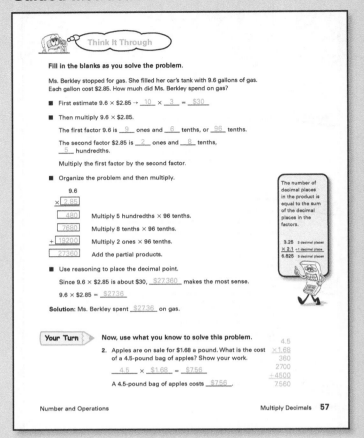

AT A GLANCE

Students learn the steps to use to find the exact product of decimal numbers.

STEP BY STEP

PAGE 56

- Introduce the **Question** at the top of the page.
- Read **Explore** with students. Reinforce that an estimate is close to the exact answer and review how to estimate products of decimal numbers.
- Read **Think** with students. Pause so students can read aloud the numbers in orange.
- Tell students to study the multiplication problem in **Connect**. Discuss each step, emphasizing the decimal place value of the digits being multiplied. Test their understanding by asking how the estimate helps them decide where to place the decimal point.
- Organize students in pairs or groups for **Let's Talk** and monitor their discussions.

- Be sure students grasp that an overestimate means the estimate is greater than the exact answer and an underestimate means the estimate is less than the exact answer. The estimate, 2, is an overestimate because it is greater than the exact answer, 1.311.

PAGE 57

- Read the **Think It Through** problem with students.
- Guide students as they solve the problem. Pause for students to fill in missing information. Then discuss each response.

Tip: Have students solve the multiplication problem on grid paper to keep the digits aligned properly.

- Monitor students as they complete **Your Turn**. Then discuss the correct answer.

Error Alert: Students who gave an answer of $75.60 may have only considered the number of decimal places in the second factor.

 ADDITIONAL ACTIVITY

See **Reteaching Activity** (page 81).

Modeled Practice

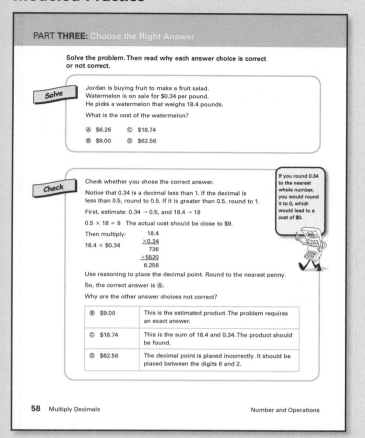

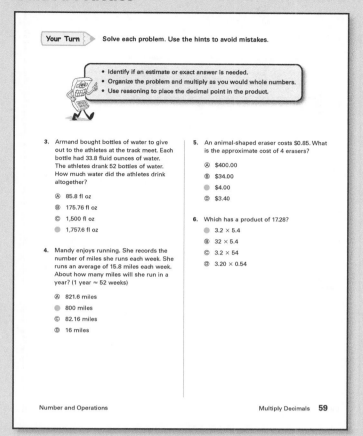

AT A GLANCE

Students reinforce their understanding of multiplying decimal numbers through solving a multiple-choice problem and analyzing correct and incorrect answer choices.

STEP BY STEP

PAGE 58

- Tell students that this page models finding the correct answer to a multiple-choice problem.
- Have students read the problem in **Solve** and choose the best answer. Remind students to check their math.
- Examine **Check** with students. Discuss why rounding 0.34 to 0 would not provide a good estimate.

PAGE 59

- Monitor students as they complete **Your Turn**.
- Organize students in pairs or small groups and have them discuss each answer choice.
- Review the answers with the class.

ADDITIONAL ACTIVITY

See **Vocabulary Activity** (page 81).

Answer Analysis

3. Ⓐ Added instead of multiplied
   Ⓑ Placed decimal point incorrectly
   Ⓒ Estimated the product
   ⬤ Multiply. $33.8 \times 52 = 1{,}757.6$

4. Ⓐ Found the exact answer instead of an estimate
   ⬤ Estimate $15.8 \to 16$; $52 \to 50$; $16 \times 50 = 800$
   Ⓒ Found the exact answer instead of an estimate and placed the decimal point incorrectly
   Ⓓ Rounded 15.8 to 16 and multiplied by 1

5. Ⓐ Rounded 0.85 to 100 instead of 1
   Ⓑ Found the exact answer instead of an estimate and placed the decimal point incorrectly
   ⬤ Estimate $0.85 \to 1$; $4 \times 1 = 4$
   Ⓓ Found the exact answer instead of an estimate

6. ⬤ $3.2 \times 5.4 = 17.28$
   Ⓑ $32 \times 5.4 = 172.8$
   Ⓒ $3.2 \times 54 = 172.8$
   Ⓓ $3.20 \times 0.54 = 1.728$

Modeled Instruction

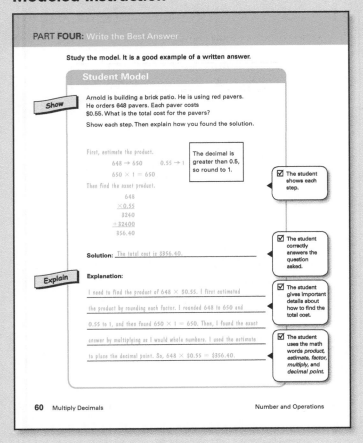

Guided Instruction

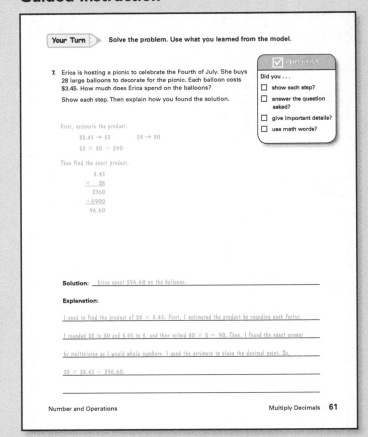

Students study a model answer to an extended-response problem.

STEP BY STEP

PAGE 60

- Tell students that this page models building the solution to a problem one step at a time and writing to explain the solution.

- Have students read the problem in **Show**. Discuss how the estimate and each mathematical step lead to the solution.

> **Tip:** Have students compare the estimate and actual answer. Explain that the estimate is much greater, because 0.55 was almost doubled when it was rounded to 1. The estimate does show how many whole-number places will be in the answer.

- Read **Explain** with students. Have students circle the math words in the explanation.

- Direct students' attention to the notes in the right margin. Tell students that this model would receive

a high score for the reasons described in these notes.

PAGE 61

- Monitor students as they complete **Your Turn**.

- Encourage students to follow the **Checklist** to write the best answer.

- Have students discuss their work with a partner. Then discuss the correct answer as a class.

Answer and Explanation

7. See the sample answer. This answer shows all of the steps taken to solve the problem, including finding an estimate and the multiplication algorithm. The solution answers the question. The explanation provides important details about how the problem was solved and uses the math words *estimate, factor, product, multiply,* and *decimal point.*

 ADDITIONAL ACTIVITY

See **Real-World Connection** (page 81).

 ADDITIONAL ACTIVITY

See **School-Home Connection** (page 81).

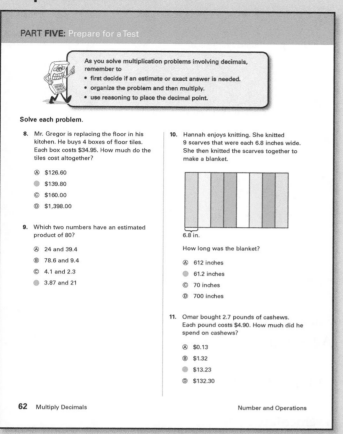

PART FIVE: Prepare for a Test

As you solve multiplication problems involving decimals, remember to
• first decide if an estimate or exact answer is needed.
• organize the problem and then multiply.
• use reasoning to place the decimal point.

Solve each problem.

8. Mr. Gregor is replacing the floor in his kitchen. He buys 4 boxes of floor tiles. Each box costs $34.95. How much do the tiles cost altogether?

Ⓐ $126.60
Ⓑ $139.80
Ⓒ $160.00
Ⓓ $1,398.00

9. Which two numbers have an estimated product of 80?

Ⓐ 24 and 39.4
Ⓑ 78.6 and 9.4
Ⓒ 4.1 and 2.3
Ⓓ 3.87 and 21

10. Hannah enjoys knitting. She knitted 9 scarves that were each 6.8 inches wide. She then knitted the scarves together to make a blanket.

6.8 in.

How long was the blanket?

Ⓐ 612 inches
Ⓑ 61.2 inches
Ⓒ 70 inches
Ⓓ 700 inches

11. Omar bought 2.7 pounds of cashews. Each pound costs $4.90. How much did he spend on cashews?

Ⓐ $0.13
Ⓑ $1.32
Ⓒ $13.23
Ⓓ $132.30

62   Multiply Decimals   Number and Operations

---

12. A fruit stand sells peaches for $1.65 a pound. Carter buys 2.4 pounds of peaches. About how much did Carter spend on peaches?

Ⓐ $3.96
Ⓑ $39.60
Ⓒ $4.00
Ⓓ $40.00

13. What is the estimated product of 5.6 × 0.37?

Ⓐ 2.072
Ⓑ 3
Ⓒ 6
Ⓓ 20.72

14. Amarion downloads 32 songs and places them in the music folder on his computer. If each song file is 5.81 MB, how much space does Amarion need for the songs he downloads?

Estimate the product. Then find the exact answer.

Estimate:
_____180 MB_____

Exact Answer:
_____185.92 MB_____

15. Loretta took 76 pictures with her new digital camera. The average file size of a picture is 3.8 MB. She transfers the pictures to her computer. How much space will the pictures take up?

Show each step. Then explain how you found the solution.

First, estimate the product.
76 → 80; 3.8 → 4
80 × 4 = 320
Then find the exact product.
```
     76
   × 3.8
    608
 +2280
  288.8
```

Solution: The pictures will take up 288.8 MB.

Explanation:
I need to find the product of 76 × 3.8. I first estimated the product by rounding each factor. I rounded 76 to 80 and 3.8 to 4, and then solved 80 × 4 = 320. I then found the exact answer by multiplying as I would whole numbers. I used the estimate to place the decimal point. So, 76 × 3.8 = 288.8 MB.

Number and Operations   Multiply Decimals   63

AT A GLANCE

Students practice multiplying decimal numbers to solve problems that might appear on a mathematics test.

STEP BY STEP

Pages 62–63

• Tell students they will practice solving multiplication problems that involve decimal numbers.

• Point out the tips at the top of page 62. Explain to students that these tips will help them answer the problems correctly.

• You may wish to have students review the hints for avoiding mistakes on page 59 as well.

• Tell students to complete problems 8–15 on pages 62 and 63. Encourage students to check their answers.

• Discuss the correct responses as a class.

Answers and Explanations

8. Ⓑ Multiply the number of boxes by the cost of each box. 4 × $34.95 = $139.80

9. Ⓓ Round the decimal number to the nearest whole number and the other factor to the nearest ten; 3.87 rounds to 4 and 21 rounds to 20. Multiply 4 × 20 = 80. So, the estimated product of 3.87 and 21 is 80.

10. Ⓑ Multiply the number of scarves by the width of each scarf. 9 × 6.8 = 61.2 inches

11. Ⓒ Multiply the number of pounds by the cost per pound. 2.7 × $4.90 = $13.23

12. Ⓒ The question asks "About how much," so estimate the product. Round each decimal to the nearest whole number. $1.65 rounds to 2 and 2.4 rounds to 2. So, 2 × 2 = $4.

13. Ⓑ Estimate by rounding 5.6 to 6, and 0.37 to 0.5; 6 × 0.5 = 3

(continued on page 80)

(continued from page 79)

14. 32 rounds to 30, and 5.81 rounds to 6. So, the estimated product is $30 \times 6 = 180$. Multiply 32 by 5.81 to find the exact answer of 185.92.

15. See the sample answer. This answer shows all of the steps the student took to solve the problem, including the steps to find the estimated product and the exact answer. The solution answers the question. The explanation provides important details about how the student solved the problem and uses the math words *estimate*, *product*, *factor*, *multiply*, and *decimal point*.

 ASSESSMENT AND REMEDIATION

- Ask students to solve the problem 3.7×6.8. *(25.16)*
- For students who are still struggling, use the chart below to guide remediation.
- After providing remediation, check students' understanding. Ask students to explain their thinking while solving the problem 0.78×3.4. *(2.652)*
- If a student is still having difficulty, use *STAMS Book E*, Lesson 1, pages 4–13.

If the error is . . .	Students may . . .	To remediate . . .
0.2516, 2.516, or 251.6	have incorrectly placed the decimal point, *or*	Show the estimate of 28. Discuss how to use it to help place the decimal point. Have students count the number of places in 28. *(2)* Explain that the exact answer will have two places to the left of the decimal point.
	made an error when estimating the product.	Have students use a number line to help them round each factor to the nearest whole number. Check their multiplication of the whole numbers: $4 \times 7 = 28$.
2,516	have multiplied like whole numbers and not placed the decimal point in the answer.	Review with students the concepts on page 56. Stress decimal place value of the digits being multiplied and the importance of placing the decimal point in the product. Have students highlight the decimal points in the factors and in the product.
a product with the incorrect digits	have made a basic fact multiplication error, *or*	Use flash cards to practice basic multiplication facts.
	made an error when recording or adding the partial products.	Review the steps to multiply multidigit numbers. Have students use grid paper or place-value charts to help them keep the digits properly aligned.

 ADDITIONAL ACTIVITY

For students who have mastered the skills in this lesson, see **Challenge Activity** (page 81).

ADDITIONAL ACTIVITIES

Hands-on Activity
Use number lines to round decimals to estimate products.

Materials: blank number lines, index cards

Organize students in four groups. Distribute blank number lines and index cards. Write the expression 57.3 × 22 and the steps to estimate a decimal product. Assign each group a step.

Have the first group plot the decimal number 57.3 on a number line. Ask, "Which whole number is the decimal number closer to?" Have the students write the rounded number on an index card and pass the card to the next group.

Have the second group plot the two whole-number factors on number lines. Ask, "Is 57 closer to 50 or 60?" "Is 22 closer to 20 or 30?" Have the students write the rounded numbers on index cards and pass the cards to the next group.

Have the third group multiply to find the estimate. They can record their answer on an index card.

Repeat with other decimal factors and assign each group a different step.

Reteaching Activity
Multiply decimal numbers.

Write these multiplication problems on the board:

$42 \times 6 = 252$ $0.42 \times 6 = 2.52$
$4.2 \times 6 = 25.2$ $0.42 \times 0.6 = 0.252$

Ask students to compare each equation: "How are the equations the same?" (*The digits are the same.*) "How are they different?" (*The digits have different place values. The decimal point is in a different place in the factors and in the products.*) Show students that the number of decimal points in the product is equal to the total number of decimal places in the factors. Have students verify this with each equation.

Provide additional examples and have students place the decimal point in the answer by counting the decimal places in the factors. This should help students to see that place value and decimal-point placement affect the value of the product.

Vocabulary Activity
Play "Quiz Show" to reinforce terms.

Materials: index cards, markers

Divide students into two groups. Provide each group with index cards and markers. Have each group sit or stand in a line. Explain that you will ask a question. The first contestant to give a correct answer will score a point for their team.

Begin with the first student in each line. Read a vocabulary term from this lesson or a related multiplication or decimal term. Have the pair of students either draw a picture of the term or write the definition. Give students a few minutes to respond. Students should raise their hand when they are ready to give their answer. The player who answers correctly earns a point for their team. Repeat for each pair of students.

Real-World Connection
Find the total cost of multiple items.

Provide grocery store advertisements. Discuss how some items are priced by weight. Have students select an item that is priced by the pound. Then have them multiply to find the total cost for 5 pounds. Repeat with other items to create a shopping list and total cost.

School-Home Connection
Inform families about multiplication.

Give each student a copy of the reproducible School-Home Connection for Lesson 6 (page 173) to share with family. This activity has the family use multiplication to find the weight of common grocery items.

Challenge Activity
Write multiplication word problems.

Have students write multiplication word problems that involve multiplying decimal numbers. Students should use a decimal number for one or both factors. One of the factors could also be a money amount given in dollars and cents. Suggest students limit the factors to 3 digits or less. Have students exchange their problem with a partner to solve.

LESSON OBJECTIVES

Students will:

- Use place value to estimate the quotient when a decimal is divided by a whole number.
- Divide decimals by whole numbers.

PREREQUISITES

Students should be able to:

- Divide whole numbers.
- Understand place value of decimal numbers.
- Multiply decimal numbers.

RELATED *STAMS*® LESSONS

- **Book E – Lesson 5**

  Zeros in the Quotient has students use long division to find quotients that have a zero for a digit.

- **Book E – Lesson 6**

  2-Digit Divisors shows students how to use long division to divide numbers by 2-digit numbers.

VOCABULARY

PAGE 64

- **estimation:** a process used to predict an answer or check an answer for reasonableness
- **quotient:** the result of division
- **whole numbers:** the numbers 0, 1, 2, 3, and so on; they have no decimal or fractional parts
- **decimal:** a number containing a decimal point that separates a whole from fractional place values (tenths, hundredths, thousandths, and so on)

PAGE 66

- **dividend:** in a division problem, the number being divided
- **divisor:** in a division problem, the number being divided by
- **compatible numbers:** numbers that are close in value to the actual numbers, but easier to add, subtract, multiply, or divide

MATH BACKGROUND

In this lesson, students learn to divide decimals by whole numbers. In Part One, students use place value to help them estimate quotients. For example, to estimate $1.85 \div 5$, students round 1.85 to 2, and think of 2 as 20 tenths. Therefore, they think of 20 tenths divided by 5.

In Part Two, students advance to using the long-division algorithm to find exact quotients. However, they still use estimation to predict and check their answers. The use of estimation helps students consider the values of the dividends and divisors.

Interactive Whiteboard

Visualize Dividing Decimals by Whole Numbers

Go to the *Interactive Whiteboard Lessons* to bring Parts One and Two to life. Use features such as sliding screens with additional practice to deepen students' understanding of dividing decimals by whole numbers.

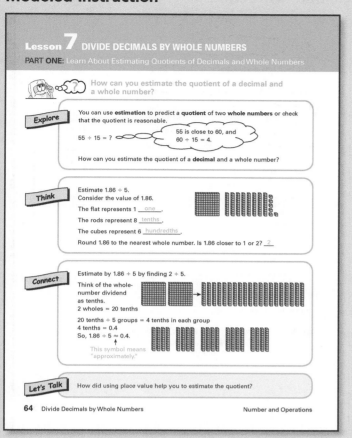

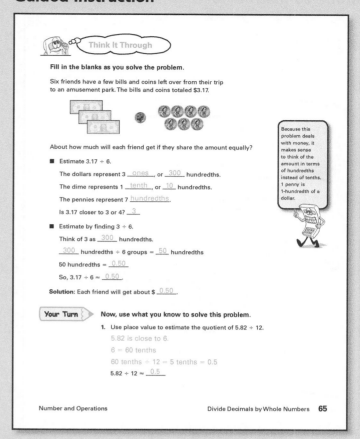

AT A GLANCE

Students activate their background knowledge about division and estimating quotients, and then learn how to use place value to estimate the quotient of a decimal and a whole number.

STEP BY STEP

PAGE 64

- Introduce the **Question** at the top of the page.
- Have students study the expressions shown in **Explore** and relate rounding to estimating the quotient.
- Read **Think** with students. Emphasize the place value of each digit in the decimal number. Pause so students can say aloud the answers in orange.
- Discuss **Connect** with students. Help students see the connection between the model and the estimate.

Tip: Have students practice rounding other decimal numbers to a whole number. Point out the need to round to a whole number that the divisor evenly divides into. Explain that these are compatible numbers.

- Organize students in pairs or groups for **Let's Talk** and monitor their discussions.
- Explain that thinking of a decimal as a number of tenths allows students to treat the decimal as a whole number.

PAGE 65

- Read the **Think It Through** problem with students.
- Help students determine that they can use estimation in this problem because the question asks *about* how much.
- Explain that 3 also equals 30 tenths, but hundredths makes more sense in the context of money.

ELL Support: Review U.S. money amounts. Relate each to place value: dollar = whole, dime = tenth, and penny = hundredth.

- Monitor students as they complete **Your Turn**. Then discuss the correct answer.

Error Alert: Students who wrote 2 may have divided 12 by 6.

 ADDITIONAL ACTIVITY

See **Hands-on Activity** (page 89).

Modeled Instruction

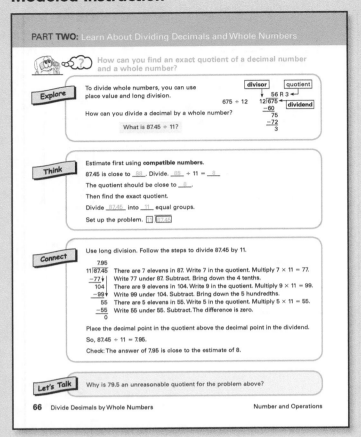

Guided Instruction

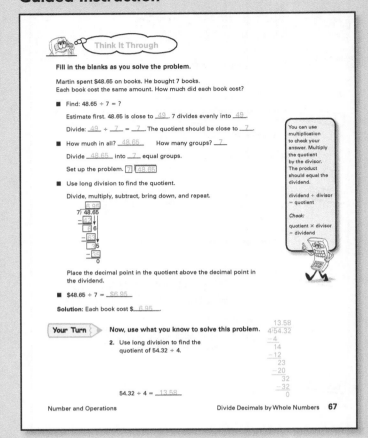

AT A GLANCE

Students learn to use long division to divide a decimal by a whole number.

STEP BY STEP

PAGE 66

- Introduce the **Question** at the top of the page.
- Read **Explore** with students. Review the steps for whole-number long division if necessary.

  ELL Support: The R in the quotient stands for *remainder*. Ensure that students understand this, as well as the definition of remainder.

- Read **Think** with students. Reinforce how to write the division expression in the long-division format.
- Have students study the long division shown in **Connect**. Make sure students understand how decimal place value affects the number being divided in each step. For example, 77 subtracted from 87 leaves 10 ones. The 104 represents 104 tenths after regrouping 10 ones as 100 tenths, and "bringing down" 4 tenths.

- Organize students in pairs or groups for **Let's Talk** and monitor their discussions.
- Explain that the placement of the decimal point changes the value of the digits by a factor of 10. Using estimation, the answer should be close to 8, not 80.

PAGE 67

- Read the **Think It Through** problem with students.
- Guide students as they solve the problem. Pause for students to fill in missing information. Then discuss each response.

  Tip: Remind students to use compatible numbers to estimate the quotient. Round 48.65 and 7 to two whole numbers that can be easily divided.

- Monitor students as they complete **Your Turn**. Then discuss the correct answer.

  Error Alert: Students who answered 1.358 or 135.8 have placed the decimal point incorrectly. Review using estimation to show that the answer is not reasonable.

ADDITIONAL ACTIVITY

See **Reteaching Activity** (page 89).

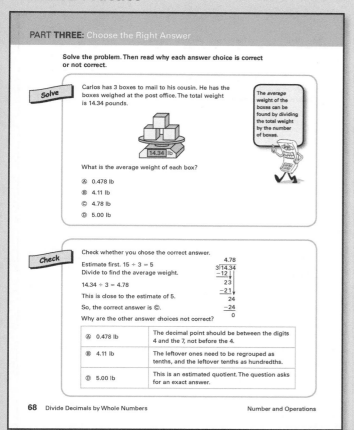

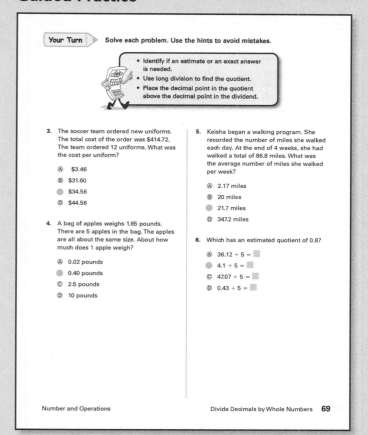

AT A GLANCE

Students reinforce their understanding of dividing decimals through solving a multiple-choice problem and analyzing correct and incorrect answer choices.

STEP BY STEP

PAGE 68

- Tell students that this page models finding the correct answer to a multiple-choice problem.

- Have students read the problem in **Solve** and choose the best answer. Remind students to check their math.

- Examine **Check** with students. Discuss the correct and incorrect choices.

PAGE 69

- Monitor students as they complete **Your Turn**.

- Organize students in pairs or small groups. Have them discuss why each answer choice is correct/not correct.

- Review the answers with the class.

 ADDITIONAL ACTIVITY

See **Vocabulary Activity** (page 89).

Answer Analysis

3. Ⓐ Placed the decimal point incorrectly
    Ⓑ Regrouped incorrectly
    ● $414.72 \div 12 = \$34.56$
    Ⓓ Basic fact error

4. Ⓐ Rounded the decimal to 2 and then moved the decimal point left 2 spaces
    ● $1.65 \div 5 \rightarrow 2 \div 5 = 0.40$.
    Ⓒ Divided 5 by 2 instead of 2 by 5
    Ⓓ Multiplied 2 by 5 instead of dividing

5. Ⓐ Placed the decimal point incorrectly
    Ⓑ Chose an estimated quotient
    ● $86.8 \div 4 = 21.7$
    Ⓓ Multiplied instead of divided

6. Ⓐ $36.12 \div 5 \approx 40 \div 5 = 8$
    ● $4.1 \div 5 \approx 400$ hundredths $\div 5 = 80$ hundredths $= 0.8$
    Ⓒ $47.07 \div 5 \approx 50 \div 5 = 10$
    Ⓓ $0.43 \div 5 \approx 0.4 \div 5 = 8$ hundredths $= 0.08$

Modeled Practice

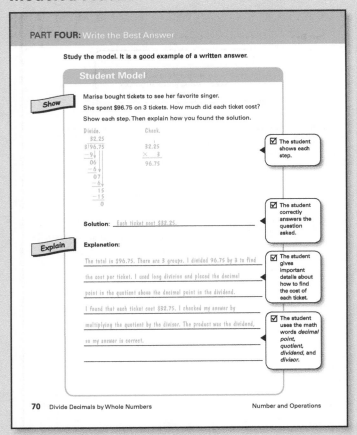

Study the model. It is a good example of a written answer.

Student Model

Show

Marisa bought tickets to see her favorite singer.
She spent $96.75 on 3 tickets. How much did each ticket cost?
Show each step. Then explain how you found the solution.

Divide.
```
   32.25
3)96.75
  -9↓
   06
  -6↓
   07
   -6↓
    15
   -15
     0
```
Check.
```
    32.25
  ×    3
    96.75
```
☑ The student shows each step.

Solution: Each ticket cost $32.25.

☑ The student correctly answers the question asked.

Explain

Explanation:

The total is $96.75. There are 3 groups. I divided 96.75 by 3 to find

the cost per ticket. I used long division and placed the decimal

point in the quotient above the decimal point in the dividend.

I found that each ticket cost $32.75. I checked my answer by

multiplying the quotient by the divisor. The product was the dividend,

so my answer is correct.

☑ The student gives important details about how to find the cost of each ticket.

☑ The student uses the math words *decimal point*, *quotient*, *dividend*, and *divisor*.

Guided Practice

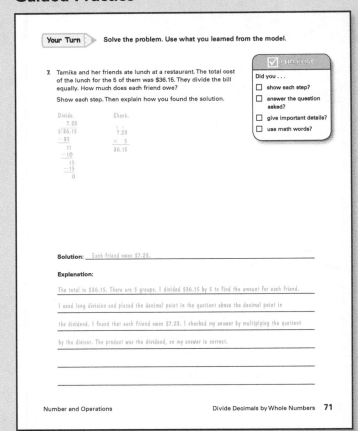

Your Turn Solve the problem. Use what you learned from the model.

7. Tamika and her friends ate lunch at a restaurant. The total cost of the lunch for the 5 of them was $36.15. They divide the bill equally. How much does each friend owe?

Show each step. Then explain how you found the solution.

Divide.
```
    7.23
5)36.15
  -35
   11
  -10
    15
   -15
     0
```
Check.
```
     7.23
  ×    5
   36.15
```

☑ CHECKLIST
Did you . . .
☐ show each step?
☐ answer the question asked?
☐ give important details?
☐ use math words?

Solution: Each friend owes $7.23.

Explanation:

The total is $36.15. There are 5 groups. I divided $36.15 by 5 to find the amount for each friend.

I used long division and placed the decimal point in the quotient above the decimal point in

the dividend. I found that each friend owes $7.23. I checked my answer by multiplying the quotient

by the divisor. The product was the dividend, so my answer is correct.

AT A GLANCE

Students study a model answer to an extended-response problem.

STEP BY STEP

PAGE 70

- Tell students that this page models building the solution to a problem one step at a time and writing to explain the solution.
- Have students read the problem in **Show**. Discuss how each mathematical step leads to the solution.

> Tip: Encourage students to multiply 32.25 by 3 to make sure it equals 96.75. If the product is *not* 96.75, then a mistake was made in one of the steps.

- Read **Explain** with students. Have students circle the math words in the explanation.
- Direct students' attention to the notes in the right margin. Tell students that this model would receive a high score for the reasons described in these notes.

PAGE 71

- Monitor students as they complete **Your Turn**.
- Encourage students to follow the **Checklist** to write the best answer.
- Have students discuss their work with a partner. Then discuss the correct answer as a class.

Answer and Explanation

7. See the sample answer. This answer shows all of the steps taken to solve the problem, including the worked-out long division and checking the quotient. The solution answers the question. The explanation provides important details about how the problem was solved and uses the math words *decimal point*, *quotient*, *dividend*, and *divisor*.

 ADDITIONAL ACTIVITY
See **Real-World Connection** (page 89).

 ADDITIONAL ACTIVITY
See **School-Home Connection** (page 89).

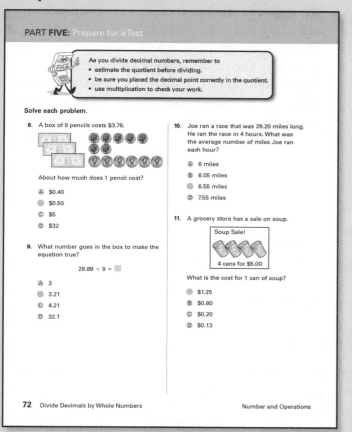

Independent Practice

PART FIVE: Prepare for a Test

As you divide decimal numbers, remember to
• estimate the quotient before dividing.
• be sure you placed the decimal point correctly in the quotient.
• use multiplication to check your work.

Solve each problem.

8. A box of 8 pencils costs $3.76.

About how much does 1 pencil cost?

Ⓐ $0.40
● $0.50
Ⓒ $5
Ⓓ $32

9. What number goes in the box to make the equation true?

28.89 ÷ 9 = ▨

Ⓐ 3
● 3.21
Ⓒ 4.21
Ⓓ 32.1

10. Joe ran a race that was 26.20 miles long. He ran the race in 4 hours. What was the average number of miles Joe ran each hour?

Ⓐ 6 miles
Ⓑ 6.05 miles
● 6.55 miles
Ⓓ 7.55 miles

11. A grocery store has a sale on soup.

Soup Sale!
4 cans for $5.00

What is the cost for 1 can of soup?

● $1.25
Ⓑ $0.80
Ⓒ $0.20
Ⓓ $0.13

72 Divide Decimals by Whole Numbers   Number and Operations

Independent Practice

12. Oscar is making potato salad for a picnic. He buys a 6-pound bag of potatoes for $3.54. What is the cost per pound?

Ⓐ $0.06   Ⓒ $5.90
● $0.59   Ⓓ $21.24

13. What is the quotient?

63.72 ÷ 6

Ⓐ 1.062   Ⓒ 16.2
● 10.62   Ⓓ 106.2

14. Riley just finished knitting a scarf. The scarf is 35.58 inches long. Riley knitted the scarf in 6 days. What is the average length of scarf Riley knit each day?

Estimate the quotient, and then find the exact answer.

Estimate:

36 in. ÷ 6 = 6 in.

Exact Answer:

35.58 in. ÷ 6 = 5.93 in.

15. The coach ordered warm-up suits for the gymnasts. The 7 warm-up suits cost a total of $296.59. How much does each gymnast owe?

Show each step. Then explain how you found the solution.

Divide.
```
    42.37
 7)296.59
  -28
   16
  -14
    25
   -21
     49
    -49
      0
```

Check.
```
  42.37
 ×    7
 296.59
```

Solution: Each gymnast owes $42.37.

Explanation:

The total is $296.59. There are 7 groups. I divided 296.59 by 7 to find the cost of each warm-up suit.

I used long division and placed the decimal point in the quotient above the decimal point in the dividend.

I found that each gymnast owes $42.37. I checked my answer by multiplying the quotient by the divisor.

The product was the dividend, so my answer is correct.

Number and Operations   Divide Decimals by Whole Numbers 73

AT A GLANCE

Students practice dividing decimals by whole numbers to solve problems that might appear on a mathematics test.

STEP BY STEP

Pages 72–73

• Tell students that they will practice solving division problems that involve a decimal and a whole number.

• Point out the tips at the top of page 72. Explain to students that these tips will help them answer the problems correctly.

• You may wish to have students review the hints for avoiding mistakes on page 69 as well.

• Tell students to complete problems 8–15 on pages 72 and 73. Encourage students to check their answers.

• Discuss the correct responses as a class.

Answers and Explanations

8. Ⓑ Round $3.76 to the nearest whole number, 4. Think of 4 dollars as 400 pennies. Divide 400 pennies by 8 to get 50 pennies, which is the same as $0.50.

9. Ⓑ 28.89 divided into 9 equal groups is 3.21. Check by multiplying: 3.21 × 9 = 28.89.

10. Ⓒ Divide 26.20 miles by 4 hours to find the average. 26.20 ÷ 4 = 6.55.

11. Ⓐ Because each can of soup costs the same, divide to find the cost per can: $5.00 ÷ 4 = $1.25.

12. Ⓑ Divide to find the cost per pound. $3.54 ÷ 6 pounds = $0.59 per pound.

13. Ⓑ Use long division to find the quotient, remembering to place the decimal point correctly. 63.72 ÷ 6 = 10.62

(continued on page 88)

(continued from page 87)

14. To estimate the quotient, round 35.58 to the nearest whole number, 36. Then divide: $36 \div 6 = 6$. Use the long-division algorithm to find the exact quotient.

$$6\overline{)35.58} = 5.93$$

15. See the sample answer. This answer shows all of the steps the student took to solve the problem, including each step of the long division and checking the quotient. The solution answers the question. The explanation provides important details about how the student solved the problem and uses the math words *decimal point*, *quotient*, *dividend*, and *divisor*.

✔ ASSESSMENT AND REMEDIATION

- Ask students to divide 4.34 by 7. *(0.62)*
- For students who are still struggling, use the chart below to guide remediation.
- After providing remediation, check students' understanding. Ask students to explain their thinking while dividing 30.56 by 8. *(3.82)*
- If a student is still having difficulty, use *STAMS Book E*, Lesson 6, pages 54–63.

If the error is . . .	Students may . . .	To remediate . . .
6.2 or 62	have placed the decimal point incorrectly, *or*	Remind students that the decimal point in the quotient lines up with the decimal point in the dividend. Have students use estimation to check the reasonableness of their answer. Students can also use a pencil to draw a line through the decimal point in the quotient and the decimal point in the dividend. If the decimal point is placed correctly, the line should be vertical.
	have not placed the digits in the quotient correctly.	For each step, have students underline the digits in the dividend they are dividing and check that they correctly place each digit in the quotient related to the place in the dividend.
0.82 or 0.72	have made a basic math error, *or*	Have students check their quotient using multiplication. If the product of quotient and divisor does not equal the dividend, have them go back and look at each step of their long division to locate the math error and correct it.
	have used an incorrect division basic fact.	Use flash cards to review division basic facts for 7s.
a different incorrect answer	have misaligned the digits during the long division.	Stress the importance of writing each step of the long division clearly and keeping the place values aligned. Have students complete the division on grid paper.

⭐ ADDITIONAL ACTIVITY

For students who have mastered the skills in this lesson, see **Challenge Activity** (page 89).

ADDITIONAL ACTIVITIES

 Hands-on Activity
Use number lines to estimate quotients.

Materials: number lines

Organize students in small groups and distribute number lines. Have students make a number line from 2.0 to 3.0 marked in tenths. Tell them to plot the decimal 2.76. Ask, "Is 2.76 closer to 2 or 3? *(3)*

Next, have students draw 3 squares to model the whole number 3. Ask, "How can you divide 3 wholes into 6 equal groups?" Discuss how the wholes can be shown as tenths or as hundredths. Have students cross out each whole and replace each with a drawing of 10 lines to represent tenths.

Guide students to see that they can divide these tenths into 6 equal groups. Have them circle the tenths to show the 6 equal groups. On the board, write $3 \div 6 = 5$ tenths $= 0.5$.

 Reteaching Activity
Use play money to model dividing decimals by whole numbers.

Materials: play money

Organize students in small groups and distribute play money. Tell students to model $2.45 using dollars, dimes, and pennies.

Write the long division on the board and have students model each step. Ask students, "Can you divide $2 into 5 equal groups?" *(no)* Have students trade the $2 for 20 dimes. Then, have them divide the dimes into 5 equal groups. *(4 dimes in each group)* Tell students to trade the leftover dimes for pennies and then divide the pennies evenly. *(9 pennies in each group)* "What is the quotient of $2.45 ÷ 5?" *(4 dimes and 9 pennies in each group, or $0.49)*

Have students repeat the activity for other division problems involving money.

 Vocabulary Activity
Use a crossword puzzle to reinforce terms

Materials: grid paper

Have each student use the vocabulary words to make a puzzle where the words share common letters.

Sample:

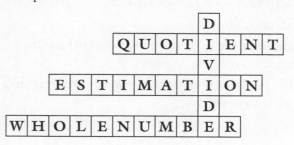

To help students check that their puzzles are complete, read a definition and have them check that they have used the corresponding word in their puzzle. Have them finalize the puzzles with numbers for each vertical and horizontal word and numbered, written definitions. Finally, have pairs exchange and complete each other's puzzle.

 Real-World Connection
Use division to find unit cost.

Display items that come in packs, such as an 8-pack of crayons, a 6-pack of juice, or a 3-pack of tennis balls, along with their corresponding prices. Discuss how division can be used to find the cost per item, or unit price. Have students divide to find each unit price.

 School-Home Connection
Inform families about division.

Give each student a copy of the reproducible School-Home Connection for Lesson 7 (page 175) to share with family. This activity has the family solve a division problem about money.

 Challenge Activity
Find the better buy.

Tell students that an 8-pack of markers sells for $5.68 and a 12-pack of markers sells for $8.76. Have them determine which is the better buy (or lesser price per marker) and explain how they found their answer. Have students write a similar problem and exchange it with a partner to solve.

Decimals

LESSON OBJECTIVES

Students will:

- Estimate the quotient of two decimal numbers using compatible numbers.
- Find the exact quotient of two decimal numbers using long division.

PREREQUISITES

Students should be able to:

- Round decimals to the nearest whole number.
- Multiply decimal numbers by powers of ten.
- Divide whole numbers using long division.

RELATED *STAMS*® LESSONS

- **Book E – Lesson 6**

  2-Digit Divisors shows students how to use long division to divide whole numbers by 2-digit divisors.

- **Book F – Lesson 7**

  Divide Decimals by Whole Numbers introduces how to find estimated and exact quotients of decimals divided by whole numbers.

VOCABULARY

PAGE 74

- **estimate:** to find an approximate answer
- **quotient:** the result of division
- **decimal number:** a number containing a decimal point that separates a whole from fractional place values (tenths, hundredths, thousandths, and so on)
- **compatible numbers:** numbers that are close in value to the actual numbers, but easier to add, subtract, multiply, or divide

PAGE 76

- **powers of ten:** numbers that are formed by multiplying 10 by itself any number of times
- **divisor:** in a division problem, the number being divided by
- **dividend:** in a division problem, the number being divided

MATH BACKGROUND

To divide by a decimal number, we multiply the divisor and dividend by a power of ten to obtain a whole-number divisor. The justification for doing this is that multiplying the divisor and dividend by the same number does not change the ratio of the two numbers. For example, these have the same ratio:

$$\frac{12}{3} \text{ or } 3\overline{)12} \text{ or } 4:1$$

$$\frac{12 \times 10}{3 \times 10} = \frac{120}{30} \text{ or } 30\overline{)120} \text{ or } 4:1$$

By the same property, these have the same ratio:

$$\frac{17.5}{2.5} \text{ or } 2.5\overline{)17.5} \text{ or } 7:1$$

$$\frac{17.5 \times 10}{2.5 \times 10} = \frac{175}{25} \text{ or } 25\overline{)175} \text{ or } 7:1$$

Because a quotient is just another way of expressing a ratio, the quotient is the same regardless of how the ratio is expressed.

Interactive Whiteboard
Visualize Dividing by Decimals

Go to the *Interactive Whiteboard Lessons* to bring Parts One and Two to life. Use features such as sliding screens with additional practice to deepen students' understanding of dividing by decimals.

Modeled Instruction

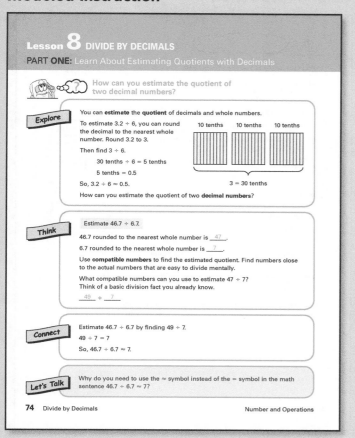

Guided Instruction

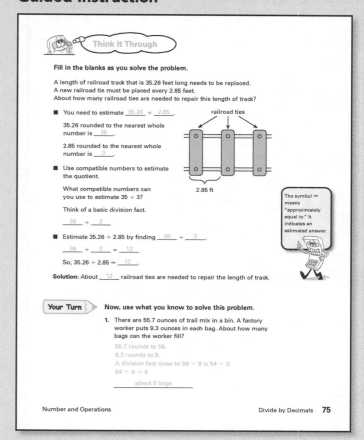

AT A GLANCE

Students activate their background knowledge about estimating the quotient of decimal and whole numbers. Then they learn to use compatible numbers to estimate the quotient of two decimals.

STEP BY STEP

PAGE 74

- Introduce the **Question** at the top of the page.
- Have students read the **Explore**.

> **Tip:** Make sure students read decimal numbers properly. This will reinforce their understanding of place value. For example, 3.2 is read "three and two tenths," not "three point two."

- Read **Think** with students. Ask students what it means for two people to be "compatible." *(They get along, they're friendly with each other, they have a lot in common.)* Relate to compatible numbers.
- Discuss **Connect** with students. Explain that there may be more than one pair of "correct" compatible numbers. Emphasize that the numbers should be close to the actual numbers.

- Organize students in pairs or groups for **Let's Talk** and monitor their discussions.
- Be sure students understand that the symbol = is only used when things are *exactly* equal. The symbol ≈ means that things are *almost* equal.

PAGE 75

- Read the **Think It Through** problem with students.

> **ELL Support:** Use the diagram to explain the problem to students. Show that the distance from the beginning of one railroad tie to the next is 2.85 feet.

- Guide students as they solve the problem.
- Monitor students as they complete **Your Turn**. Then discuss the correct answer. Use a calculator to show students that the exact quotient is 5.9892….

> **Error Alert:** Students who got the answer 7 may have rounded the dividend 55.7 to the greatest place value (tens) instead of the nearest whole number (ones).

 ADDITIONAL ACTIVITY

See **Hands-on Activity** (page 97).

Modeled Instruction

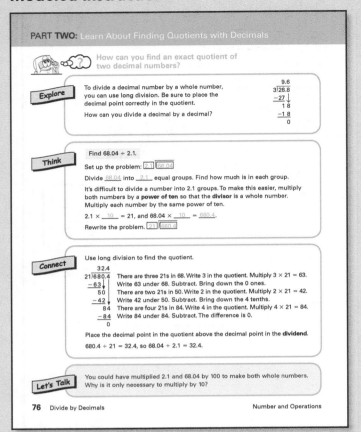

Guided Instruction

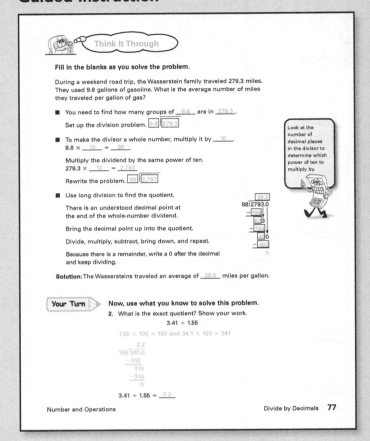

AT A GLANCE

Students find the exact quotient of two decimal numbers by multiplying the divisor and dividend by the same power of ten and using long division.

STEP BY STEP

PAGE 76

- Introduce the **Question** at the top of the page.
- Read **Explore** with students. Write the steps for long division on the board: *divide, multiply, subtract, bring down, repeat.*

ELL Support: Tell students that the word *decimal* is not interchangeable with *decimal point. Decimal* refers to a decimal number, which has a *decimal point* in it.

- Read **Think** with students.

Tip: Review powers of ten: $10^1 = 10 \times 1$; $10^2 = 10 \times 10 = 100$; $10^3 = 10 \times 10 \times 10 = 1{,}000$; etc. Remind students that because we use a base-ten number system, we can simply move the decimal point the number of places to the right that equals the number of tens being multiplied.

- Read through the solution steps in **Connect**.
- Organize students in pairs or groups for **Let's Talk** and monitor their discussions.
- Be sure students understand that the purpose of multiplying by a power of ten is to create a whole-number *divisor* to simplify the computation.

PAGE 77

- Read the **Think It Through** problem with students.
- Guide students as they solve the problem. Pause as they fill in missing information. Have them estimate the answer to check for reasonableness. *(280 ÷ 10 = 28)*
- Monitor students as they complete **Your Turn**. Then discuss the correct answer.

Error Alert: Students who got the answer 2 may have stopped dividing when reaching the end of the dividend. Remind them to write as many zeros after the decimal point in the dividend as needed, bring down, and continue dividing until the subtraction results in a zero.

ADDITIONAL ACTIVITY

See **Reteaching Activity** (page 97).

Modeled Practice

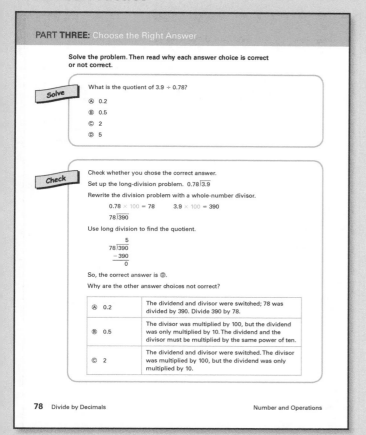

Guided Practice

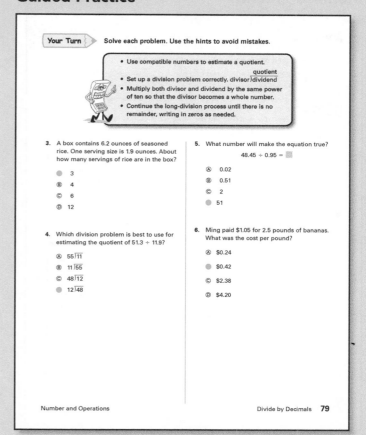

AT A GLANCE

Students reinforce their understanding of decimal division through solving a multiple-choice problem and analyzing correct and incorrect answer choices.

STEP BY STEP

PAGE 78

- Tell students that this page models finding the correct answer to a multiple-choice problem.

- Have students read the problem in **Solve** and choose the best answer. Remind students to check their math.

- Examine **Check** with students. Discuss the correct and incorrect choices.

PAGE 79

- Monitor students as they complete **Your Turn**.

- Organize students in pairs or small groups and have them discuss why each answer choice is correct or not and what errors may have been made.

- Review the answers with the class.

 ADDITIONAL ACTIVITY

See **Vocabulary Activity** (page 97).

Answer Analysis

3. ● This is the quotient of compatible numbers 6 ÷ 2.
   Ⓑ Found 6 − 2
   Ⓒ Divided 6 by 1
   Ⓓ Multiplied 6 by 2

4. Ⓐ Rounded numbers incorrectly, and switched dividend and divisor
   Ⓑ Rounded numbers incorrectly
   Ⓒ Switched dividend and divisor
   ● This problem uses closest compatible numbers.

5. Ⓐ Switched dividend and divisor; rounded quotient
   Ⓑ Multiplied both parts by different powers of ten
   Ⓒ Switched dividend and divisor, and multiplied them by different powers of ten
   ● $4,845 \div 95 = 51$

6. Ⓐ Switched dividend and divisor, and multiplied them by different powers of ten
   ● $\$10.50 \div 25 = \$0.42$
   Ⓒ Switched dividend and divisor
   Ⓓ Multiplied dividend and divisor by different powers of ten

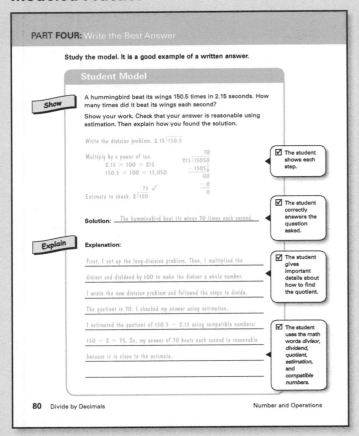

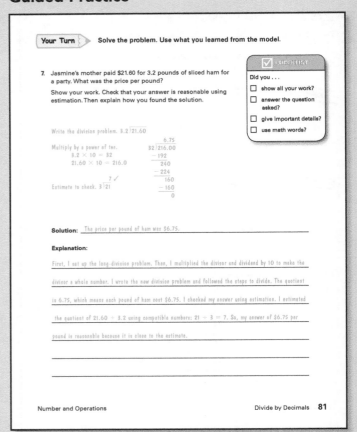

AT A GLANCE

Students study a model answer to an extended-response problem.

STEP BY STEP

PAGE 80

- Tell students that this page models building the solution to a problem one step at a time and writing to explain the solution.

- Have students read the problem in **Show**. Discuss how each mathematical step leads to the solution.

> Tip: Explain that decimal points are not removed from the dividend and divisor. Both values have been multiplied by 100. The resulting whole numbers have an understood decimal point to the right of the ones place.

- Read **Explain** with students. Have students circle the math words in the explanation.

- Tell students that this model would receive a high score for the reasons described in the right margin.

PAGE 81

- Monitor students as they complete **Your Turn**.
- Encourage students to follow the **Checklist** to write the best answer.
- Have students discuss their work with a partner. Then discuss the correct answer as a class.

Answer and Explanation

7. See the sample answer. It shows all of the steps taken to solve the problem, by setting up a decimal division problem, multiplying the dividend and divisor by powers of ten, finding the quotient using long division, and checking with estimation. The solution answers the question. The explanation provides important details about how the problem was solved and uses the math words *divisor*, *dividend*, *quotient*, *estimation*, and *compatible numbers*.

ADDITIONAL ACTIVITY

See **Real-World Connection** (page 97).

ADDITIONAL ACTIVITY

See **School-Home Connection** (page 97).

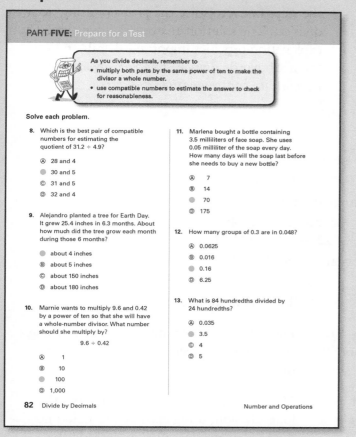

PART FIVE: Prepare for a Test

As you divide decimals, remember to
• multiply both parts by the same power of ten to make the divisor a whole number.
• use compatible numbers to estimate the answer to check for reasonableness.

Solve each problem.

8. Which is the best pair of compatible numbers for estimating the quotient of 31.2 ÷ 4.9?
   Ⓐ 28 and 4
   ⬤ 30 and 5
   Ⓒ 31 and 5
   Ⓓ 32 and 4

9. Alejandro planted a tree for Earth Day. It grew 25.4 inches in 6.3 months. About how much did the tree grow each month during those 6 months?
   ⬤ about 4 inches
   Ⓑ about 5 inches
   Ⓒ about 150 inches
   Ⓓ about 180 inches

10. Marnie wants to multiply 9.6 and 0.42 by a power of ten so that she will have a whole-number divisor. What number should she multiply by?
    9.6 ÷ 0.42
    Ⓐ 1
    Ⓑ 10
    ⬤ 100
    Ⓓ 1,000

11. Marlena bought a bottle containing 3.5 milliliters of face soap. She uses 0.05 milliliter of the soap every day. How many days will the soap last before she needs to buy a new bottle?
    Ⓐ 7
    Ⓑ 14
    ⬤ 70
    Ⓓ 175

12. How many groups of 0.3 are in 0.048?
    Ⓐ 0.0625
    Ⓑ 0.016
    ⬤ 0.16
    Ⓓ 6.25

13. What is 84 hundredths divided by 24 hundredths?
    Ⓐ 0.035
    ⬤ 3.5
    Ⓒ 4
    Ⓓ 5

82 Divide by Decimals   Number and Operations

14. Estimate the quotient. Explain how you got your answer.
    77.5 ÷ 10.2 ≈ ▦

    77.5 and 10.2 rounded to the nearest whole numbers are 78 and 10. The closest compatible numbers

    for division are 80 and 10. Because 80 ÷ 10 = 8, 77.5 ÷ 10.2 ≈ 8.

15. Layla and her mother are sewing costumes for the school play. They purchased 6.8 yards of fabric for $67.66. What was the price for each yard of fabric?
    Show your work. Check the reasonableness of your answer using estimation.
    Then explain how you found the solution.

    Write the division problem. 6.8⟌67.66

    Multiply by a power of ten.
    6.8 × 10 = 68
    67.66 × 10 = 676.6

    Check. 7⟌70

    $$\begin{array}{r} 9.95 \\ 68\,\overline{)676.60} \\ -612 \\ \hline 646 \\ -612 \\ \hline 340 \\ -340 \\ \hline 0 \end{array}$$

    10 ✓

    Solution: ___The fabric cost $9.95 for each yard.___

    Explanation:

    First, I set up the long-division problem. Then, I multiplied the divisor and dividend by 10 to make

    the divisor a whole number. I wrote the new division problem and followed the steps to divide.

    The quotient is 9.95, which means each yard of fabric cost $9.95. I checked my answer using estimation.

    I estimated the quotient of 67.66 ÷ 6.8 using compatible numbers: 70 ÷ 7 = 10. So, my answer

    of $9.95 per yard is reasonable because it is close to the estimate.

Number and Operations   Divide by Decimals **83**

AT A GLANCE

Students practice solving decimal division problems that might appear on a mathematics test.

STEP BY STEP

PAGES 82–83

• Tell students that they will practice solving decimal division problems. They should estimate when the question asks for an approximate answer. If a problem does not specifically mention an estimate, or use clue words such as *about* or *approximately*, an exact answer is needed.

• Point out the tips at the top of page 82. Explain to students that these tips will help them answer the problems correctly.

• You may wish to have students review the hints for avoiding mistakes on page 79 as well.

• Tell students to complete problems 8–15 on pages 82 and 83. Encourage students to check their answers.

• Discuss the correct responses as a class.

Answers and Explanations

8. Ⓑ Round 31.2 and 4.9 to the nearest whole numbers: 31 and 5. The closest compatible numbers for division are 30 and 5, so the quotient is approximately 6.

9. Ⓐ Round 25.4 and 6.3 to the nearest whole numbers: 25 and 6. Using compatible numbers, $24 \div 6 = 4$, so the tree grew about 4 inches each month.

10. Ⓒ The divisor has two decimal places, so multiply the divisor and dividend by 10^2, or 100, to create a whole-number divisor.

11. Ⓒ Divide 3.5 by 0.05 to find the number of days the soap will last. Multiply both the divisor and dividend by 100 and divide.
    $3.5 \div 0.05 \rightarrow 350 \div 5 = 70$

12. Ⓒ Divide 0.048 by 0.3.
    $0.048 \div 0.3 \rightarrow 0.48 \div 3 = 0.16$

13. Ⓑ Divide 0.84 by 0.24.
    $0.84 \div 0.24 \rightarrow 84 \div 24 = 3.5$

(continued on page 96)

(continued from page 95)

14. Round both dividend and divisor to the nearest whole number: $78 \div 10$. Then use the closest compatible numbers, 80 and 10, for division to find an estimated quotient of approximately 8.

15. See the sample answer. This answer shows all of the steps taken to solve the problem using decimal division. The solution answers the question. The explanation provides important details and uses the math words *divisor*, *dividend*, *quotient*, *estimation*, and *compatible numbers*.

 ASSESSMENT AND REMEDIATION

- Ask students to find the quotient of $7.6 \div 2.5$. *(7.6 ÷ 2.5 → 76 ÷ 25 = 3.04)*
- For students who are still struggling, use the chart below to guide remediation.
- After providing remediation, check students' understanding. Ask students to explain their steps while finding the quotient of $3.78 \div 0.12$. *(3.78 ÷ 0.12 → 378 ÷ 12 = 31.5)*
- If a student is still having difficulty, use *STAMS Book F*, Lesson 7, pages 64–73.

If the error is . . .	Students may . . .	To remediate . . .
0.304	have multiplied the divisor by 10 to get a whole number, but not multiplied the dividend, *or*	Have students estimate the quotient, using compatible numbers, to see if their answer makes sense.
	have not brought the decimal point from the dividend straight up to the quotient.	Have students use grid paper to work the long division, using each box to hold one digit. The decimal point in the (adjusted) dividend should be written on a grid line, and should be brought straight up into the quotient, lying on the same grid line.
3.4	have misaligned digits in the quotient and dividend, *or*	Have students use grid paper to work out long-division problems, using the grid lines to keep digits and decimal points lined up correctly.
	have neglected to place a zero in the tenths place of the quotient, simply bringing down the next digit to continue dividing.	Explain the importance of writing a zero in the tenths place. Show that 3.4 is quite different than 3.04. Have students think of $3.40 and $3.04; they are different amounts of money.
304	have placed a zero at the end of the dividend to keep dividing, but have forgotten to first write the decimal point.	Remind students that every whole number has an understood decimal point to the right of the ones place, separating whole from fractional place values. So, 76 must be written 76.0 when the need to write in a zero arises. Use $5 and $5.00 as an example, as students have likely seen prices displayed in both of these ways in stores.

 ADDITIONAL ACTIVITY

For students who have mastered the skills in this lesson, see **Challenge Activity** (page 97).

ADDITIONAL ACTIVITIES

 Hands-on Activity
Use a multiplication chart to find compatible numbers.

Materials: 1 multiplication chart per person

Have students use a 12 × 12 multiplication chart to look for compatible numbers when estimating quotients for decimal division. Teach them how to use it by doing the following:

Write the problem 49.3 ÷ 5.8 on the board. Ask, "What is the dividend 49.3 rounded to the nearest whole number?" *(50)* "What is the divisor 5.8 rounded to the nearest whole number?" *(6)* Tell students that they can use the multiplication chart to find the closest compatible numbers for 50 ÷ 6. First, look for 6 down the first column. Then move across that row until reaching the number nearest 50. Students should identify 48. Now direct students to move up the column containing 48 to find the estimated quotient. *(8)* Ask, "What division fact did you just use to estimate 49.3 ÷ 5.8?" *(48 ÷ 6 = 8)* Write the estimated quotient next to the problem on the board, using the approximately equal symbol: 49.3 ÷ 5.8 ≈ 8.

 Reteaching Activity
Multiply by powers of 10 by moving the decimal points.

One of the most common errors in decimal division is placement of the decimal point in the quotient. Reinforce the practice of multiplying the divisor and dividend by the same power of 10 by having students draw curved arrows under each digit to show moving the decimal point to the right. When students can visually confirm the same number of arrows appear under both the dividend and divisor, they are ready to proceed with the division process. Encourage students to record the decimal points in their new positions, even if at the end of a whole number. This will reduce possible errors later on. Also, have students immediately bring the decimal point in the dividend up into place in the quotient before beginning the division.

 Vocabulary Activity
Play "Quiz Show" to reinforce terms.

Materials: index cards, markers

Divide students into two groups and provide each group with index cards and markers. As you read a vocabulary term aloud, the first contestant in each group writes a definition or draws a picture for the term. The two contestants raise their hands as soon as they have a response ready. The one with the first correct response earns a point for his or her team. Repeat with a new vocabulary term for each pair of contestants.

 Real-World Connection
Do grocery store math.

Bring in (or mock up) a grocery store receipt with several items that were charged per pound, such as produce or lunch meat. Black out the per-pound price. Ask students to calculate the cost for each pound of that item based on the number of pounds (divisor) and total cost (dividend).

 School-Home Connection
Inform families about decimal division.

Give each student a copy of the reproducible School-Home Connection for Lesson 8 (page 177) to share with family. This activity has the family solve division problems about the cost of snacks.

 Challenge Activity
Find quotients with repeating decimals.

Have students work a division problem that has a repeating decimal quotient. For example, 6.1 ÷ 0.18 to the first three decimal places is 33.888. Explain that if they keep dividing and repeatedly get the same digit or series of digits in a quotient, the answer is a *repeating* decimal. There are two ways to express this type of number. For this example, the answer can be written 33.888 … or 33.$\overline{8}$.

Lesson **9** UNDERSTAND RATIOS

LESSON OBJECTIVES

Students will:

• Write a ratio to compare two quantities.

• Use multiplication and division to find equivalent ratios.

PREREQUISITES

Students should be able to:

• Understand and write fractions and equivalent fractions.

• Multiply and divide whole numbers.

RELATED *STAMS*® LESSON

• Book D – Lesson 8

   Equivalent Fractions shows students how to find equivalent fractions.

VOCABULARY

PAGE 84

• **fraction:** a part of a whole

• **whole:** the total number of all items being compared

• **ratio:** a comparison of two quantities by division; can be part to part, part to whole, or whole to part

PAGE 86

• **equivalent:** equal

• **equivalent ratios:** two or more ratios that are equal to one another

PAGE 87

• **proportion:** an equation that shows two ratios are equivalent

MATH BACKGROUND

A ratio is a comparison of two quantities by division. The ratio of 3 boys to 2 girls can be written 3 to 2, 3:2, or $\frac{3}{2}$. The last form represents the division, $3 \div 2 = 1.5$, which means 3 boys are 1.5 times as many as 2 girls. It also represents a fraction, meaning 3 boys are $\frac{3}{2}$ times as many as 2 girls.

In Part One, students learn that ratios can compare parts and wholes. In Part Two, they learn about equivalent ratios such as 4 to 6 and 8 to 12. Students tend to have difficulty with the order of the quantities in equivalent ratios. For example, if one ratio is written as miles to gallons, an equivalent ratio must also be written in this order.

Ratio is the foundation for the next two topics students will study: percent (a ratio that compares a number to 100) and rate (a ratio of quantities that have different units, such as 30 miles per gallon).

Interactive Whiteboard
Visualize Ratio Concepts

Go to the *Interactive Whiteboard Lessons* to bring Parts One and Two to life. Use features such as interactive models to deepen students' understanding of ratios.

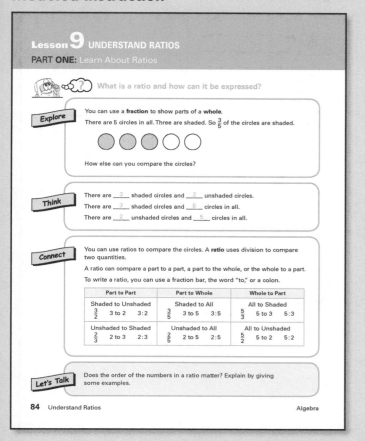

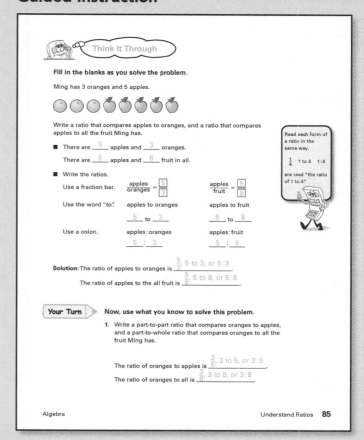

AT A GLANCE
. . . .

Students activate their background knowledge about fractions, and then learn about ratios as a way to compare two quantities.

STEP BY STEP
. . . .

PAGE 84

- Introduce the **Question** at the top of the page.
- Have students study the circles shown in **Explore** and connect the image to the fraction.
- Read **Think** with students. Emphasize that there are two types of circles, shaded and unshaded. Pause so students can say aloud the numbers in orange.
- Discuss **Connect** with students. Help students see the connection between the circles and the ratios. Focus on the order of the words and the order of the numbers.

ELL Support: Underline the prefix *un-*. Discuss how *un-* means "not," or "opposite of." Point to the picture to reinforce the definition. Give other examples such as *un*happy, *un*likely, and *un*equal.

- Organize students in pairs or groups for **Let's Talk** and monitor their discussions.

- Be sure students understand that the order of the numbers must match the comparison being made.

Tip: Have students draw a picture to represent the ratio of shaded to unshaded circles as being 2 to 4. Check students have drawn 2 shaded and 4 unshaded circles and not vice versa.

PAGE 85

- Read the **Think It Through** problem with students.
- Guide students as they solve the problem. Help them determine that they need to write a part-to-part ratio to compare the apples and oranges and part-to-whole ratio to compare apples to all the fruit.
- Help students see that each ratio can be written three different ways.
- Monitor students as they complete **Your Turn**. Then discuss the correct answer.

Error Alert: Students who wrote 5 to 3 for the first answer confused the order of apples and oranges.

 ADDITIONAL ACTIVITY
. . . .
See **Hands-on Activity** (page 105).

Modeled Instruction

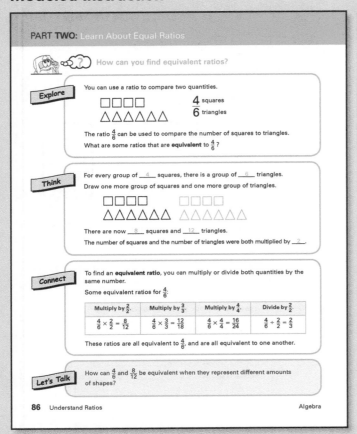

Guided Instruction

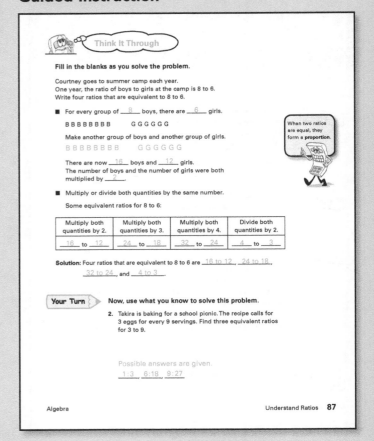

AT A GLANCE

Students learn to use multiplication and division to write equivalent ratios.

STEP BY STEP

PAGE 86

- Introduce the **Question** at the top of the page.
- Read **Explore** with students. Reinforce that a ratio can compare a part to a part.
- Read **Think** with students. Pause so students can read aloud the numbers in orange and study the drawing.
- Tell students to study the chart in **Connect**. Test their understanding by asking if 5 to 7 is equivalent to 4 to 6.

> Tip: Write out the multiplication to show how each equivalent ratio was found $\left(\frac{4}{6} = \frac{(4 \times 2)}{(6 \times 2)} = \frac{8}{12} \right)$.
>
> Then ask students to find some other ratios that are equivalent to the ratio 4:6.

- Organize students in pairs or groups for **Let's Talk** and monitor their discussions.

- Be sure students grasp that although the ratios contain different numbers, they both represent 4 squares for every 6 triangles.

PAGE 87

- Read the **Think It Through** problem with students.
- Guide students as they solve the problem. Pause for students to fill in missing information. Then discuss each response.
- Monitor students as they complete **Your Turn**. Then discuss the correct answer. (There are infinitely many correct answers, so be sure to check students' work.)

> Error Alert: Students who wrote 4:10 as an equivalent ratio for 3:9 thought that they could add the same number to both quantities to produce equivalent fractions. Stress that the only operations that produce equivalent fractions in this manner are multiplication and division.

 ADDITIONAL ACTIVITY

See **Reteaching Activity** (page 105).

Modeled Practice

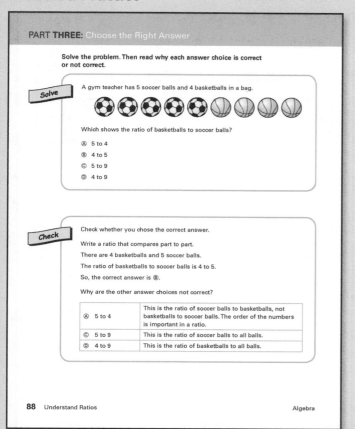

Guided Practice

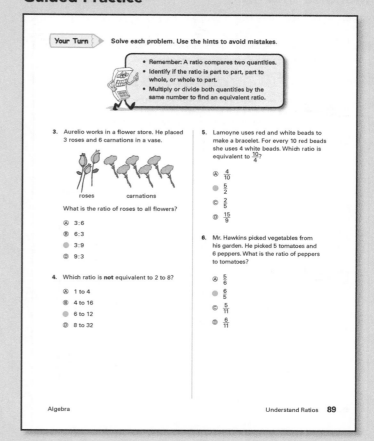

AT A GLANCE

Students reinforce their understanding of ratio by solving a multiple-choice problem and analyzing correct and incorrect answer choices.

STEP BY STEP

PAGE 88

- Tell students that this page models finding the correct answer to a multiple-choice problem.
- Have students read the problem in **Solve** and choose the best answer. Remind students to check their math.
- Examine **Check** with students. Discuss the correct and incorrect choices.

PAGE 89

- Monitor students as they complete **Your Turn**.
- Organize students in pairs or small groups and have them discuss why each answer choice is correct or not and what errors may have been made.
- Review the answers with the class.

 ### ADDITIONAL ACTIVITY

See **Vocabulary Activity** (page 105).

Algebra

Answer Analysis

3. Ⓐ Chose the ratio of roses to carnations
   Ⓑ Chose the ratio of carnations to roses
   ⬤ There are 3 roses and 9 flowers in all. The ratio of roses to all flowers is $3:9$.
   Ⓓ Chose the ratio of all flowers to roses

4. Ⓐ Divided both quantities by 2
   Ⓑ Multiplied both quantities by 2
   ⬤ The student added 4 to both quantities; 6 to 12 is not equivalent to 2 to 8.
   Ⓓ Multiplied both quantities by 4

5. Ⓐ Reversed order of the two quantities in the ratio
   ⬤ $\dfrac{10}{4} = \dfrac{10 \div 2}{4 \div 2} = \dfrac{5}{2}$
   Ⓒ Divided both quantities by 2 but reversed their order in the ratio
   Ⓓ Added 5 to both quantities

6. Ⓐ Chose the ratio of tomatoes to peppers
   ⬤ The ratio of tomatoes to peppers is 6 to 5 or $\dfrac{6}{5}$.
   Ⓒ Chose the ratio of tomatoes to all vegetables
   Ⓓ Chose the ratio of peppers to all vegetables

Modeled Practice

Guided Practice

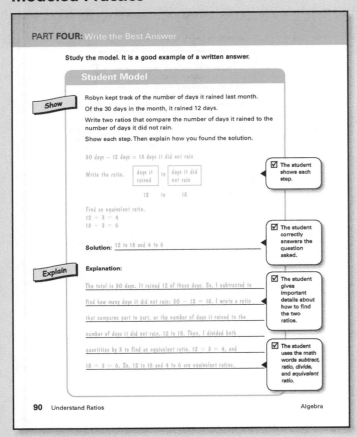

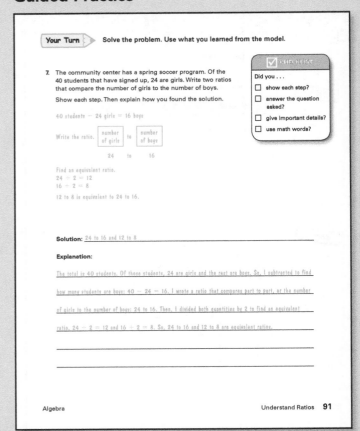

AT A GLANCE

Students study a model answer to an extended-response problem.

STEP BY STEP

PAGE 90

- Tell students that this page models building the solution to a problem one step at a time and writing to explain the solution.
- Have students read the problem in **Show**. Discuss how each mathematical step leads to the solution.

Tip: Explain that subtraction can be used to find the other part if you know the whole and one part.

- Read **Explain** with students. Have students circle the math words in the explanation.
- Direct students' attention to the notes in the right margin. Tell students that this model would receive a high score for the reasons described in these notes.

PAGE 91

- Monitor students as they complete **Your Turn**.
- Encourage students to follow the **Checklist** to write the best answer.
- Have students discuss their work with a partner. Then discuss the correct answer as a class.

Answer and Explanation

7. See the sample answer. This answer shows all of the steps taken to solve the problem, including expressing the ratio and writing equations to find an equivalent ratio. The solution answers the question. The explanation provides important details about how the problem was solved and uses the math words *subtract*, *ratio*, *divide*, and *equivalent ratio*.

   There are infinitely many correct answers, so be sure to check students' work.

 ADDITIONAL ACTIVITY

See **Real-World Connection** (page 105).

 ADDITIONAL ACTIVITY

See **School-Home Connection** (page 105).

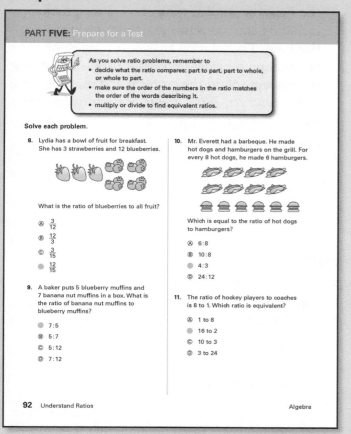

PART FIVE: Prepare for a Test

As you solve ratio problems, remember to
• decide what the ratio compares: part to part, part to whole, or whole to part.
• make sure the order of the numbers in the ratio matches the order of the words describing it.
• multiply or divide to find equivalent ratios.

Solve each problem.

8. Lydia has a bowl of fruit for breakfast. She has 3 strawberries and 12 blueberries.

What is the ratio of blueberries to all fruit?

Ⓐ $\frac{3}{12}$

Ⓑ $\frac{12}{3}$

Ⓒ $\frac{3}{15}$

● $\frac{12}{15}$

9. A baker puts 5 blueberry muffins and 7 banana nut muffins in a box. What is the ratio of banana nut muffins to blueberry muffins?

● 7:5

Ⓑ 5:7

Ⓒ 5:12

Ⓓ 7:12

10. Mr. Everett had a barbeque. He made hot dogs and hamburgers on the grill. For every 8 hot dogs, he made 6 hamburgers.

Which is equal to the ratio of hot dogs to hamburgers?

Ⓐ 6:8

Ⓑ 10:8

● 4:3

Ⓓ 24:12

11. The ratio of hockey players to coaches is 8 to 1. Which ratio is equivalent?

Ⓐ 1 to 8

● 16 to 2

Ⓒ 10 to 3

Ⓓ 3 to 24

92 Understand Ratios   Algebra

Independent Practice

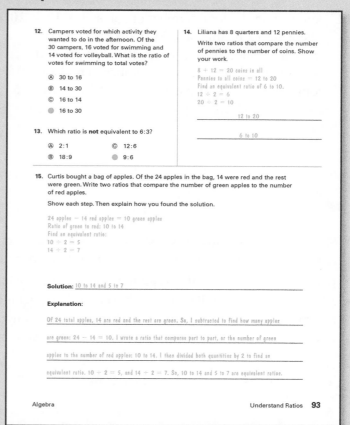

12. Campers voted for which activity they wanted to do in the afternoon. Of the 30 campers, 16 voted for swimming and 14 voted for volleyball. What is the ratio of votes for swimming to total votes?

Ⓐ 30 to 16

Ⓑ 14 to 30

Ⓒ 16 to 14

● 16 to 30

13. Which ratio is **not** equivalent to 6:3?

Ⓐ 2:1   Ⓒ 12:6

Ⓑ 18:9   ● 9:6

14. Liliana has 8 quarters and 12 pennies. Write two ratios that compare the number of pennies to the number of coins. Show your work.

8 + 12 = 20 coins in all
Pennies to all coins = 12 to 20
Find an equivalent ratio of 6 to 10.
12 ÷ 2 = 6
20 ÷ 2 = 10

_____ 12 to 20 _____

_____ 6 to 10 _____

15. Curtis bought a bag of apples. Of the 24 apples in the bag, 14 were red and the rest were green. Write two ratios that compare the number of green apples to the number of red apples.

Show each step. Then explain how you found the solution.

24 apples — 14 red apples = 10 green apples
Ratio of green to red: 10 to 14
Find an equivalent ratio:
10 ÷ 2 = 5
14 ÷ 2 = 7

Solution: 10 to 14 and 5 to 7

Explanation:

Of 24 total apples, 14 are red and the rest are green. So, I subtracted to find how many apples

are green: 24 — 14 = 10. I wrote a ratio that compares part to part, or the number of green

apples to the number of red apples: 10 to 14. I then divided both quantities by 2 to find an

equivalent ratio. 10 ÷ 2 = 5, and 14 ÷ 2 = 7. So, 10 to 14 and 5 to 7 are equivalent ratios.

Algebra   Understand Ratios 93

AT A GLANCE

Students practice using ratios to solve problems that might appear on a mathematics test.

STEP BY STEP

PAGES 92–93

• Tell students that they will practice solving problems that involve ratios and equivalent ratios.

• Point out the tips at the top of page 92. Explain to students that these tips will help them answer the problems correctly.

• You may wish to have students review the hints for avoiding mistakes on page 89 as well.

• Tell students to complete problems 8–15 on pages 92 and 93. Encourage students to check their answers.

• Discuss the correct responses as a class.

Answers and Explanations

8. Ⓓ Add to find the total fruit: $3 + 12 = 15$. There are 12 blueberries and 15 fruit in all. So, the ratio of blueberries to all fruit is 12 to 15, or $\frac{12}{15}$.

9. Ⓐ There are 7 banana nut muffins and 5 blueberry muffins. So, the ratio of banana nut to blueberry is 7 to 5, or 7:5.

10. Ⓒ There are 8 hot dogs and 6 hamburgers. So, the ratio of hot dogs to hamburgers is 8:6. Find an equivalent ratio by multiplying or dividing. Divide both quantities by 2 to get the ratio 4:3.

11. Ⓑ Multiply both quantities of the ratio by 2. $8 \times 2 = 16$, and $1 \times 2 = 2$. So, 16 to 2 is equivalent to 8 to 1.

12. Ⓓ There are 16 votes for swimming and 30 votes in all. So, the ratio of votes for swimming to total votes is 16 to 30.

13. Ⓓ Multiply or divide both quantities by the same number. Multiply by 2 to get 12:6. Multiply by 3 to get 18:9. Divide by 2 to get 2:1. So, 9:6 is not equivalent to 6:3.

(continued on page 104)

(continued from page 103)

14. Add to find the total number of coins: $8 + 12 = 20$. There are 12 pennies and 20 coins in all. So the ratio of pennies to coins is $12:20$. Multiply or divide both quantities by the same number to find an equivalent ratio. Possible answers include $6:10$, $3:5$, $24:40$, $36:60$, and any other ratio that simplifies to $3:5$.

15. See the sample answer. This answer shows all of the steps the student took to solve the problem, including equations to show the student's thinking. The solution answers the question. The explanation provides important details about how the student solved the problem and uses the math words *subtract*, *ratio*, *divide*, and *equivalent ratio*.

There are infinitely many correct answers, so be sure to check the student's work.

 ## ASSESSMENT AND REMEDIATION

- Show students a drawing of 9 shapes: 6 circles and 3 stars.
  Ask students to write two ratios comparing stars to circles. *(Sample answer: $3:6$ and $1:2$)*
- For students who are still struggling, use the chart below to guide remediation.
- After providing remediation, check students' understanding. Ask students to explain their thinking while writing two ratios to compare hearts to all shapes for a picture of 4 hearts and 4 stars. *(Sample answer: $4:8$ and $2:4$)*
- If a student is still having difficulty, use *STAMS Book D*, Lesson 8, pages 74–83.

If the error is . . .	Students may . . .	To remediate . . .
$6:3$ (or equivalent ratio)	have mistakenly reversed the quantities, *or*	Encourage students to write the words for the ratio and check that the order of the numbers matches the order of the words. For example: stars to circles = 3 stars to 6 circles = $3:6$.
	not understand the importance of the order in a ratio.	Clarify that the order of the numbers in the ratio is important. Demonstrate this by drawing a picture that shows each ratio of circles to stars: 3 to 6 and 6 to 3.
$3:9$ (or equivalent ratio)	have written the number of stars as a fraction of the whole.	Discuss the difference between a ratio and a fraction. Explain that a fraction is a part of a whole. Show that a ratio can compare a part to a part.
a different ratio that is not equivalent to $3:6$	have miscounted, *or*	Have students list and carefully count each shape: "circles: 6; stars: 3; total: 9." Ask students to identify from the list which quantities are needed for the ratio of stars to circles. Guide them to write the ratio.
	not understand the concept of ratio.	Review with students the concepts on page 84. Have students practice finding the ratio for different groups of items.

 ## ADDITIONAL ACTIVITY

For students who have mastered the skills in this lesson, see **Challenge Activity** (page 105).

ADDITIONAL ACTIVITIES

 Hands-on Activity
Use counters to model ratios.

Materials: two-color counters

Organize students in small groups and distribute counters. Have students create a group of 8 counters, 3 red and 5 yellow.

Write the ratio 3 to 5 on the board. Then ask students, "How many red counters? How many yellow counters?" Say, "The ratio of red counters to yellow counters is 3 to 5." Ask students to describe the counters using other ratios such as yellow to red, yellow to all, and red to all.

Write another ratio on the board. Have students model it using counters. Then ask them to describe the group of counters using other part-to-part and part-to-whole ratios.

 Reteaching Activity
Use connecting cubes to model equivalent ratios.

Materials: connecting cubes (different colors)

Distribute connecting cubes to each student. Tell students to link together 2 cubes of one color and 4 cubes of another color to make a pattern unit, such as 2 blue, 4 red.

Ask students, "What is the ratio of blue cubes to red cubes?" *(2 to 4)* Have students repeat the pattern unit and again count the blue cubes and red cubes. "What is the ratio of blue cubes to red cubes?" *(4 to 8)* Repeat several times to form equivalent ratios. *(6 to 10, 8 to 16, and so on)*

Have students look at the original pattern unit of 2 to 4. Have students make equal groups of blue and red cubes (1 blue and 2 red per group). Discuss how this is the ratio in simplest form. Say, "1 to 2 is equivalent to 2 to 4. For every 1 blue cube, there are 2 red cubes."

 Vocabulary Activity
Play Concentration to reinforce terms.

Materials: index cards

In pairs, have students write one vocabulary term on each index card. Then have students write a definition or example of each term on another index card. Have students shuffle the cards and place them face down in an array. Students take turns flipping over two cards. If the player chooses a matching term and definition, he keeps the pair. If the cards do not match, he replaces them. The student with the most matched pairs wins.

 Real-World Connection
Apply ratios to real-world situations.

Discuss everyday examples of ratios, such as recipes (2 eggs per batch), map distance (2 miles to 1 inch), and scale drawings (2 meters to 1 cm). Then have students name other examples of ratios. If reasonable, have students use ratios to describe situations in the classroom (for example, windows to doors, or chairs to desks).

 School-Home Connection
Inform families about ratios.

Give each student a copy of the reproducible School-Home Connection for Lesson 9 (page 179) to share with family. This activity has the family use ratios to design book covers.

 Challenge Activity
Use equivalent ratios to finding a missing value.

Present this problem: *The ratio of boys to girls is 3 to 2. If there are 18 boys, how many girls are there?* Have students use equivalent ratios to find the answer. *(3 to 2 → 18 to 12; 12 girls)* Ask students write a similar problem, and then exchange with a partner and solve.

LESSON OBJECTIVES

Students will:

- Write ratios as percents.
- Compare ratios and percents.

PREREQUISITES

Students should be able to:

- Write equivalent ratios.
- Divide a whole number by a decimal.
- Multiply a decimal by 100.

RELATED *STAMS*® LESSONS

- **Book E – Lesson 9**

  Compare Unlike Fractions shows students how to rewrite equivalent fractions with different denominators.

- **Book F – Lesson 7**

  Divide Decimals by Whole Numbers shows students how to use long division to divide decimals.

- **Book F – Lesson 9**

  Understand Ratios teaches students how to write ratios and find equivalent ratios.

VOCABULARY

PAGE 94

- **ratio:** a comparison of two quantities by division; can be part to part, part to whole, or whole to part

- **percent:** a ratio that compares a number to 100

- **percent sign (%):** a symbol that means *per hundred,* or *hundredths*

- **equivalent ratios:** two or more ratios that are equal to one another

PAGE 96

- **operation:** an action that is performed on numbers or variables (such as addition, subtraction, multiplication, or division)

MATH BACKGROUND

Students have learned that ratios can compare part to part, whole to part, and part to whole. In this lesson, they learn that a percent is a special ratio that compares a number to 100, where 100 represents the whole. So, a percent is a part-to-whole ratio.

Percents are useful because they provide an easy way to compare ratios to each other. For example, suppose basketball players A, B, and C make 28 of 50, 24 of 40, and 30 of 48 shots. You can compare percents to decide who has the best record.

Player A: $\dfrac{28}{50} = \dfrac{28 \times 2}{50 \times 2} = \dfrac{56}{100} = 56\%$

Player B: $\dfrac{24}{40} \rightarrow 40\overline{)24.00}^{0.60} \rightarrow 60\%$

Player C: $\dfrac{30}{40} \rightarrow 40\overline{)30.00}^{0.75} \rightarrow 75\%$ (greatest percent; best ratio)

Note that two methods of writing a ratio in fraction form as a ratio in percent form are shown above: writing an equivalent ratio with a denominator of 100 and dividing to obtain a decimal. Both are demonstrated in this lesson.

Interactive Whiteboard
···
Visualize Percent Concepts

Go to the *Interactive Whiteboard Lessons* to bring Parts One and Two to life. Use features such as sliding screens with additional practice to deepen students' understanding of percent.

Modeled Instruction

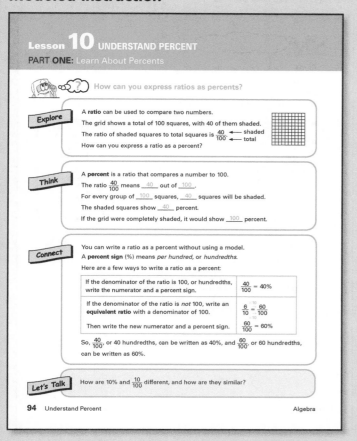

Guided Instruction

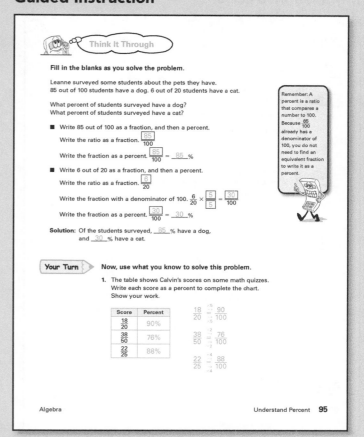

AT A GLANCE

Students activate their background knowledge about ratios, and then learn that percent is a ratio that compares a number to 100.

STEP BY STEP

PAGE 94

- Introduce the **Question** at the top of the page.
- Have students study the grid shown in **Explore** and connect the image to the ratio.
- Read **Think** with students. Emphasize that 100% is a whole, and percents less than 100% are parts of a whole. Pause so students can say aloud the numbers in orange.
- Discuss **Connect** with students. Emphasize that an equivalent ratio is only needed when the denominator is not equal to 100.

Tip: Give students other ratios with denominators of 2, 4, 5, 20, 25, and 50. Have them practice multiplying both terms by the same number to find an equivalent ratio with the whole represented by 100.

- Organize students in pairs or groups for **Let's Talk** and monitor their discussions.
- Be sure students understand that the percent and fraction are equal, but that they are different ways to express the same amount.

PAGE 95

- Read the **Think It Through** problem with students.
- Help them determine that they must write an equivalent ratio to find the percent of surveyed students with a cat.

ELL Support: Explain that the percent sign means *per hundred*. So, students should not write $\frac{85\%}{100}$ to show 85%. This means 85 per hundred, over 100.

- Monitor students as they complete **Your Turn**. Then discuss the correct answer.

Error Alert: If students wrote $\frac{38}{50}$ as 88%, they may have added 50 to the numerator and denominator, instead of multiplying each by 2.

 ADDITIONAL ACTIVITY

See **Hands-on Activity** (page 113).

Modeled Instruction

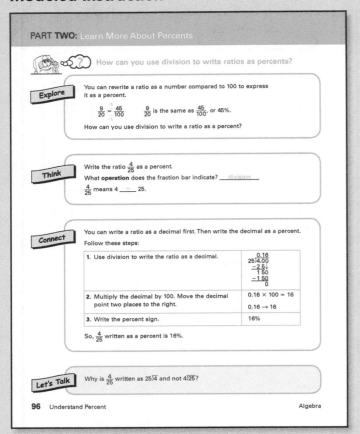

Guided Instruction

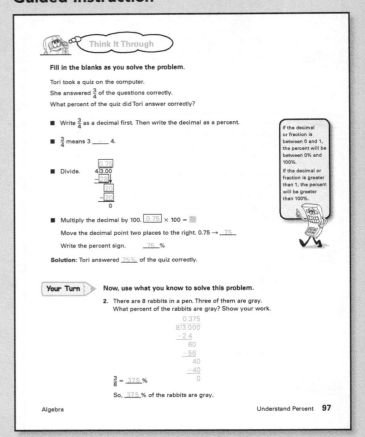

AT A GLANCE
. . . .

Students learn how to use long division to write a ratio as a percent.

STEP BY STEP
. . . .

PAGE 96

• Introduce the **Question** at the top of the page.

• Read **Explore** with students. Review how to use equivalent ratios to write ratios as percents.

• Read **Think** with students.

• Tell students to study the steps and example in **Connect**. Test their understanding by asking why 4 is divided by 25 (and not vice versa).

ELL Support: Review the directional words *right* and *left*. Have students point or raise the appropriate hand to indicate which way to move the decimal point when multiplying by 100.

• Organize students in pairs or groups for **Let's Talk** and monitor their discussions.

• Be sure students understand that all fractions indicate the numerator should be divided by the denominator.

PAGE 97

• Read the **Think It Through** problem with students.

• Guide students as they solve the problem. Pause as they fill in missing information. Then discuss each response.

Tip: Have students check their work by writing the ratio $\frac{3}{4}$ as an equivalent ratio out of 100. $\left(\frac{3}{4} = \frac{75}{100}\right)$

• Monitor students as they complete **Your Turn**. Then discuss the correct answer.

Error Alert: Students who answered 375% might be placing the decimal point after the last digit when multiplying the decimal by 100.

 ADDITIONAL ACTIVITY
. . . .

See **Reteaching Activity** (page 113).

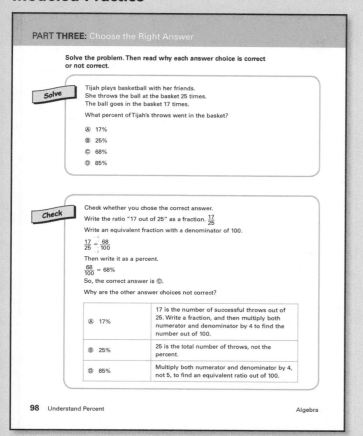

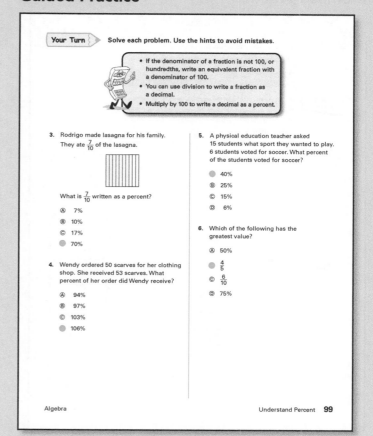

AT A GLANCE

Students reinforce their understanding of percents through solving a multiple-choice problem and analyzing correct and incorrect answer choices.

STEP BY STEP

PAGE 98

- Tell students that this page models finding the correct answer to a multiple-choice problem.
- Have students read the problem in **Solve** and choose the best answer. Remind students to check their math.
- Examine **Check** with students. Discuss the correct and incorrect choices.

PAGE 99

- Monitor students as they complete **Your Turn**.
- Organize students in pairs or small groups and have them discuss why each answer choice is correct or not and what errors may have been made.
- Review the answers with the class.

 ADDITIONAL ACTIVITY

See **Vocabulary Activity** (page 113).

Algebra

Answer Analysis

3. Ⓐ Chose the numerator as the percent
   Ⓑ Chose the denominator as the percent
   Ⓒ Added the numerator and denominator
   ● $\frac{7}{10} = \frac{70}{100} = 70\%$

4. Ⓐ Divided 50 by 53 instead of 53 by 50
   Ⓑ Solved $\frac{50}{53} = \frac{x}{100}$, and subtracted 3 from 100 because 50 is 3 less than 53
   Ⓒ Solved $\frac{53}{50} = \frac{x}{100}$, but added 3 to 100 because 53 is 3 more than 50
   ● $\frac{53}{50} = \frac{106}{100} = 106\%$

5. ● $6 \div 15 = 0.40 = 40\%$
   Ⓑ Divided 15 by 6, placed decimal point incorrectly
   Ⓒ Chose the total number of students as the percent
   Ⓓ Chose the number that voted for soccer as the percent

6. Ⓐ Chose the least value
   ● $4 \div 5 = 0.80 = 80\%$, which is the greatest value.
   Ⓒ Six tenths is 60%, and not the greatest value.
   Ⓓ Did not rename $\frac{4}{5}$ correctly

Modeled Practice

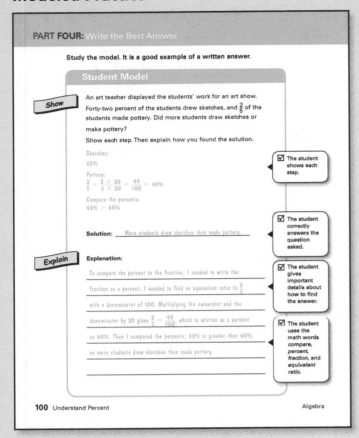

Guided Practice

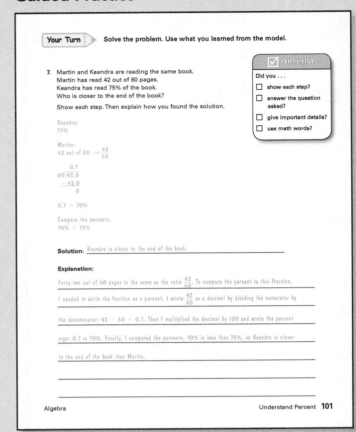

AT A GLANCE

Students study a model answer to an extended-response problem.

STEP BY STEP

PAGE 100

- Tell students that this page models building the solution to a problem one step at a time and writing to explain the solution.
- Have students read the problem in **Show**. Discuss how each mathematical step leads to the solution.

> Tip: Although the given solution only shows how to use equivalent ratios to find the answer, explain that students may use either method—equivalent ratios or division—as long as they are able to explain their reasoning.

- Read **Explain** with students. Have students circle the math words in the explanation.
- Direct students' attention to the notes in the right margin. Tell students that this model would receive a high score for the reasons described in these notes.

PAGE 101

- Monitor students as they complete **Your Turn**.
- Encourage students to follow the **Checklist** to write the best answer.
- Have students discuss their work with a partner. Then discuss the correct answer as a class.

Answer and Explanation

7. See the sample answer. This answer shows all of the steps taken to solve the problem, including long division to write the ratio as a decimal. The solution answers the question. The explanation provides important details about how the problem was solved and uses the math words *ratio*, *compare*, *percent*, *fraction*, and *decimal*. (If students use equivalent ratios to find the percent, accept that response.)

 ADDITIONAL ACTIVITY

See **Real-World Connection** (page 113).

 ADDITIONAL ACTIVITY

See **School-Home Connection** (page 113).

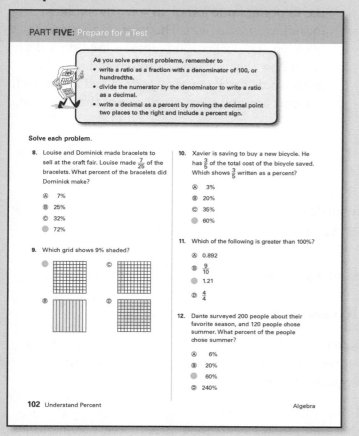

Independent Practice

AT A GLANCE

Students practice solving percent problems that might appear on a mathematics test.

STEP BY STEP

PAGES 102–103

- Tell students that they will practice solving problems that involve writing ratios as percents.
- Point out the tips at the top of page 102. Explain to students that these tips will help them answer the problems correctly.
- You may wish to have students review the hints for avoiding mistakes on page 99 as well.
- Have students complete problems 8–15 on pages 102 and 103. Encourage students to check their answers.
- Discuss the correct responses as a class.

Answers and Explanations

8. ⒟ Louise made $\frac{7}{25}$, so Dominick made $\frac{18}{25}$. Write an equivalent ratio out of 100.
$$\frac{18}{25} = \frac{18 \times 4}{25 \times 4} = \frac{72}{100} = 72\%$$

9. Ⓐ 9% means *9 per hundred*. So, the grid that has 9 squares out of 100 squares shaded shows 9% shaded.

10. ⒟ Write an equivalent ratio out of 100.
$$\frac{3}{5} = \frac{3 \times 20}{5 \times 20} = \frac{60}{100} = 60\%$$

11. Ⓒ 1.21 is more than 1 whole, so it is greater than 100%. 1.21 = 121%

12. Ⓒ Write an equivalent ratio comparing to 100.
$$\frac{120}{200} = \frac{120 \div 2}{200 \div 2} = \frac{60}{100} = 60\%$$

13. Ⓒ Write an equivalent ratio comparing to 100.
$$\frac{39}{50} = \frac{39 \times 2}{50 \times 2} = \frac{78}{100} = 78\%$$

(continued on page 112)

(continued from page 111)

14. Divide 5 by 8 to write the ratio as a decimal. Multiply the decimal by 100, and then write the percent symbol. $5 \div 8 = 0.625 = 62.5\%$

15. See the sample answer. This answer shows all of the steps the student took to solve the problem, including long division. The solution answers the question. The explanation provides important details about how the problem was solved and uses the math words *ratio, compare, percent,* and *decimal.* (If students use equivalent ratios, accept that response.)

ASSESSMENT AND REMEDIATION

- Ask students to write $\frac{3}{10}$ as a percent. *(30%)*
- For students who are still struggling, use the chart below to guide remediation.
- After providing remediation, check students' understanding. Ask students to explain their thinking while writing $\frac{1}{5}$ as a percent. *(20%)*
- If a student is still having difficulty, use *STAMS Book F,* Lesson 9, pages 84–93.

If the error is . . .	Students may . . .	To remediate . . .
3%	have written the numerator as the percent, *or*	Remind students that percent means *per hundred.* The numerator can be used as the percent only if the denominator is 100.
	have misplaced the decimal point while using long division.	Have students use a hundred grid to shade $\frac{3}{10}$. Be sure that they shade 3 of 10 equal parts. Point out that when a hundred grid is divided into 10 equal parts, one part consists of 10 small squares.
10%	not understand percent and have merely written the denominator as the percent, *or*	Review with students the concepts on page 94. Have students model ratios and percents on a hundred grid. Reinforce that *percent* represents a ratio of a number to 100.
	have written the number that the numerator and denominator must be multiplied by to obtain an equivalent ratio with a denominator of 100.	Have students write out the steps of finding equivalent ratios, including arrows to show the multiplication of both numerator and denominator by the same number. Tell students to then circle the numerator of the fraction with a denominator of 100. Point out that the circled number is the percent.
any other percent	have guessed or made a basic math error.	Review with students the concepts on pages 94 and 96. Use grids to model percents and practice rewriting the percent as a fraction with a denominator of 100. It may also prove helpful to have students revisit long division involving decimals, from lessons 7 and 8, particularly using grid paper to keep place values and decimal points aligned.

ADDITIONAL ACTIVITY

For students who have mastered the skills in this lesson, see **Challenge Activity** (page 113).

ADDITIONAL ACTIVITIES

Hands-on Activity
Use grids to model percents.

Materials: hundred-grid paper and colored pencils

Organize students in small groups and distribute hundred-grid paper and colored pencils. Have each group shade 8 full rows of squares to show 80%.

Ask, "How many total squares are on the grid?" *(100)* "How many squares did you shade?" *(80)* "How many rows are on the grid?" *(10)* "How many rows did you shade?" *(8)*

Write the percent and both ratios on the board: $80\% = \frac{80}{100} = \frac{8}{10}$. Discuss how each representation names the same amount.

Have students shade other hundred grids to model different percents and write equivalent ratios, where applicable.

Reteaching Activity
Write ratios as percents.

Write the ratio $\frac{3}{5}$ on the board. Ask students, "How can you write the ratio as a percent?" *(Find an equivalent ratio out of 100 or use division.)*

Divide students into pairs. Have one student use an equivalent ratio to find the percent and have the other use division. $\left(\frac{3}{5} = 60\%\right)$

Repeat for $\frac{7}{20}$, $\frac{3}{25}$, and $\frac{5}{8}$.

Discuss which method they found easier for each ratio and whether there are any times when division is the best method. Students should find that it is better to use division if the denominator is not a factor of 100, because finding equivalent ratios involves the use of mental math.

Vocabulary Activity
Play "What Am I?" to reinforce terms.

Materials: index cards for each pair

Have students write the vocabulary words on index cards, mix up the cards, and place them facedown in a stack. The first student picks a card and gives an example of the vocabulary word. For example, if a student picks *decimal point*, she or he might write 5.25 and circle the decimal point. The other player tries to guess the word. Continue until all the cards have been used. Conclude the activity by having student pairs work together to agree on the best example for each vocabulary word, and then draw or write that on the back of its card.

Real-World Connection
Identify everyday examples of percents.

Discuss everyday examples of percents, such as information presented in circle graphs, test grades, results of surveys, population, and sale prices. Discuss the difference between $85 off the price and 85% off the price.

School-Home Connection
Inform families about percents.

Give each student a copy of the reproducible School-Home Connection for Lesson 10 (page 181) to share with family. This activity has the family solve percent problems involving money.

Challenge Activity
Record results of a survey in percents.

Have students write a survey question to ask 10 classmates. Suggest that students use a question that has a limited number of responses, such as: *What is your favorite season?* or *Which do you like better, swimming or biking?* Have them ask their classmates the question and record the responses in an organized manner, such as a table. Have students find the percent of respondents for each answer. Then, challenge them to ask more people (for a total of 20 or 25) and check whether the percents changed.

Lesson **11** UNIT RATES

LESSON OBJECTIVES

Students will:

- Understand unit rates and how they are used.
- Learn how to use proportions to solve problems involving unit rate.

PREREQUISITES

Students should be able to:

- Multiply whole numbers, fractions, and decimals.
- Divide whole numbers, fractions, and decimals.

RELATED *STAMS*® LESSON

- Book F – Lesson 9

  Understand Ratios teaches students how to write ratios and find equivalent ratios.

VOCABULARY

PAGE 104

- **ratio:** a comparison of two quantities by division; can be part-to-part, part-to-whole, or whole-to-part
- **rate:** a ratio that compares two quantities measured in different units
- **unit rate:** a rate that shows how much for 1
- **per:** for 1

PAGE 106

- **equivalent rates:** two or more rates that are equal to one another
- **equivalent ratios:** two or more ratios that are equal to one another
- **variable:** a letter or symbol that stands for an unknown
- **proportion:** an equation that shows two ratios are equivalent

MATH BACKGROUND

In this lesson, students solve problems involving unit rates. A unit rate means *how much for one*. Unit rates are used in real-world applications, taking forms such as miles per gallon, cost per item, and items per package.

In Part One, students learn to either multiply or divide to solve unit-rate problems depending upon context. When given the unit rate, they can use multiplication. When solving for the unit rate, they can use division.

In Part Two, they learn to use proportions, which offer a more organized way of solving unit-rate problems. Students write two equivalent rates involving an unknown, and then use number sense to solve the proportion. A mistake that students may make is to set up the proportion incorrectly. They should use the order of units to guide them, making sure the comparison is the same. For example, if they express the first rate comparing miles to gallons, then they must also express the second rate comparing miles to gallons.

Interactive Whiteboard
Visualize Unit Rates

Go to the *Interactive Whiteboard Lessons* to bring Parts One and Two to life. Use features such as drag and drop to deepen students' understanding of unit rates.

Modeled Instruction

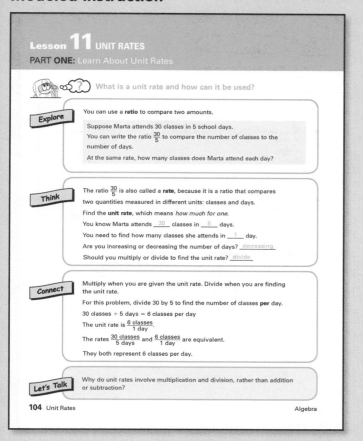

Guided Instruction

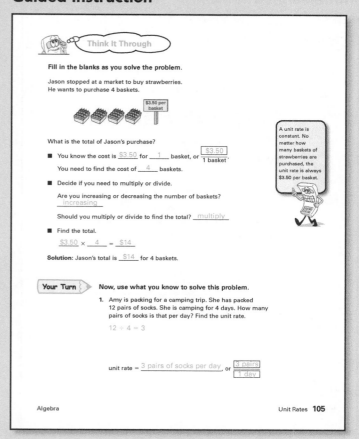

AT A GLANCE

Students activate their background knowledge about ratios and then learn about rates and unit rates.

STEP BY STEP

PAGE 104

- Introduce the **Question** at the top of the page.
- Have students study the problem shown in **Explore** and connect the ratio to the problem.
- Read **Think** with students. Emphasize that you are looking for the number of classes in 1 day, which indicates a unit rate. Pause so students can say aloud the words and numbers in orange.

ELL Support: Compare the meaning of the term *rate* used to compare two quantities and the everyday usage as a verb meaning to evaluate. When you rate a book or movie, you are also comparing it to a standard.

- Discuss **Connect** with students. Help students see the connection between the numerators and the denominators; that is, they are related by a factor of 5.

Tip: Point out that both rates show *classes* on top and *days* on the bottom. Explain the need for consistency in the order of the units compared. This will help students be successful with Part Two.

- Organize students in pairs or groups for **Let's Talk** and monitor their discussions.
- Explain that unit rates involve equal groups, which relate to multiplication and division.

PAGE 105

- Read the **Think It Through** problem with students.
- Guide students as they solve the problem. Help them determine that they can use multiplication in this problem because they are given the unit rate.
- Monitor students as they complete **Your Turn**. Remind them that *per* means "for 1." Then discuss the correct answer.

Error Alert: Students who gave an answer of 48 used multiplication instead of division.

 ADDITIONAL ACTIVITY

See **Hands-on Activity** (page 121).

Algebra

Modeled Instruction

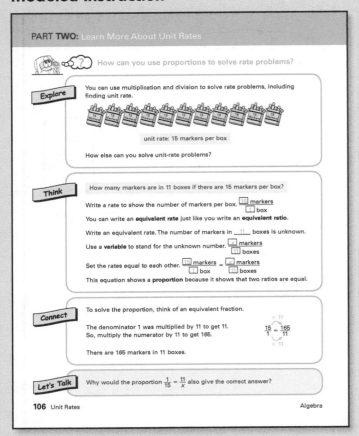

Guided Instruction

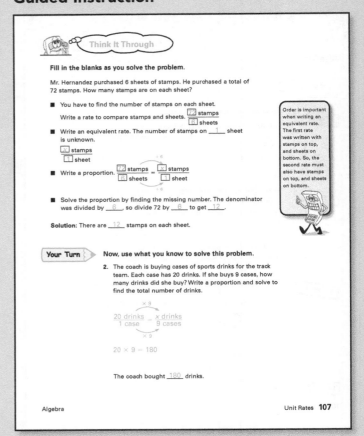

AT A GLANCE
. . . .
Students learn how to use proportions to solve unit-rate problems.

STEP BY STEP
. . . .
PAGE 106
- Introduce the **Question** at the top of the page.
- Read **Explore** with students. Reinforce that each box shows an equal number of markers.
- Read **Think** with students. Pause so students can read aloud the numbers and variables in orange.

ELL Support: Students may confuse the word *proportion* with *portion*, or a part of a whole. Explain that the two terms mean very different things, although they sound very much alike.

- Tell students to study the proportion in **Connect**. Test their understanding by asking how they know to multiply the numerator by 11.
- Organize students in pairs or groups for **Let's Talk** and monitor their discussions.

- Be sure students grasp that a correct answer can be found as long as the same units are placed in the numerators of each rate and the same units are in the denominator or each rate.

PAGE 107
- Read the **Think It Through** problem with students.
- Guide students as they solve the problem. Pause for students to fill in missing information. Then discuss each response.

Tip: Some students might be able to mentally divide 72 by 6 and determine that the answer is 12. Encourage them to still set up and solve a proportion as a way to organize the problem and verify their work.

- Monitor students as they complete **Your Turn**. Then discuss the correct answer.

Error Alert: If students gave an answer of 28, they found 20 − 1 to get 19, and then added 19 to 9.

 ADDITIONAL ACTIVITY
. . . .
See **Reteaching Activity** (page 121).

Modeled Practice

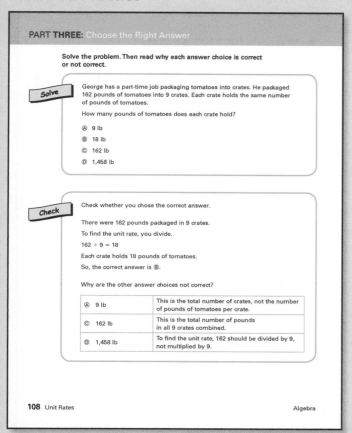

Guided Practice

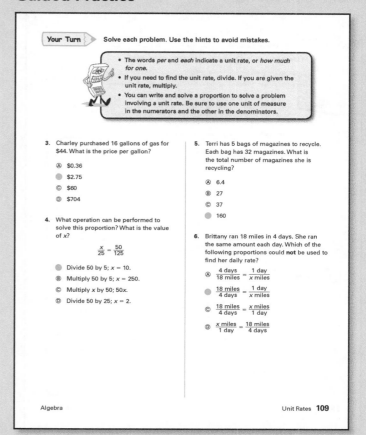

AT A GLANCE

Students reinforce their understanding of unit rates and proportions through solving a multiple-choice problem and analyzing correct and incorrect answer choices.

STEP BY STEP

PAGE 108

- Tell students that this page models finding the correct answer to a multiple-choice problem.
- Have students read the problem in **Solve** and choose the best answer. Remind students to check their math.
- Examine **Check** with students. Discuss the correct and incorrect choices.

PAGE 109

- Monitor students as they complete **Your Turn**.
- Organize students in pairs or small groups and have them discuss why each answer choice is correct or not and what errors may have been made.
- Review the answers with the class.

 ADDITIONAL ACTIVITY

See **Vocabulary Activity** (page 121).

Answer Analysis

3. Ⓐ Divided 16 by 44
   ● Correctly divided 44 by 16 to get $2.75
   Ⓒ Added 16 + 44
   Ⓓ Multiplied 16 by 44 instead of dividing

4. ● 125 is divided by 5 to get 25, so 50 must be divided by 5 to get 10.
   Ⓑ 50 should be divided by 5, not multiplied by 5.
   Ⓒ Multiplied value of x by 50
   Ⓓ 50 should be divided by 5, not by 25.

5. Ⓐ Divided 32 by 5 instead of multiplying
   Ⓑ Subtracted 5 from 32 instead of multiplying
   Ⓒ Added 5 to 32 instead of multiplying
   ● The unit rate is given, so multiply to find the answer: $32 \times 5 = 160$.

6. Ⓐ Chose both rates as days compared to miles
   ● The first rate shows miles to days, but the second rate shows days to miles, so this cannot be used.
   Ⓒ Chose both rates as miles to days
   Ⓓ Chose both rates as miles to days

Modeled Practice

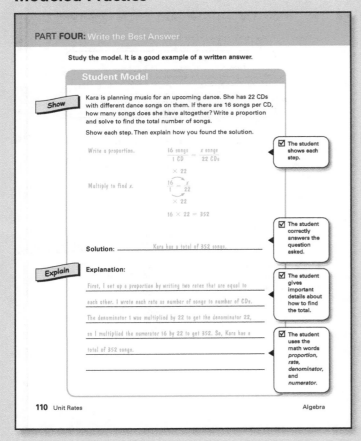

Study the model. It is a good example of a written answer.

Student Model

Show

Kara is planning music for an upcoming dance. She has 22 CDs with different dance songs on them. If there are 16 songs per CD, how many songs does she have altogether? Write a proportion and solve to find the total number of songs.

Show each step. Then explain how you found the solution.

Write a proportion. $\frac{16\ songs}{1\ CD} = \frac{x\ songs}{22\ CDs}$

$\times\ 22$

Multiply to find x. $\frac{16}{1} = \frac{x}{22}$

$\times\ 22$

$16 \times 22 = 352$

☑ The student shows each step.

Solution: _____ Kara has a total of 352 songs. _____

☑ The student correctly answers the question asked.

Explain

Explanation:

First, I set up a proportion by writing two rates that are equal to each other. I wrote each rate as number of songs to number of CDs.

The denominator 1 was multiplied by 22 to get the denominator 22, so I multiplied the numerator 16 by 22 to get 352. So, Kara has a total of 352 songs.

☑ The student gives important details about how to find the total.

☑ The student uses the math words *proportion, rate, denominator,* and *numerator.*

Guided Practice

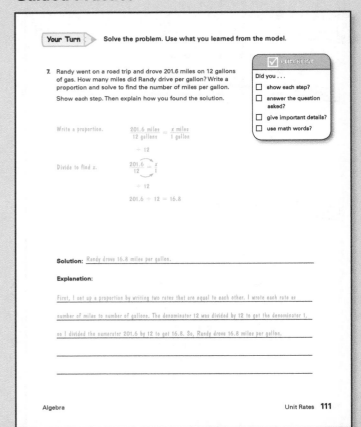

Your Turn ▷ Solve the problem. Use what you learned from the model.

7. Randy went on a road trip and drove 201.6 miles on 12 gallons of gas. How many miles did Randy drive per gallon? Write a proportion and solve to find the number of miles per gallon.

Show each step. Then explain how you found the solution.

CHECKLIST
Did you . . .
☐ show each step?
☐ answer the question asked?
☐ give important details?
☐ use math words?

Write a proportion. $\frac{201.6\ miles}{12\ gallons} = \frac{x\ miles}{1\ gallon}$

$\div\ 12$

Divide to find x. $\frac{201.6}{12} = \frac{x}{1}$

$\div\ 12$

$201.6 \div 12 = 16.8$

Solution: _____ Randy drove 16.8 miles per gallon. _____

Explanation:

First, I set up a proportion by writing two rates that are equal to each other. I wrote each rate as number of miles to number of gallons. The denominator 12 was divided by 12 to get the denominator 1, so I divided the numerator 201.6 by 12 to get 16.8. So, Randy drove 16.8 miles per gallon.

AT A GLANCE

Students study a model answer to an extended-response problem.

STEP BY STEP

PAGE 110

- Tell students that this page models building the solution to a problem one step at a time and writing to explain the solution.
- Have students read the problem in **Show**. Discuss how the proportion and each step lead to the solution.
- If students point out that a proportion is not needed to solve this, they are correct. Explain that there is more than one way to solve some problems.

Tip: The proportion could be set up with *CDs* in the numerators and *songs* in the denominators. However, it is good practice for students to associate the fraction bar with the word *per*, and write *16 songs per CD* as the rate $\frac{16\ songs}{1\ CD}$.

- Read **Explain** with students. Have students circle the math words in the explanation.

- Direct students' attention to the notes in the right margin. Tell them that this model would receive a high score for the reasons described in these notes.

PAGE 111

- Monitor students as they complete **Your Turn**.
- Encourage students to follow the **Checklist** to write the best answer.
- Have students discuss their work with a partner. Then discuss the correct answer as a class.

Answer and Explanation

7. See the sample answer. This answer shows all of the steps taken to solve the problem, including setting up a proportion and dividing. The solution answers the question. The explanation provides important details about how the problem was solved and uses the math words *proportion, rate, denominator,* and *numerator.*

 ADDITIONAL ACTIVITY
See **Real-World Connection** (page 121).

 ADDITIONAL ACTIVITY
See **School-Home Connection** (page 121).

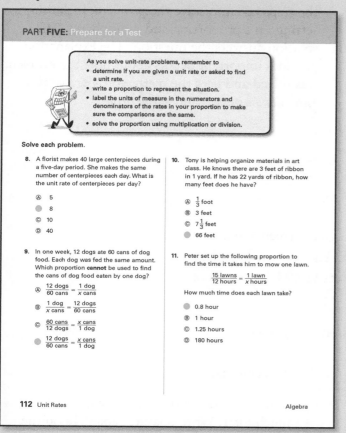

Independent Practice

Independent Practice

AT A GLANCE

Students practice using proportions to solve unit-rate problems that might appear on a mathematics test.

STEP BY STEP

PAGES 112–113

- Tell students that they will practice solving multiplication problems that involve unit rates and proportions.

- Point out the tips at the top of page 112. Explain to students that these tips will help them answer the problems correctly.

- You may wish to have students review the hints for avoiding mistakes on page 109 as well.

- Tell students to complete problems 8–15 on pages 112 and 113. Encourage them to check their answers.

- Discuss the correct responses as a class.

Answers and Explanations

8. Ⓑ To find the unit rate, divide: 40 centerpieces divided by 5 days is 8 centerpieces per day.

9. Ⓓ This is an incorrect proportion because the first rate shows dogs to cans, and the second rate shows cans to dogs. The comparisons are not the same.

10. Ⓓ To use the unit rate, multiply: 22 yards times 3 feet per yard is 66 feet.

11. Ⓐ The numerator 15 was divided by 15 to get 1, so divide the denominator 12 by 15 to get 0.8.

12. Ⓑ To find the unit rate, divide: $10 divided by 4 pounds is $2.50 per pound of potatoes.

13. Ⓒ To use the unit rate, multiply: 14 hours times $8.50 per hour is $119.

(continued on page 120)

Algebra

(continued from page 119)

14. To find the unit rate, divide 2.5 inches by 5 days to get 0.5 inch per day.

15. See the sample answer. This answer shows all of the steps taken to solve the problem, including setting up a proportion and multiplying. The solution answers the question. The explanation provides important details about how the problem was solved and uses the math words *proportion*, *rate*, *denominator*, and *numerator*.

 ASSESSMENT AND REMEDIATION

- Ask students to use a proportion to find the unit rate of $15 for 3 T-shirts. *($5 per T-shirt)*
- For students who are still struggling, use the chart below to guide remediation.
- After providing remediation, check students' understanding. Ask students to explain their thinking while setting up a proportion to solve: If it costs $1.49 for 1 pound of apples, find cost of 6 pounds. $\left(\dfrac{\$1.49}{1\ pound} = \dfrac{x}{6\ pounds}; \$8.94 \right)$
- If a student is still having difficulty, use *STAMS Book F*, Lesson 9, pages 84–93.

If the error is . . .	Students may . . .	To remediate . . .
$45	have multiplied $15 by 3.	Remind students that unit rate means how much for 1. Write 3 large, capital Ts on the board to represent 3 T-shirts. Explain that the total cost is $15. The problem asks them to find the cost for only one T-shirt. Tell them they can use division when they are asked to find the unit rate.
$0.20	have divided 3 by $15.	Encourage students to inspect their proportions carefully to see that it is organized correctly, with each rate comparing the two quantities in the same order. This will help them to see which numbers—and their corresponding units—need to be divided, in which order.
$13	found 15 − 3 to get 12, and then added 12 to 1. They may think that equal rates are related by a common difference, rather than a common factor.	Start with the rate of $5 per T-shirt. Write $\dfrac{\$5}{1\ \text{T-shirt}}$. Then have students write rates for 2 T-shirts, 3 T-shirts, and 4 T-shirts. Have them examine the equivalent rates. Show that the numerators and denominators are changing by a factor of 5.

 ADDITIONAL ACTIVITY

For students who have mastered the skills in this lesson, see **Challenge Activity** (page 121).

ADDITIONAL ACTIVITIES

Hands-on Activity
Use cups and counters to model proportions.

Materials: 50 counters and 5 small cups per group

Organize students in small groups and distribute cups and counters. Set up the scenario 15 counters/3 cups.

Have students identify if they know the unit rate or if they need to find the unit rate. Write the phrase "___ *counter per cup*" on the board. Then ask students, "Do you know the unit rate? If so, what is it? If not, how can you find the unit rate?"

Repeat the activity, with the scenario of 4 counters in 1 cup, asking students to find the number in 5 cups. *(20 counters)*

Reteaching Activity
Use money to model proportions and rates.

Materials: play money

Have students find the unit rate for $7.14 for 6 pounds. Ask if 7.14 should be divided by 6, or if 6 should be divided by 7.14. After students respond, write a proportion on the board. Show that a proportion with labeled rates will make it much clearer as to which numbers to multiply or divide, and in what order. Encourage students to set up proportions to organize all unit rate problems.

Vocabulary Activity
Make a crossword puzzle to reinforce terms.

Materials: grid paper

Have each student use the vocabulary terms to make a puzzle where the words share common letters. Sample:

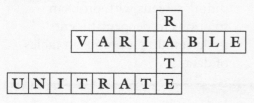

To help students check that their puzzles are complete, read a definition and have them check that they have used the corresponding word in their puzzle. Have them finish the puzzles with numbers for each vertical and horizontal word and numbered, written definitions. Finally, have pairs exchange and complete each other's puzzles.

Real-World Connection
Identify everyday examples of unit rates.

Explain that unit rates can be used to help compare prices. Write these two rates on the board: $\frac{\$8.40}{7 \text{ cans}}$ and $\frac{\$8.80}{8 \text{ cans}}$. Ask students to find the unit rate for each. *($1.20 per can and $1.10 per can)* Show that although $8.80 is more expensive, this rate shows a lower cost per can.

School-Home Connection
Inform families about proportions.

Give each student a copy of the reproducible School-Home Connection for Lesson 11 (page 183) to share with family. This activity has the family determine the better buy between different grocery store items.

Challenge Activity
Explain proportions to another person.

Have students write a letter that explains rates and proportions to a classmate who has missed this lesson. The letter should include examples of rates and proportions, along with vocabulary definitions and example problems.

Expressions and Equations

LESSON OBJECTIVES

Students will:

- Find missing values in tables of data.
- Write a multiplication or division equation to represent data in a table.

PREREQUISITES

Students should be able to:

- Write a ratio to compare two quantities.
- Write and solve proportions using number sense.

RELATED *STAMS*® LESSONS

- **Book F – Lesson 9**

  Understand Ratios teaches students how to write ratios and find equivalent ratios.

- **Book F – Lesson 11**

  Unit Rates shows students how to write and solve proportions.

VOCABULARY

PAGE 114

- **table:** a visual display of data in rows and columns
- **data:** a collection of facts or information
- **ratio:** a comparison of two quantities by division; can be part to part, part to whole, or whole to part
- **equivalent ratios:** two or more ratios that are equal to one another
- **proportion:** an equation that shows two ratios are equivalent

PAGE 116

- **equation:** a number sentence that contains an equal sign and shows two quantities have the same value
- **pattern:** a set of data values that share a common relationship

MATH BACKGROUND

In this lesson, students learn two different but related skills for working with tables of data. Each table in the lesson shows pairs of data that have a constant ratio. In Part One, students find missing data values by writing and solving equations in the form of proportions. In Part Two, they write equations, not in the form of proportions, to show how the data values are related.

The examples below illustrate these skills.

a	b
5	1
10	2
30	

a	b
5	1
10	2
30	6

Solve the proportion $\frac{5}{1} = \frac{30}{b}$ to find the missing b-value.

Write the equations $b = \frac{a}{5}$ and $a = 5b$ to show the relationship between a and b.

Students will learn in later grades that when two quantities have a constant ratio, as shown in the tables in this lesson, then those quantities are said to have *direct variation*.

Interactive Whiteboard

Visualize Ratios in Tables of Data

Go to the *Interactive Whiteboard Lessons* to bring Parts One and Two to life. Use features such as sliding screens with problem solutions to deepen students' understanding of ratios in tables of data.

Modeled Instruction

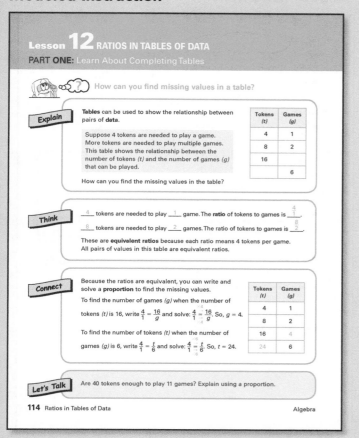

Guided Instruction

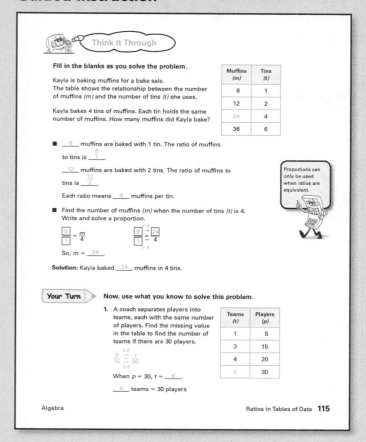

. . . .

Students activate their background knowledge about ratios and then learn that they can use equivalent ratios to find missing values in data tables.

STEP BY STEP
. . . .

PAGE 114

• Introduce the **Question** at the top of the page.

• Have students study the table of data shown in **Explore**.

> **ELL Support:** Discuss the word *relationship*. Explain that each value of t is related, or connected, to its corresponding value of g, and each pair of values are connected in the same way.

• Read **Think** with students. Emphasize that the pairs of values in the table form equivalent ratios. Pause so students can say aloud the numbers in orange.

• Discuss **Connect** with students. Help them see the connection between solving the proportion and finding the missing value in the table. Be sure students see that the ratio $\frac{4}{1}$ is $\frac{t}{g}$, not $\frac{g}{t}$.

> **Tip:** Explain to students that not all tables show the same ratio in all rows. Give some examples and have students identify which show the same ratio.

• Organize students in pairs or groups for **Let's Talk** and monitor their discussions.

• Be sure students understand that 40 tokens is not enough because solving the proportion shows that for 11 games 44 tokens are needed.

PAGE 115

• Read the **Think It Through** problem with students.

• Guide students as they solve the problem. Help them write and solve a proportion to find the missing value.

• Show that multiplying the numerator and denominator by the same number results in an equivalent ratio.

• Monitor students as they complete **Your Turn**. Then discuss the correct answer.

> **Error Alert:** Students who gave an answer of $t = 5$ wrote the number that each t-value is multiplied by.

 ADDITIONAL ACTIVITY
. . . .

See **Hands-on Activity** (page 129).

Modeled Instruction

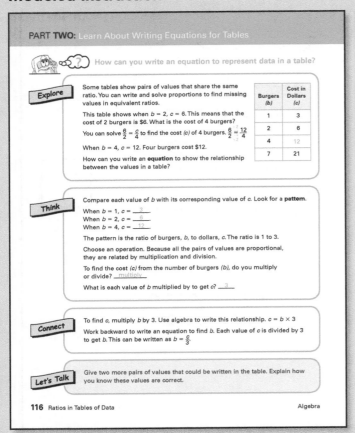

Guided Instruction

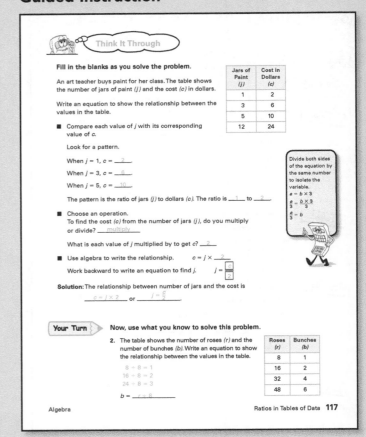

Students learn that a multiplication or division equation can be used to represent data in a table.

STEP BY STEP

PAGE 116

- Introduce the **Question** at the top of the page.
- Read **Explore** with students. Reinforce that pairs of values in the table are equivalent ratios by having students write each as a ratio and then compare.
- Read **Think** with students. Pause so students can read aloud the numbers and words in orange.
- Tell students to study the multiplication and division sentences in **Connect**. Test their understanding by asking students to explain how $c = b \times 3$ and $b = \frac{c}{3}$ show the same relationship.

ELL Support: Point out that the word *equation* begins with the same letters as the word *equal*. Explain that an equation will always contain an equal sign.

- Organize students in pairs or groups for **Let's Talk** and monitor their discussions.
- Be sure students have found any two pairs of values where one is 3 times the other. Check that students are specific about which is the *b*-value, and which is the *c*-value.

PAGE 117

- Read the **Think It Through** problem with students.
- Guide students as they solve the problem. Pause as they fill in missing information. Then discuss each response.

Tip: Have students show their steps to write both a multiplication and division equation.

- Monitor students as they complete **Your Turn**. Then discuss the correct answer.

Error Alert: Students who wrote $b = r \times 8$ reversed the relationship between the variables.

 ADDITIONAL ACTIVITY

See **Reteaching Activity** (page 129).

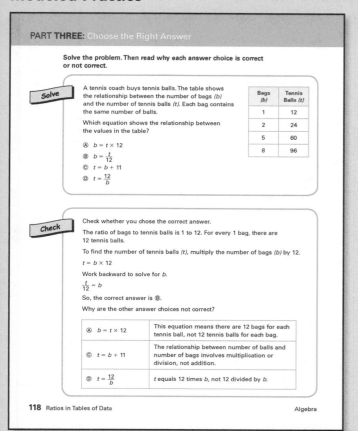

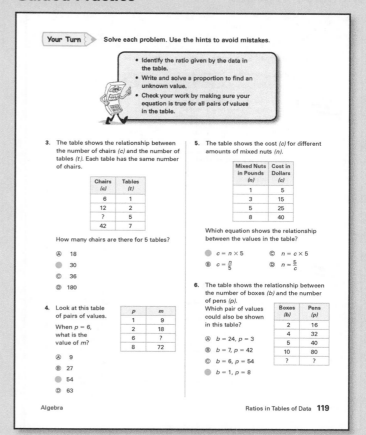

AT A GLANCE

Students reinforce their analysis of data in tables through solving a multiple-choice problem and analyzing correct and incorrect answer choices.

STEP BY STEP

PAGE 118

- Tell students that this page models finding the correct answer to a multiple-choice problem.

- Have students read the problem in **Solve** and choose the best answer. Remind students to check their math.

- Examine **Check** with students. Discuss the correct and incorrect choices.

PAGE 119

- Monitor students as they complete **Your Turn**.

- Organize students in pairs or small groups and have them discuss why each answer choice is correct or not and what errors may have been made.

- Review the answers with the class.

 ADDITIONAL ACTIVITY

See **Vocabulary Activity** (page 129).

Answer Analysis

3. Ⓐ Added 6 to the number in the row above
   ● The ratio is 6 chairs to 1 table. Write and solve a proportion: $\frac{6}{1} = \frac{c}{5}$; multiply 6 by 5 to find $c = 30$.
   Ⓒ Subtracted 6 from the number in the row below
   Ⓓ Set up the proportion incorrectly

4. Ⓐ Chose the number of mugs per pack
   Ⓑ Added 9 to the number in the row above
   ● The ratio of p to m is 1 to 9. Write and solve a proportion: $\frac{1}{9} = \frac{6}{m}$; multiply 9 by 6 to find $m = 54$.
   Ⓓ Subtracted 9 from the number in the row below

5. ● The cost per pound is $5. Multiply number of pounds by 5 to get the total cost.
   Ⓑ Confused multiplication and division
   Ⓒ Reversed the variables
   Ⓓ Flipped the numerator and denominator

6. Ⓐ Reversed the variables
   Ⓑ Thought values of b were multiplied by 6
   Ⓒ Thought values of b were multiplied by 9
   ● The ratio of b to p is 1 to 8.

Modeled Practice

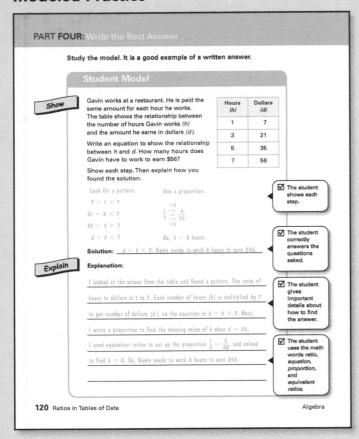

Guided Practice

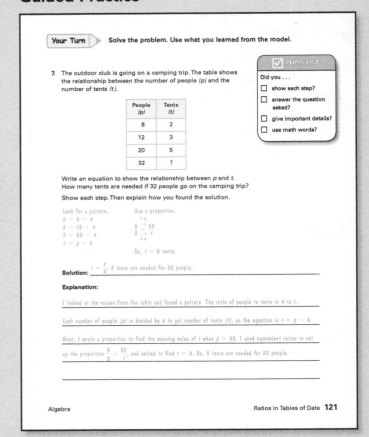

AT A GLANCE

Students study a model answer to an extended-response problem.

STEP BY STEP

PAGE 120

- Tell students that this page models building the solution to a problem one step at a time and writing to explain the solution.

- Have students read the problem in **Show**. Discuss how the ratio of the data values and each mathematical step lead to the solution.

> Tip: The problems in this lesson can all be solved by either using a proportion or by finding a pattern to write an equation. Suggest that students use both methods to check their work.

- Read **Explain** with students. Have students circle the math words in the explanation.

- Direct students' attention to the notes in the right margin. Tell students that this model would receive a high score for the reasons described in these notes.

PAGE 121

- Monitor students as they complete **Your Turn**.
- Encourage students to follow the **Checklist** to write the best answer.
- Have students discuss their work with a partner. Then discuss the correct answer as a class.

Answer and Explanation

7. See the sample answer. This answer shows all of the steps taken to solve the problem, including writing an equation and setting up a proportion. The solution answers the question. The explanation provides important details about how the problem was solved and uses the math words *ratio*, *equation*, *proportion*, and *equivalent ratio*.

   Also accept the equation $p = 4 \times t$ as a correct answer.

 ADDITIONAL ACTIVITY

See **Real-World Connection** (page 129).

 ADDITIONAL ACTIVITY

See **School-Home Connection** (page 129).

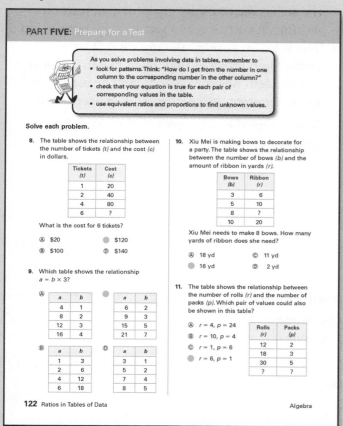

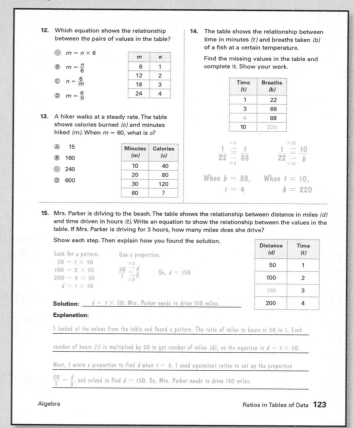

AT A GLANCE

Students practice using data in tables and ratios to solve problems that might appear on a mathematics test.

STEP BY STEP

PAGES 122–123

- Tell students that they will practice solving ratio problems involving data in tables and their related equations.

- Point out the tips at the top of page 122. Explain to students that these tips will help them answer the problems correctly.

- You may wish to have students review the hints for avoiding mistakes on page 119 as well.

- Tell students to complete problems 8–15 on pages 122 and 123. Encourage students to check their answers.

- Discuss the correct responses as a class.

Answers and Explanations

8. Ⓒ The ratio of tickets to cost is 1 to 20. Write and solve a proportion: $\frac{1}{20} = \frac{6}{c}$; multiply 20 by 6 to find $c = 120$.

9. Ⓒ For the table to have equation $a = b \times 3$, the ratio of a to b must be 3 to 1, for all pairs of a and b. 6 to 2, 9 to 3, 15 to 5, and 21 to 7 are all ratios equivalent to 3 to 1.

10. Ⓑ The ratio of bows to ribbon is 3 to 6, or 1 to 2. Write and solve a proportion: $\frac{1}{2} = \frac{8}{r}$; multiply 2 by 8 to find $r = 16$.

11. Ⓓ The ratio of rolls to packs is 12 to 2, or 6 to 1. So, $r = 6$ and $p = 1$ satisfies the relationship shown in the table.

12. Ⓐ The ratio of m to n is 6 to 1. So, to get m you can multiply n by 6: $m = n \times 6$.

13. Ⓒ The ratio of c to m is 40 to 10 or 4 to 1. Write and solve a proportion: $\frac{4}{1} = \frac{c}{60}$; multiply 4 by 60 to find $c = 240$.

(continued on page 128)

(continued from page 127)

14. The ratio of *t* to *b* is 1 to 22. Write and solve a proportion for each missing value.

To find *t* when *b* = 88, write and solve $\frac{1}{22} = \frac{t}{88}$. Multiply 1 by 4 to find *t* = 4.

To find *b* when *t* = 10, write and solve $\frac{1}{22} = \frac{10}{b}$. Multiply 22 by 10 to find *b* = 220.

15. See the sample answer. This answer shows all of the steps taken to solve the problem, including writing an equation and setting up a proportion. The solution answers the question. The explanation provides important details about how the problem was solved and uses the math words *ratio*, *equation*, *proportion*, and *equivalent ratio*.

Also accept the equation *t* = *d* ÷ 50 as a correct answer.

 ASSESSMENT AND REMEDIATION

- Ask students to write an equation to show the relationship between the values in this table. Then have them find the missing value. *(d = t × 7 or t = $\frac{d}{7}$; 56)*
- For students who are still struggling, use the chart below to guide remediation.
- After providing remediation, check students' understanding. Ask students to explain their thinking while writing an equation and finding the missing value for this table. *(f = 3 × y or y = $\frac{f}{3}$; 30)*
- If a student is still having difficulty, use *STAMS Book F*, Lesson 9, pages 84–93.

Distance *(d)*	Time *(t)*
7	1
21	3
28	4
?	8

Yards *(y)*	Feet *(f)*
1	3
2	6
4	12
10	?

If the error is . . .	Students may . . .	To remediate . . .
writing an equation of *t* = *d* × 7 or *d* = $\frac{t}{7}$	have reversed the variables.	Encourage students to describe the relationship in words before writing an equation. (Each value of *d* is 7 times the corresponding value of *t*.)
writing an equation of *d* = *t* + 6	have written an equation that only works for the first pair of data values	Encourage students to always get in the habit of checking their work. Here, they should substitute *all* given pairs of values from the table into their equation to verify that the equation is true.
a missing value of 32	have added 7 to the number in the row above it.	Explain that if the numbers in the second column were 1, 2, 3, and 4, students *could* simply find multiples of 7 for the first column. However, the numbers in the second column do *not* increase by 1, so you need to consider each pair independently of the others.
some other missing value	have difficulty with basic multiplication facts.	Have students review basic multiplication and division facts by drawing arrays, skip counting, or using flash cards with a partner.

 ADDITIONAL ACTIVITY

For students who have mastered the skills in this lesson, see **Challenge Activity** (page 129).

ADDITIONAL ACTIVITIES

Hands-on Activity
Use counters to model ratios and make a table.

Materials: 40 counters and 5 small cups per group

Organize students in small groups and distribute cups and counters. Have students divide the counters equally among the cups. *(8 counters per cup.)*

Draw a table on the board and label the columns "Counters *(a)*" and "Cups *(b)*." Have students select one cup and ask, "How many counters are in 1 cup? What is the ratio of counters to cups?" Write the ratio *8 to 1* on the board and write the values in the table. Repeat for 2 and 3 cups. Then ask, "How many counters are in 5 cups?" *(40.)*

Have students compare each ratio. Discuss the relationship between the number of counters and the number of cups and how this is shown in the table. *(Each number in the Cup column is equal to the corresponding number in the Counters column divided by 8.)*

Reteaching Activity
Write equations for data tables.

Have students copy this table.

a	b
1	4
2	8
4	
8	

Have students study the first two rows in the table. Ask, "What do you do to *a* to get *b*?" *(Multiply by 4.)* "Is this true for the next row also?" *(Yes.)* Write "multiply *a* by 4 to get *b*" on the board. Then write the equation $a \times 4 = b$ on the board. Have students use this rule to complete the table. *(16, 32.)*

Ask students similar questions for another table in which the rule is divide by 2.

Vocabulary Activity
Play "Concentration" to reinforce terms.

Materials: index cards

In pairs, have students write one vocabulary term on each index card. Then have students write a definition or example of each term on another index card. Have students shuffle the cards and place them facedown in an array. Students take turns flipping over two cards. If the player chooses a matching term and definition, he or she keeps the pair. If the cards do not match, the student replaces them. The student with the most matched pairs wins.

Real-World Connection
Explore equations based on ratios.

Discuss how ratios are used in real-world situations such as miles per hour, pay rate (dollars per hour), cost per pound, and items per pack. Ask students to share some examples and, if possible, have them write equations, data tables, and proportions showing the ratios. For example: If a person runs at a rate of 6 miles per hour, how long will it take the person to run 12 miles? *(2 hours.)*

School-Home Connection
Inform families about ratios in equations.

Give each student a copy of the reproducible School-Home Connection for Lesson 12 (page 185) to share with family. This activity has the family think of situations for given tables of data.

Challenge Activity
Make a table with missing values.

Have students make a table of values based on a given ratio. Remind students that the pairs of values must share the same ratio. Students should include at least five pairs of values in their table, including two pairs in which one value is unknown. After students have written the values in their table, have them exchange with a partner to find the missing values.

Expressions and Equations

LESSON OBJECTIVES

Students will:

- Write addition, subtraction, multiplication, and division equations to represent a given situation, with a variable representing the unknown.
- Solve equations using number sense.

PREREQUISITES

Students should be able to:

- Add, subtract, multiply, and divide whole numbers.
- Compute with fractions and decimals.

RELATED *STAMS*® LESSONS

- **Book E – Lesson 11**

  Add and Subtract Mixed Numbers shows students how to add and subtract fractions and mixed numbers.

- **Book F – Lesson 8**

  Divide Decimals by Decimals shows students how to divide decimals.

VOCABULARY

PAGE 124

- **equation:** a number sentence that contains an equal sign and shows two quantities have the same value
- **expression:** a mathematical phrase that contains at least one number or variable, and can also contain operation symbols
- **sum:** the result of addition
- **variable:** a letter or symbol that stands for an unknown
- **solution:** a value of the variable that makes an equation true
- **substitute:** to replace an unknown with a value

PAGE 125

- **difference:** the result of subtraction

PAGE 127

- **quotient:** the result of division
- **product:** the result of multiplication

MATH BACKGROUND

In this lesson, students use reasoning and number sense to solve equations. The table below shows the thinking for each type.

To solve:	Think:
$x + 5 = 8$	What number plus 5 equals 8?
$x - 2 = 3$	What number minus 2 equals 3?
$2x = 10$	2 times what number equals 10?
$\frac{x}{3} = 4$	What number divided by 3 equals 4?

To solve these equations, it is helpful if students can refer to fact families. To solve $x + 5 = 8$, the reasoning might be, "After adding 5 to a number, the result is 8. So, 8 is the largest number in the addition/subtraction family, and the numbers in the family are ___, 5, 8." The fact family is: $3 + 5 = 8$, $5 + 3 = 8$, $8 - 5 = 3$, $8 - 3 = 5$.

Remind students that addition and multiplication are commutative, so $x + 5 = 8$ and $5 + x = 8$ are equivalent, and $2x = 10$ and $x \cdot 2 = 10$ are equivalent. Remind that subtraction and division are *not* commutative.

Interactive Whiteboard
Visualize Using Number Sense to Solve Equations

Go to the *Interactive Whiteboard Lessons* to bring Parts One and Two to life. Use features such as clonable art to deepen students' understanding of using number sense to solve equations.

Modeled Instruction

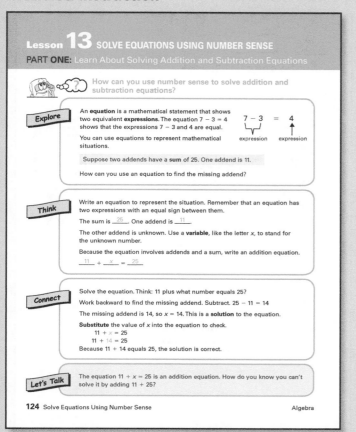

Guided Instruction

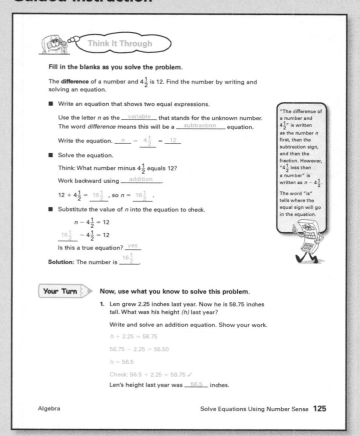

AT A GLANCE

Students learn how to write addition and subtraction equations containing a variable, and then use number sense to solve the equations.

STEP BY STEP

PAGE 124

- Introduce the **Question** at the top of the page.
- Have students read the **Explore** section. Explain that $7 - 3 = 4$ is a *numerical* equation because it contains only numbers and operations. Discuss why $4 = 7 - 3$ is an equivalent numerical equation.

  Tip: Write a numerical equation, and then circle each side of the equation. Show that the equal sign is not necessarily in the middle of an equation.

- Read **Think** with students. Tell students that a variable can be any letter, but x and n are most commonly used to represent unknowns.
- Discuss **Connect** with students. Discuss pairs of operations that "undo" each other. Explain that the strategy of working backward relates to operations that "undo" each other.

- Organize students in pairs or groups for **Let's Talk** and monitor their discussions.
- Students should conclude that if they added $11 + 25$ and substituted the sum for x, the result would not be a true statement.

PAGE 125

- Read the **Think It Through** problem with students.

  ELL Support: Help students to associate the term *difference* with subtraction. Explain that they can determine how *different* two numbers are by finding how far apart they are.

- Guide students as they solve the problem. As needed, review addition and subtraction with mixed numbers.
- Monitor students as they complete **Your Turn**.

  Error Alert: Students who wrote $h = 2.25 + 58.75$, thought they should add the two numbers. Explain that Len used to be a certain height (h), then he increased by 2.25 inches, and now he is 58.75 inches tall. Show that 58.75 represents a sum.

 ADDITIONAL ACTIVITY

See **Hands-on Activity** (page 137).

Modeled Instruction

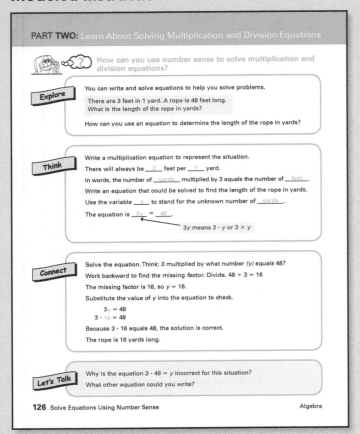

Guided Instruction

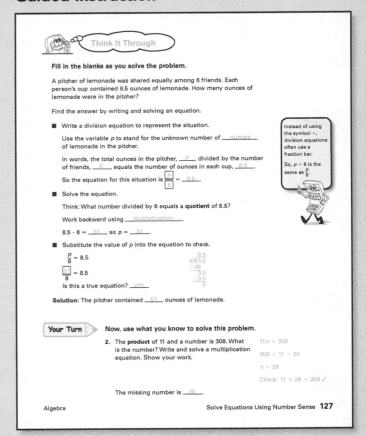

AT A GLANCE

Students extend their understanding of writing and solving equations using number sense to multiplication and division situations.

STEP BY STEP

Page 126

- Introduce the **Question** at the top of the page.
- Read **Explore** with students.

  ELL Support: Eliminate any confusion about the multiple meanings of *foot* and *yard* by explaining that these are units of measure in the English system.

- Read **Think** with students. Explain that multiplication in variable expressions is written with a dot or no sign, instead of ×, to avoid confusion with the variable *x*.

  Tip: Clarify the foot/yard relationship. Draw a model of a yard with 1 foot markings, labeling 1 yd and 3 ft. Draw another yard next to it and prompt students to identify labels of 2 yd and 6 ft.

- Read through the solution steps in **Connect**.

- Organize students in pairs or groups for **Let's Talk** and monitor their discussions.
- Be sure students understand that *each* yard represents 3 feet, so the variable *y* must be multiplied by 3. The other possible equation is $\frac{48}{3} = y$.

Page 127

- Read the **Think It Through** problem with students. Establish the concept of division. Ask students to imagine a pitcher of lemonade (starting amount: dividend) that is poured among cups (number of groups: divisor), resulting in equal portions (amount in each group: quotient).
- Guide students as they solve the problem. Pause as they fill in missing information.
- Monitor students as they complete **Your Turn**. Then discuss the correct answer.

  Error Alert: Students who answered 3,388 may have calculated the product of the two numbers given. Ask them to re-read the problem carefully.

 ### ADDITIONAL ACTIVITY

See **Reteaching Activity** (page 137).

Modeled Practice

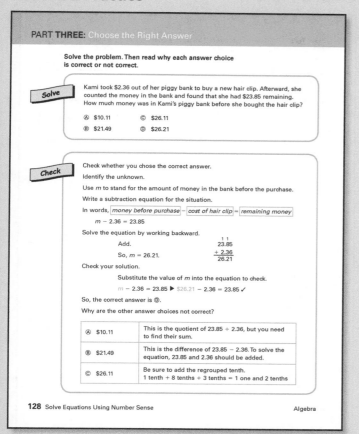

Guided Practice

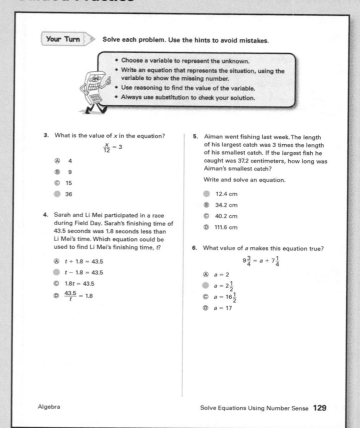

AT A GLANCE

Students reinforce their understanding of writing and solving equations with a multiple-choice word problem, and analyze correct and incorrect answer choices.

STEP BY STEP

PAGE 128

- Have students read the problem in **Solve** and choose the best answer. Remind students to check their work.

- Examine **Check** with students. Discuss the correct and incorrect choices. Give examples of when the actual (not opposite) operation is used to solve an equation. That is, when the unknown is the sum, difference, product, or quotient, such as $15 - 3 = x$.

PAGE 129

- Monitor students as they complete **Your Turn**.

- Organize students in pairs or small groups to discuss answer choices and errors that may have been made.

- Review the answers with the class.

 ADDITIONAL ACTIVITY

See **Vocabulary Activity** (page 137).

Answer Analysis

3. Ⓐ Divided 12 by 3
   Ⓑ Subtracted 3 from 12
   Ⓒ Added 12 and 3
   ● The dividend is 36: $\frac{36}{12} = 3$.

4. Ⓐ Chose incorrect operation: addition
   ● This equation shows that 1.8 seconds less than Lei Mei's time is equal to Sarah's time.
   Ⓒ Chose incorrect operation: multiplication
   Ⓓ Chose incorrect operation: division

5. ● This answer is the result of solving the equation $3f = 37.2$ using division.
   Ⓑ Subtracted 3 from 37.2
   Ⓒ Added 3 to 37.2
   Ⓓ Multiplied 3 by 37.2

6. Ⓐ Subtracted whole numbers; ignored fractions
   ● $9\frac{3}{4} - 7\frac{1}{4} = 2\frac{2}{4} = 2\frac{1}{2}$
   Ⓒ Added whole numbers, subtracted fractions
   Ⓓ Added given numbers instead of working backward by using subtraction

Modeled Practice

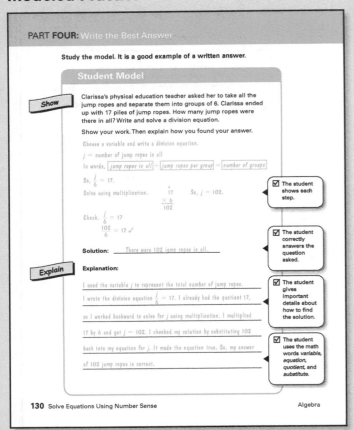

Guided Practice

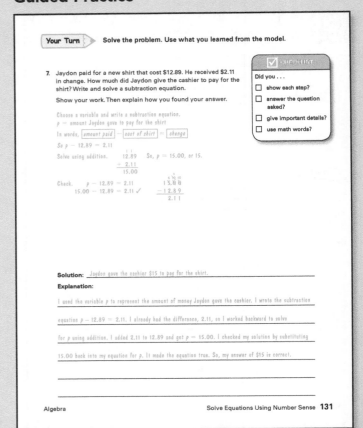

AT A GLANCE
. . . .

Students study a model answer to an extended-response problem.

STEP BY STEP
. . . .

PAGE 130

- Tell students that this page models building the solution to a real-world problem one step at a time and writing to explain the solution.

- Have students read the problem in **Show**. Discuss how each mathematical step leads to the solution.

Tip: Make sure students don't look at the phrase "in all" and immediately think this must be an addition situation. Have students visualize the process of Clarissa taking a large number of jump ropes and separating them into groups of 6.

- Read **Explain** with students. Have students circle the math words in the explanation.

- Direct students' attention to the notes in the right margin. Tell them that this model would receive a high score for the reasons described in these notes.

PAGE 131

- Monitor students as they complete **Your Turn**.
- Encourage students to follow the **Checklist** to write the best answer.
- Have students discuss their work with a partner. Then discuss the correct answer as a class.

Answer and Explanation

7. See the sample answer. It shows all of the steps taken to solve the problem: defining a variable, writing an equation, solving the equation using number sense, and checking the answer. The solution answers the question. The explanation provides important details about how the problem was solved and uses the math words *variable*, *equation*, *difference*, and *substitute*.

ADDITIONAL ACTIVITY
. . . .
See **Real-World Connection** (page 137).

ADDITIONAL ACTIVITY
. . . .
See **School-Home Connection** (page 137).

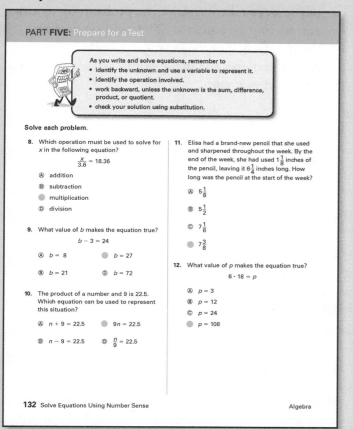

PART FIVE: Prepare for a Test

> As you write and solve equations, remember to
> • identify the unknown and use a variable to represent it.
> • identify the operation involved.
> • work backward, unless the unknown is the sum, difference, product, or quotient.
> • check your solution using substitution.

Solve each problem.

8. Which operation must be used to solve for x in the following equation?
$$\frac{x}{3.6} = 18.36$$
Ⓐ addition
Ⓑ subtraction
● multiplication
Ⓓ division

9. What value of b makes the equation true?
$$b - 3 = 24$$
Ⓐ $b = 8$ ● $b = 27$
Ⓑ $b = 21$ Ⓓ $b = 72$

10. The product of a number and 9 is 22.5. Which equation can be used to represent this situation?
Ⓐ $n + 9 = 22.5$ ● $9n = 22.5$
Ⓑ $n - 9 = 22.5$ Ⓓ $\frac{n}{9} = 22.5$

11. Elisa had a brand-new pencil that she used and sharpened throughout the week. By the end of the week, she had used $1\frac{1}{8}$ inches of the pencil, leaving it $6\frac{1}{4}$ inches long. How long was the pencil at the start of the week?
Ⓐ $5\frac{1}{8}$
Ⓑ $5\frac{1}{2}$
Ⓒ $7\frac{1}{6}$
● $7\frac{3}{8}$

12. What value of p makes the equation true?
$$6 \cdot 18 = p$$
Ⓐ $p = 3$
Ⓑ $p = 12$
Ⓒ $p = 24$
● $p = 108$

13. The area of the rug in Martin's bedroom is 35 square feet. If the length of the rug is 7 feet, what is the width?
Hint: area = length · width
● 5 ft   Ⓒ 42 ft
Ⓑ 28 ft   Ⓓ 245 ft

14. The quotient of a number, n, and 1.5 is 26. What is the number?
Write and solve a division equation.
Equation: $\frac{n}{1.5} = 26$
$$26 \times 1.5 = 130 + 260 = 39.0$$
$n = 39$

15. Donna was playing a game. After she scored 45 bonus points, her total score was 825. What was her initial score before she earned the bonus points? Write and solve an addition equation.
Show your work. Then explain how you found answer.

Choose a variable and write an equation.
s = Donna's initial score
In words, [initial score] + [bonus points] = [total score]
$s + 45 = 825$

Solve using subtraction.
$$\begin{array}{r} 7\ 12 \\ 8\,2\,5 \\ -\ 4\,5 \\ \hline 7\,8\,0 \end{array}$$
So, $s = 780$.

Check. $s + 45 = 825$
$780 + 45 = 825$ ✓
$$\begin{array}{r} 1 \\ 7\,8\,0 \\ +\ 4\,5 \\ \hline 8\,2\,5 \end{array}$$

Solution: Donna's initial score was 780.
Explanation:
I used the variable s to represent Donna's initial score. I wrote the addition equation $s + 45 = 825$.
I already had the sum 825, so I worked backward to solve for s using subtraction.
I subtracted 45 from 825 and got $s = 780$. I checked my solution by substituting 780 back into my
equation. It made the equation true. So, my answer of 780 is correct.

AT A GLANCE

Students practice solving problems involving using number sense to solve one-step equations that might appear on a mathematics test.

STEP BY STEP

PAGES 132–133

• Tell students that they will practice answering questions that involve writing and solving equations.

• Point out the tips at the top of page 132. Explain to students that these tips will help them answer the problems correctly.

• You may wish to have students review the hints for avoiding mistakes on page 129 as well.

• Tell students to complete problems 8–15 on pages 132 and 133. Encourage students to check their answers. When they've solved an equation, they can substitute the value for the variable back into the equation to see if the expressions on both sides of the equal sign are equivalent.

• Discuss the correct responses as a class.

Answers and Explanations

8. Ⓒ Working backward, this division equation is solved using multiplication.

9. Ⓒ This is a subtraction equation. Work backward using addition. $b = 24 + 3 = 27$

10. Ⓒ The word *product* indicates the relationship is multiplication. The multiplication equation represents the stated relationship.

11. Ⓓ The scenario describes a relationship involving subtraction. Write the equation $p - 1\frac{1}{8} = 6\frac{1}{4}$ and solve by adding. $6\frac{1}{4} + 1\frac{1}{8} = 6\frac{2}{8} + 1\frac{1}{8} = 7\frac{3}{8}$

12. Ⓓ Because the unknown is the product, use the given operation, multiplication. The value of p is 108.

13. Ⓐ This answer reflects setting up the equation $A = l \cdot w$ as $35 = 7w$ and solving for w using division.

(continued on page 136)

(continued from page 135)

14. The word *quotient* indicates division. Write the division equation $\frac{n}{1.5} = 26$. Word backward using multiplication to find that $n = 39$.

15. See the sample answer. This answer shows all of the steps taken to solve the problem by writing and solving an equation. The solution answers the question. The explanation provides important details and uses the math words *variable*, *equation*, *sum*, and *substitute*.

 ASSESSMENT AND REMEDIATION

- Ask students to write and solve an equation to find the unknown number: "The product of 1.2 and a number is 8.4." *(1.2n = 8.4; n = 7)*
- For students who are still struggling, use the chart below to guide remediation.
- After providing remediation, check students' understanding. Ask students to explain their steps while finding the unknown number in the following problem: "The difference of a number and 45 is 5." *(n − 45 = 5; n = 50)*
- If a student is still having difficulty, use *STAMS Book F*, Lesson 8, pages 74–83.

If the error is . . .	Students may . . .	To remediate . . .
writing and solving the equation $1.2 \times 8.4 = n$	be struggling with translating words into equations.	Have students map each word or phrase in the given word sentence to a mathematical sentence (equation). *The product of 1.2 and a number is 8.4.* multiplication $1.2 \cdot n = 8.4$
not writing an equation	not understand what is meant by "write an equation," or not understand the need for writing an equation.	Reiterate the importance of writing an equation to represent the situation first and then solving to arrive at the correct answer. Explain that this lesson is laying the foundation for procedures needed in further work with algebra.
0.7 or 70	have misplaced the decimal point when performing division.	Review the steps for decimal division. Remind students to multiply the divisor and dividend by the same power of ten (having the effect of moving the decimal point the same number of places to the right in each) so that the divisor is a whole number.

 ADDITIONAL ACTIVITY

For students who have mastered the skills in this lesson, see **Challenge Activity** (page 137).

ADDITIONAL ACTIVITIES

Hands-on Activity
Use number lines to model addition and subtraction equations.

Materials: blank sheets of paper, straightedge

Have students use number lines with whole numbers to model solving addition and subtraction equations. To prepare, have students sketch a number line from 0 to 25. Teach the concept as follows:

Write the numerical equation $14 + 5 = 19$ on the board. Tell students to make a mark at the starting value, 14. Ask, "To add 5, which direction do you move along the number line?" *(Right.)* Direct students to move 5 units to the right from 14 to confirm that they end at the sum 19. Write the equation $x + 13 = 22$ on the board. Ask, "What does this equation say?" *(An unknown number plus 13 equals 22.)* Ask, "What is the starting value?" *(Unknown.)* Tell students that we do know moving 13 units to the right will give the sum of 22. Ask, "How can you work backward with the number line to find the starting value?" *(Begin at the sum 22 and move left 13 places.)* This will result in the missing number, $x = 9$. Follow the same procedure, but moving left for a numerical subtraction equation like $20 - 8 = 12$.

Solve the equation $s - 15 = 8$ by starting at 8 and moving right 15 places. *(s = 23)*

Reteaching Activity
Reinforce new representations for multiplication and division with a chart.

In this lesson, students encounter several ways to write multiplication and division expressions. Explain that because unknowns in equations are written with symbols (letters of the alphabet), these new ways of expressing multiplication and division help to avoid confusion between variables and operation symbols. Help students keep track of these equivalent representations by creating a two-column chart. Under the header *Multiplication*, include: 3 times 5; 3×5; $3 \cdot 5$; $3(5)$. Under the header *Division*, include: 8 divided by 4; $8 \div 4$; $4)\overline{8}$; $\frac{8}{4}$.

Vocabulary Activity
Play "Quiz Show" to reinforce terms.

Materials: index cards, markers

Divide students into two groups and provide each group with index cards and markers. As you read a vocabulary term aloud, the first contestant in each group writes a definition or draws a picture for the term. The two contestants raise their hands as soon as they have a response ready. The one with the first correct response earns a point for his or her team. Repeat with a new vocabulary term for each pair of contestants.

Real-World Connection
Write and exchange word problems.

Have each student write four real-world word problems. Each one should represent a different operation and be solvable using simple one-step equations. As needed, provide some topics for real-world ideas, such as *grocery store*, *roller-skating rink*, *party decorations*, *video games*, and *gardening*.

School-Home Connection
Inform families about solving equation using number sense.

Give each student a copy of the reproducible School-Home Connection for Lesson 13 (page 187) to share with the family. The activity in the letter has the family write equations to solve several word problems.

Challenge Activity
Write equations for a given solution.

Rather than giving students equations and having them solve them, do the opposite. Give students solutions and have them write the equations. For each solution, have them write 4 equations—one for each operation.

Example:

$x = 4 \rightarrow 10 + x = 14, \; x - 1 = 3, \; 32 = 8x, \; \frac{x}{1} = 4$

LESSON OBJECTIVES

Students will:

- Use inverse operations to solve one-step addition and subtraction equations.
- Use inverse operations to solve one-step multiplication and division equations.

PREREQUISITES

Students should be able to:

- Add, subtract, multiply, and divide whole numbers and decimals.
- Write equations to represent word problems.

RELATED *STAMS*® LESSON

- **Book F – Lesson 13**

  Solve Equations Using Number Sense introduces students to writing equations. Students use reasoning and number sense to solve them.

VOCABULARY

PAGE 134

- **number sense:** an understanding of numbers and how they relate to one another
- **equation:** a number sentence that contains an equal sign and shows two quantities with the same value
- **inverse operations:** operations that undo each other; for example, addition and subtraction or multiplication and division
- **simplify:** make the expression less complicated, such as performing all possible operations
- **solution:** a value of the variable that makes an equation true

PAGE 135

- **substitute:** to replace an unknown with a value

PAGE 136

- **quotient:** the result of division
- **dividend:** in a division problem, the number being divided

PAGE 137

- **product:** the result of multiplication
- **factor:** a number that is multiplied by another number

MATH BACKGROUND

This lesson has the same types of equations as in Lesson 13, and the conceptual basis for solving them is the same. But students will need a structured format for solving more difficult equations in later grades. That format is presented in this lesson, along with the formal vocabulary, *inverse operations*. The table compares the methods of solving $x + 5 = 8$.

Lesson 13	Lesson 14
"What number plus 5 equals 8?" Work backward. Subtract: $8 - 5 = 3$. So $x = 3$.	"5 is being added to x." Perform the *inverse operation*. Subtract 5 from both sides. $$x + 5 = 8$$ $$x + 5 - 5 = 8 - 5$$ $$x = 3$$

Students will solve one-step equations by determining in each case what is being done to the variable and then performing the appropriate inverse operation on both sides of the equation.

Interactive Whiteboard

Visualize Using Inverse Operations to Solve Equations

Go to the *Interactive Whiteboard Lessons* to bring Parts One and Two to life. Use features such as sliding screens with additional practice to deepen students' understanding of using inverse operations to solve equations.

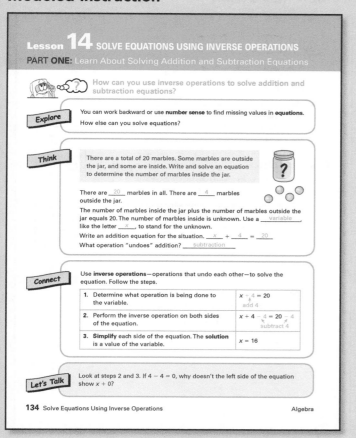

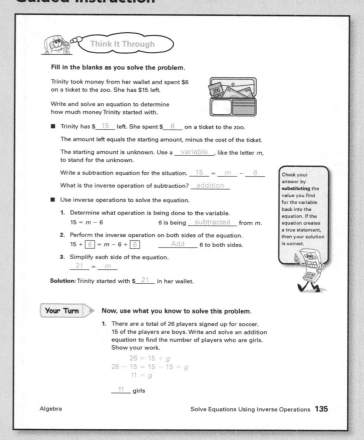

AT A GLANCE

Students activate their background knowledge about equations and then learn how to use inverse operations to solve addition and subtraction equations.

STEP BY STEP

Page 134

- Introduce the **Question** at the top of the page.
- Have students read the statement in **Explore**.
- Read **Think** with students. Emphasize that the number of marbles in the jar is the unknown. Pause so students can say aloud the numbers in orange.

  Tip: Explain the meaning of "sides" of an equation. Show that the equal sign splits the equation into two sides that are expressions with equal value.

- Discuss **Connect** with students. Help students see that subtracting the same amount from both sides will isolate the variable and help to find the solution.

  ELL Support: Define *inverse*. Show that opening and closing the door are inverses of each other—one "undoes" the other. Ask students for other examples.

- Organize students in pairs or groups for **Let's Talk** and monitor their discussions.
- Be sure students understand that zero added to any number equals the number. There is no need to write $x + 0$ because the expression simplifies to x.

Page 135

- Read the **Think It Through** problem with students.
- Guide students as they solve the problem. Point out that the equation $15 = m - 6$ is the same as $m - 6 = 15$, and that the variable can appear on either side of the equation.
- Help students see that addition, the inverse of subtraction, can be used to find the solution.
- Monitor students as they complete **Your Turn**. Then discuss the correct answer.

  Error Alert: Students who answered 41 may have added 15 to both sides of the equation instead of subtracting.

 ADDITIONAL ACTIVITY

See **Hands-on Activity** (page 145).

Modeled Instruction

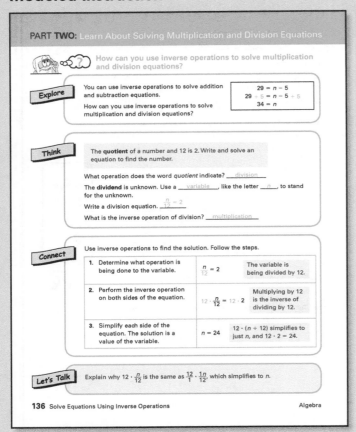

Guided Instruction

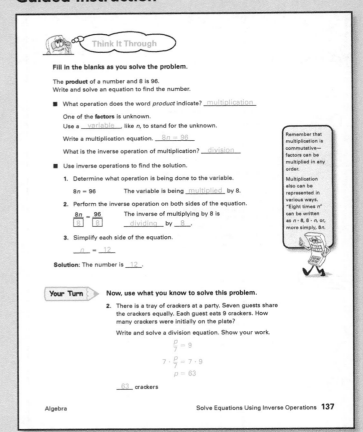

Students learn how to use inverse operations to solve multiplication and division equations.

STEP BY STEP

Page 136

- Introduce the **Question** at the top of the page.
- Read **Explore** with students. Reinforce that addition and subtraction are inverse operations, as are multiplication and division.

  ELL Support: Review the words associated with the different operations such as *quotient, dividend, divisor, product, factor, sum, addend,* and *difference.* Organize the terms in a chart to display in the room.

- Read **Think** with students.
- Tell students to study the steps in **Connect**. Test their understanding by asking why 2 is multiplied by 12. Explain that performing the same operation to both sides will keep both sides, or expressions, equal.
- Organize students in pairs or groups for **Let's Talk** and monitor their discussions.

- Be sure students understand that a whole number can be written as a fraction with a denominator of 1, and that the coefficient of the variable n is understood to be 1. Show how to use cross-simplification to simplify the product.

Page 137

- Read the **Think It Through** problem with students.
- Guide students as they solve the problem. Then discuss each response.

  Tip: Allow students to complete the problem using the equivalent equation $n \cdot 8 = 96$ or $8 \cdot n = 96$.

- Monitor students as they complete **Your Turn**. Then discuss the correct answer.

  Error Alert: Students who wrote a correct equation but did not find a correct solution may not have performed the inverse operation to both sides of the equation, or may have made a basic math error.

 ADDITIONAL ACTIVITY

See **Reteaching Activity** (page 145).

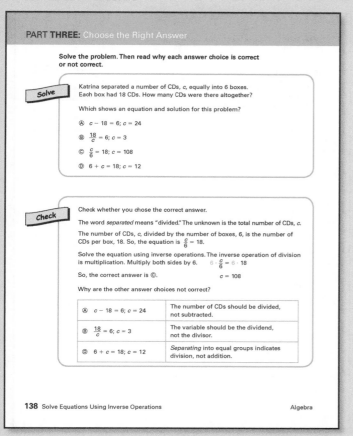

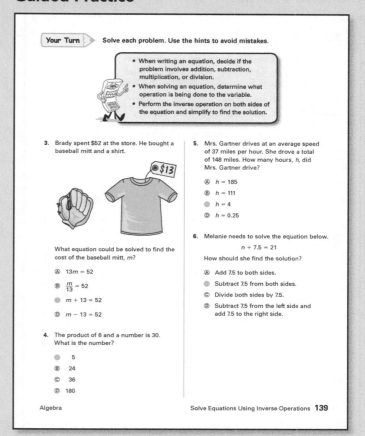

AT A GLANCE

Students reinforce their understanding of inverse operations through solving a multiple-choice problem and analyzing correct and incorrect answer choices.

STEP BY STEP

PAGE 138

- Tell students that this page models finding the correct answer to a multiple-choice problem.

- Have students read the problem in **Solve** and choose the best answer. Remind students to check their math.

- Examine **Check** with students. Discuss the correct and incorrect choices.

PAGE 139

- Monitor students as they complete **Your Turn**.

- Organize students in pairs or small groups and have them discuss why each answer choice is correct or not and what errors may have been made.

- Review the answers with the class.

 ADDITIONAL ACTIVITY

See **Vocabulary Activity** (page 145).

Answer Analysis

3. Ⓐ Chose a multiplication equation

   Ⓑ Chose a division equation

   ⬤ The cost of the mitt + the cost of the shirt = the total cost.

   Ⓓ Chose a subtraction equation

4. ⬤ $6n = 30$; divide both sides by 6 to find $n = 5$.

   Ⓑ Subtracted 6 from 30

   Ⓒ Added 6 and 30

   Ⓓ Multiplied 6 and 30

5. Ⓐ Solved $148 = h - 37$

   Ⓑ Solved $148 = h + 37$

   ⬤ $37h = 148$; divide both sides by 37 to find $h = 4$.

   Ⓓ Solved $148h = 37$

6. Ⓐ Selected the operation shown in the equation

   ⬤ The inverse of adding 7.5 is subtracting 7.5.

   Ⓒ Thought division and addition are inverse operations

   Ⓓ Selected inverse operation for left side of equation but selected operation used in equation for right side

Modeled Practice

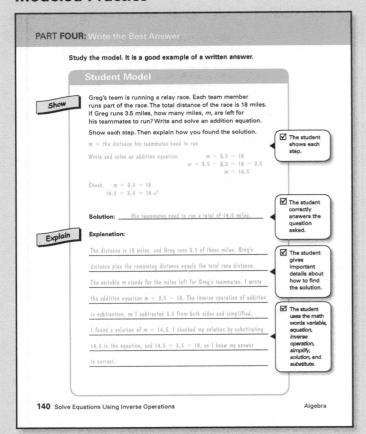

Guided Practice

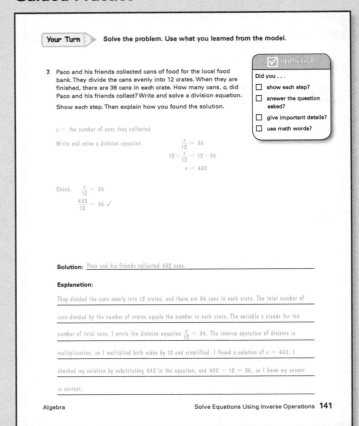

AT A GLANCE
· ·

Students study a model answer to an extended-response problem.

STEP BY STEP
· ·

PAGE 140

- Tell students that this page models building the solution to a problem one step at a time and writing to explain the solution.

- Have students read the problem in **Show**. Discuss how each mathematical step leads to the solution.

> Tip: Explain that a multiplication equation can't be used, because you don't know if the members are all running the same distance. Also, the question doesn't ask for the distance that *each* member will run.

- Read **Explain** with students. Have students circle the math words in the explanation.

- Direct students' attention to the notes in the right margin. Tell students that this model would receive a high score for the reasons described in these notes.

PAGE 141

- Monitor students as they complete **Your Turn**.

- Encourage students to follow the **Checklist** to write the best answer.

- Have students discuss their work with a partner. Then discuss the correct answer as a class.

Answer and Explanation

7. See the sample answer. This answer shows all of the steps taken to solve the problem, including writing an equation and using an inverse operation to solve. The solution answers the question. The explanation provides important details about how the problem was solved and uses the math words *variable*, *equation*, *inverse operation*, *simplify*, *solution*, and *substitute*.

 ADDITIONAL ACTIVITY
· ·
See **Real-World Connection** (page 145).

 ADDITIONAL ACTIVITY
· ·
See **School-Home Connection** (page 145).

Independent Practice

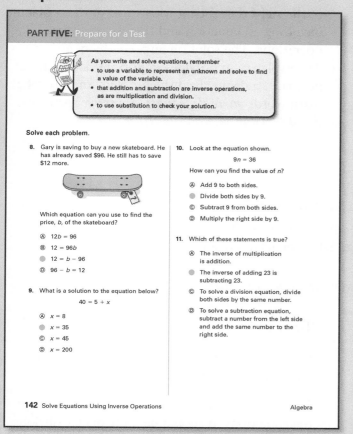

PART FIVE: Prepare for a Test

As you write and solve equations, remember
- to use a variable to represent an unknown and solve to find a value of the variable.
- that addition and subtraction are inverse operations, as are multiplication and division.
- to use substitution to check your solution.

Solve each problem.

8. Gary is saving to buy a new skateboard. He has already saved $96. He still has to save $12 more.

Which equation can you use to find the price, *b*, of the skateboard?

Ⓐ $12b = 96$
Ⓑ $12 = 96b$
Ⓒ $12 = b - 96$
Ⓓ $96 - b = 12$

9. What is a solution to the equation below?
$$40 = 5 + x$$

Ⓐ $x = 8$
Ⓑ $x = 35$
Ⓒ $x = 45$
Ⓓ $x = 200$

10. Look at the equation shown.
$$9n = 36$$

How can you find the value of *n*?

Ⓐ Add 9 to both sides.
Ⓑ Divide both sides by 9.
Ⓒ Subtract 9 from both sides.
Ⓓ Multiply the right side by 9.

11. Which of these statements is true?

Ⓐ The inverse of multiplication is addition.
Ⓑ The inverse of adding 23 is subtracting 23.
Ⓒ To solve a division equation, divide both sides by the same number.
Ⓓ To solve a subtraction equation, subtract a number from the left side and add the same number to the right side.

142 Solve Equations Using Inverse Operations · Algebra

---

12. The quotient of a number and 4.5 is 8. What is the number?

Ⓐ 1.77
Ⓑ 3.5
Ⓒ 12.5
Ⓓ 36

13. An art teacher divided the total number of students who signed up for an after-school art program into 6 groups. Each group had 12 students. How many students signed up for the after-school program?

Ⓐ 72
Ⓑ 18
Ⓒ 6
Ⓓ 2

14. A softball team is raising money for a local charity. They raised $90 at the bake sale on Saturday. They have $450 left to raise to meet their fundraising goal.

Write and solve a subtraction equation to find the team's fundraising goal, *g*. Show your work.

Equation:
$$g - 90 = 450$$

$$g - 90 = 450$$
$$g - 90 + 90 = 450 + 90$$
$$g = 540$$

Fundraising Goal: $___540___

15. There are a total of 42 products behind the counter at a convenience store. Some of them are on a shelf, and some are in a box. If there are 8 products in the box, how many products are on the shelf? Write and solve an addition equation.

Show each step. Then explain how you found the solution.

$p =$ the number of products on the shelf

Write and solve an addition equation.
$$p + 8 = 42$$
$$p + 8 - 8 = 42 - 8$$
$$p = 34$$

Check.
$$p + 8 = 42$$
$$34 + 8 = 42 ✓$$

Solution: There are 34 products on the shelf.

Explanation:
The number of products on the shelf plus the number of products in the box equals 42. I used the variable *p* to stand for the number of products on the shelf. I wrote the addition equation $p + 8 = 42$. The inverse operation of addition is subtraction, so I subtracted 8 from both sides and simplified. I found a solution of $p = 34$. I checked my solution by substituting 34 in the equation, and $34 + 8 = 42$, so I know my answer is correct.

Algebra · Solve Equations Using Inverse Operations 143

AT A GLANCE

Students practice using inverse operations to solve problems that might appear on a mathematics test.

STEP BY STEP

PAGES 142–143

- Tell students that they will practice solving problems that involve solving equations using inverse operations.

- Point out the tips at the top of page 142. Explain to students that these tips will help them answer the problems correctly.

- You may wish to have students review the hints for avoiding mistakes on page 139 as well.

- Tell students to complete problems 8–15 on pages 142 and 143. Encourage students to check their answers.

- Discuss the correct responses as a class.

Answers and Explanations

8. Ⓒ The price of the skateboard minus the amount Gary has saved equals the amount he still has to save. $12 = b - 96$

9. Ⓑ The inverse operation of addition is subtraction. To solve for *x*, subtract 5 from both sides. $40 - 5 = 35$

10. Ⓑ $9n$ means 9 times *n*. The inverse operation of multiplication is division. Divide both sides by 9.

11. Ⓑ Addition and subtraction are inverse operations. So, the inverse of adding 23 is subtracting 23.

12. Ⓓ The word *quotient* indicates division. Letting $n =$ the unknown number, solve $\frac{n}{4.5} = 8$ by multiplying both sides by 4.5: $n = 36$.

13. Ⓐ The total number of students, divided into 6 groups gives 12 students in each group. Write the equation $\frac{s}{6} = 12$. Solve by multiplying both sides by 6: $s = 72$.

(continued on page 144)

(continued from page 143)

14. The fundraising goal minus the amount raised at the bake sale equals the amount left to raise. Write the equation: $g - 90 = 450$. Solve for g by adding 90 to both sides. $g = 450 + 90 = 540$

15. See the sample answer. This answer shows all of the steps the student took to solve the problem, including an equation and the use of inverse operations. The solution answers the question. The explanation provides important details about how the student solved the problem and uses the math words *variable*, *equation*, *inverse operation*, *simplify*, *solution*, and *substitute*.

✔ ASSESSMENT AND REMEDIATION

- Ask students to use inverse operations to solve the equation $5a = 15$. *(a = 3)*
- For students who are still struggling, use the chart below to guide remediation.
- After providing remediation, check students' understanding. Ask students to explain their thinking while solving $8 + y = 24$. *(y = 16)*
- If a student is still having difficulty, use *STAMS Book F*, Lesson 13, pages 124–133.

If the error is . . .	Students may . . .	To remediate . . .
$a = 75$	have multiplied both sides by 5.	Discuss how the inverse, or *opposite*, operation must be used to find the solution. Remind students of the importance of checking their solutions. It should be immediately obvious to students that 5×75 does not equal 15.
added 15 and 5 to get $a = 20$, or subtracted 5 from 15 to get $a = 10$	have selected an incorrect inverse operation, *or*	Review the meaning of inverse operations. Write the pairs of inverse operations on the board: addition/subtraction and multiplication/division. Provide examples of operations using counters, such as *adding 6* and have students show and say the inverse: *subtracting 6*.
	have misread the equation as an addition equation.	Point out that a variable next to a number indicates multiplication. Show this by rewriting the equation as $5 \cdot a = 15$ or $5 \times a = 15$.
any other value for a	have made a basic math error.	Have students check their work using substitution to see their work is incorrect. Then review basic multiplication and division facts. Show how to solve the equation on the board, step by step.

☆ ADDITIONAL ACTIVITY

For students who have mastered the skills in this lesson, see **Challenge Activity** (page 145).

ADDITIONAL ACTIVITIES

Hands-on Activity
Use counters and cups to model keeping both sides of an equation equal.

Materials: 30 counters and 3 plastic cups per pair

Organize students into pairs. Student A should hold 1 cup, and Student B should hold 2 cups. Ask Student A to place 5 counters in his cup. Ask Student B to place 1 counter in one cup and 4 counters in the other cup. Show that the students have the same number of counters.

Ask each student to take 1 more counter and add them to a cup. Do they still have the same number? *(Yes.)* Now ask Student A to remove 2 counters, and ask Student B to remove 2 counters from *each* cup. Do they still have the same number? *(No.)* Explain that 2 were subtracted from Student A, but 4 were subtracted from Student B. So now they do not have an equal number of counters. This shows that if you do not do the same thing to both sides of an equation, the two sides will not remain equal.

Reteaching Activity
Use counters to model solving multiplication and division equations.

Materials: 30 counters, 3 cups, and a marker per pair

Write the equation $3n = 18$ on the board. Organize students in pairs and distribute cups and counters. Have one student in each pair model the left side of the equation by writing the letter n on each of 3 cups. Have the partner model the right side of the equation by counting out 18 counters.

Point out that the equal sign shows that both sides have the same value. Then ask students, "What operation is the opposite of multiplication?" *(Division.)* Have each student show dividing by 3 by making 3 equal groups. Ask pairs to rewrite the equation based on their models now. *(n = 6)*

Repeat with other multiplication and division equations.

Vocabulary Activity
Play "What Am I?" to reinforce terms.

Materials: index cards for each pair

Have students write the vocabulary words on index cards, mix up the cards, and place them facedown in a stack. The first student picks a card and gives an example of the vocabulary word. For example, if a student picks *solution*, she or he might write $3d = 21$, solve the equation, and circle the solution, $d = 7$. The other player tries to guess the word. Continue until all the cards have been used. Conclude the activity by having student pairs work together to agree on the best example for each vocabulary word and draw or write that on the back of its card.

Real-World Connection
Write and solve equations for real-life situations.

Explain that equations are frequently used in the real world to solve problems involving money, temperature, and measurement. Have students write and solve an equation to determine the number of days that is equivalent to 120 hours. *(24d = 120; d = 5)*

School-Home Connection
Inform families about solving equations.

Give each student a copy of the reproducible School-Home Connection for Lesson 14 (page 189) to share with the family. The activity in the letter has the family write and solve equations to solve various problems.

Challenge Activity
Solve a set of equations.

Have students apply what they have learned about solving equations to solve these two problems:

1. If $a + b = 12$ and $6a = 18$, what is b?
   (a = 3, b = 9)

2. If $d - c = 7$ and $\frac{d}{3} = 3$, what is c?
   (d = 9, c = 2)

Expressions and Equations

LESSON OBJECTIVES

Students will:

- Select and use the appropriate formula for a situation.
- Solve problems involving distance/rate/time relationships, as well as area.

PREREQUISITES

Students should be able to:

- Solve equations using inverse operations.
- Perform addition, subtraction, multiplication, and division on whole numbers, decimals, and fractions.

RELATED *STAMS*® LESSONS

- **Book F – Lesson 8**

  Divide by Decimals introduces students to decimal division.

- **Book F – Lesson 14**

  Solve Equations Using Inverse Operations shows students how to solve one-step equations.

VOCABULARY

PAGE 144

- **rate:** a ratio that compares two different units such as distance and time
- **constant rate:** a rate that does not change
- **formula:** an equation that shows the relationship among quantities
- **substitute:** to replace an unknown with a value
- **variable:** a letter or symbol that stands for an unknown
- **inverse operations:** operations that undo each other
- **simplify:** make the expression less complicated, such as performing all possible operations
- **solution:** a value of the variable that makes an equation true

PAGE 146

- **isolate the variable:** get the variable by itself on one side of an equation to find its value

MATH BACKGROUND

Students have seen equations that have only numbers, such as $7 - 3 = 4$, and equations that have a variable, such as $11 + x = 25$. In this lesson they will work with formulas—equations that have more than one variable, such as $d = rt$ (*distance = rate × time*). They will substitute given values into the formulas and then solve the resulting one-variable equations. For example, substituting 48 for d and 6 for r in the formula $d = rt$ yields the equation $48 = 6t$, which is solved by dividing both sides by 6.

At the sixth-grade level, units of measure are not included when solving equations. But students will learn in later grades how to include units when solving equations, as shown below on the right.

Solving without units:

$$d = rt$$
$$48 = 6t$$
$$\frac{48}{6} = \frac{6t}{6}$$
$$8 = t$$

Solving with units:

$$d = rt$$
$$48\text{ ft} = \frac{6\text{ ft}}{1\text{ min}} \cdot t$$
$$\frac{1\text{ min}}{6\text{ ft}} \cdot 48\text{ ft} = \frac{1\text{ min}}{6\text{ ft}} \cdot \frac{6\text{ ft}}{1\text{ min}} \cdot t$$
$$8\text{ min} = t$$

Interactive Whiteboard
- -
Visualize Using Formulas

Go to the *Interactive Whiteboard Lessons* to bring Parts One and Two to life. Use features such as sliding screens with additional practice to deepen students' understanding of using formulas to solve problems.

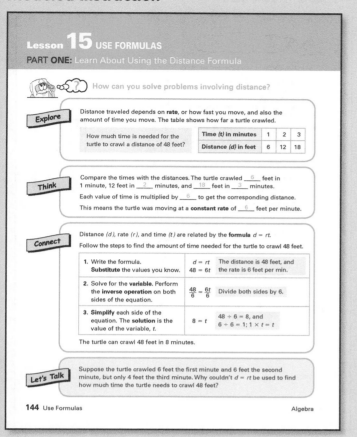

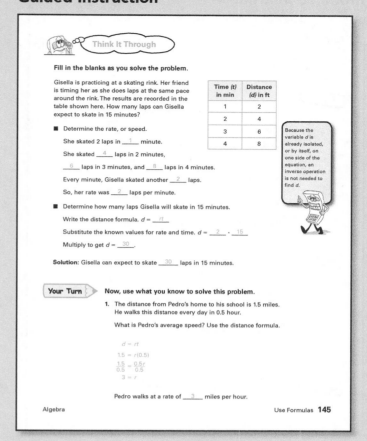

AT A GLANCE

Students activate their prior knowledge about data in tables. They then apply their equation-solving skills to the distance formula $d = rt$.

STEP BY STEP

PAGE 144

- Introduce the **Question** at the top of the page.
- Have students read the **Explore**. Discuss the importance of all components of the table, including headings, variables, and units.
- Read **Think** with students.

  Tip: Reinforce the concept of a *constant rate* by writing the distance/time relationships from the table as ratios with units, then simplifying: $\frac{6 \text{ ft}}{1 \text{ min}} = 6 \text{ ft/min}$; $\frac{12 \text{ ft}}{2 \text{ min}} = 6 \text{ ft/min}$.

- Discuss **Connect** with students. State the relationship given by the formula $d = rt$ in a sentence: *distance traveled is equal to rate times time.*

- Organize students in pairs or groups for **Let's Talk** and monitor their discussions.

- Students should conclude that they could not use the distance formula because they wouldn't have a single value (constant rate) to substitute for the variable r.

PAGE 145

- Read the **Think It Through** problem with students.

  ELL Support: Some students may not be familiar with *roller skating*, *rink*, and *lap*. Describe this recreational activity and use a diagram to clarify what a *rink* is and what one *lap* would mean.

- Guide students as they solve the problem. Confirm that each distance vs. time pair of values in the table simplifies to the rate 2 laps per minute.

- Monitor students as they complete **Your Turn**.

  Error Alert: Students who found an answer of 0.75 mile per hour multiplied instead of divided. Remind them that, in this case, they are solving for r and must use the inverse operation (division) to solve.

 ADDITIONAL ACTIVITY

See **Hands-on Activity** (page 153).

Modeled Instruction

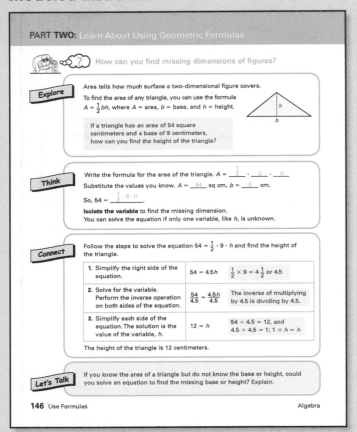

Guided Instruction

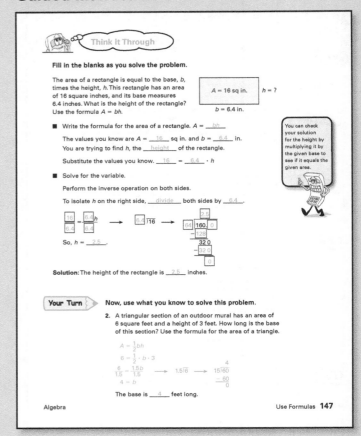

AT A GLANCE

Students extend their understanding of using formulas to find the areas of geometric figures.

STEP BY STEP

PAGE 146

- Introduce the **Question** at the top of the page.

ELL Support: Students may not be familiar with the word *dimensions*. Define it as a general term for measurements such as length, width, and height. In this lesson, they will encounter the dimensions for area only, which will be referred to as base and height.

- Read **Explore** with students. Remind students that base and height are units of length, but area is a measure of square units, even for nonsquare figures.
- Read **Think** with students. Discuss what *isolate the variable* means.
- Work through the solution steps in **Connect**.

Tip: Show students that sometimes, when solving equations, expressions can be simplified before inverse operations are performed. Here, students find $\frac{1}{2} \cdot 9$ before performing division.

- Organize students in pairs or groups for **Let's Talk** and monitor their discussions.
- Students should conclude that an equation cannot be solved for more than one missing variable.

PAGE 147

- Read the **Think It Through** problem with students. Make sure students understand that the formula $A = bh$ is the same as the more familiar formula $A = lw$.
- Guide students as they solve the problem. Have students check their solution. Ask, "Does $16 = 6.4(2.5)$?" *(yes)*
- Monitor students as they complete **Your Turn**. Then discuss the correct answer.

Error Alert: Students who found an answer of 2 feet may have used an incorrect formula.

 ADDITIONAL ACTIVITY

See **Reteaching Activity** (page 153).

Modeled Practice

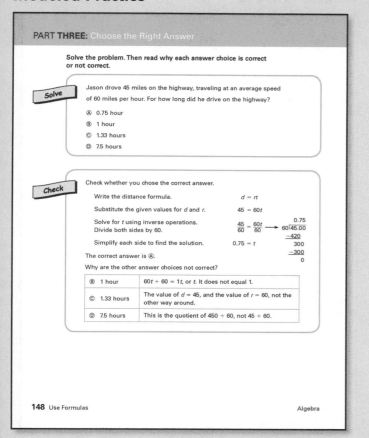

Guided Practice

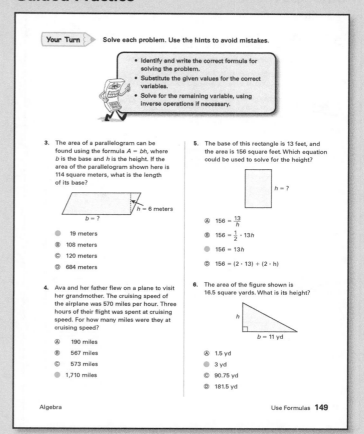

AT A GLANCE

Students reinforce their understanding of formulas with a multiple-choice word problem and analyze correct and incorrect answer choices.

STEP BY STEP

PAGE 148

- Have students read the problem in **Solve** and choose the best answer. Remind students to check their work.

- Examine **Check** with students. Ask students to think about the meaning of 0.75 hour. How many minutes is that? Use an analog clock to count the minutes in three-fourths of an hour.

PAGE 149

- Monitor students as they complete **Your Turn**.

- Organize students in pairs or small groups to discuss answer choices and errors that may have been made.

- Review the answers with the class.

 ADDITIONAL ACTIVITY

See **Vocabulary Activity** (page 153).

Answer Analysis

3.   ●   Use division to solve for b in $114 = 6b$.
   - Ⓑ Subtracted 6 from 114
   - Ⓒ Added 6 and 114
   - Ⓓ Multiplied 6 and 114

4. Ⓐ Divided 570 by 3
   - Ⓑ Subtracted 3 from 570
   - Ⓒ Added 3 and 570
   - ● Use the distance formula $d = rt$; multiply to solve for d: $d = 570 \cdot 3 = 1{,}710$ mi.

5. Ⓐ Used formula implying that 13 is the area
   - Ⓑ Used formula for the area of a triangle
   - ● This equation relates area, base, and height of a rectangle.
   - Ⓓ Used formula relating perimeter (instead of area) with base and height

6. Ⓐ Used incorrect area formula, $A = bh$
   - ● Using the formula, $A = \frac{1}{2}bh$, $16.5 = \frac{1}{2} \cdot 11 \cdot h$; $16.5 = 5.5h$; $h = 3$ yd.
   - Ⓒ Used correct formula but substituted values for the wrong variables
   - Ⓓ Multiplied the given values

Modeled Practice

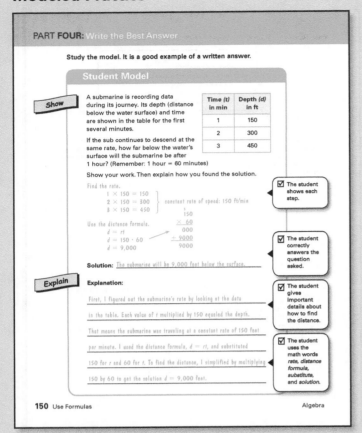

Guided Practice

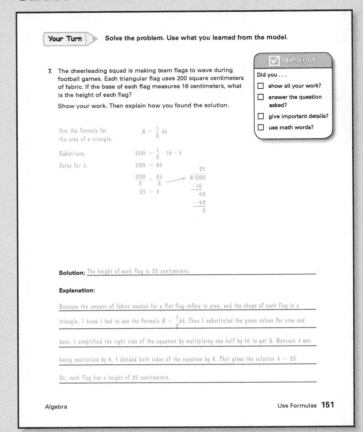

AT A GLANCE

Students study a model answer to an extended-response problem.

STEP BY STEP

PAGE 150

- Tell students that this page models building the solution to a real-world problem one step at a time and writing to explain the solution.

- Have students read the problem in **Show**. Discuss how each mathematical step leads to the solution.

> **Tip:** Make sure students recognize that the only value given in the problem that can be substituted directly into the distance formula is the time ($t = 60$). The unknown is the distance, d. So before using the formula, they must find the rate, r, using the data given in the table.

- Read **Explain** with students. Have students circle the math words in the explanation.

- Direct students' attention to the notes in the right margin. Tell students that this model would receive a high score for the reasons described in these notes.

PAGE 151

- Monitor students as they complete **Your Turn**.
- Encourage students to follow the **Checklist** to write the best answer.
- Have students discuss their work with a partner. Then discuss the correct answer as a class.

Answer and Explanation

7. See the sample answer. It shows all of the steps taken to solve the problem: identifying the correct formula; substituting known values for the variables; and solving the equation by simplifying and using inverse operations. The solution answers the question. The explanation provides important details about how the problem was solved and uses the math terms *formula*, *substitute*, *simplify*, and *solution*.

ADDITIONAL ACTIVITY

See **Real-World Connection** (page 153).

ADDITIONAL ACTIVITY

See **School-Home Connection** (page 153).

Independent Practice

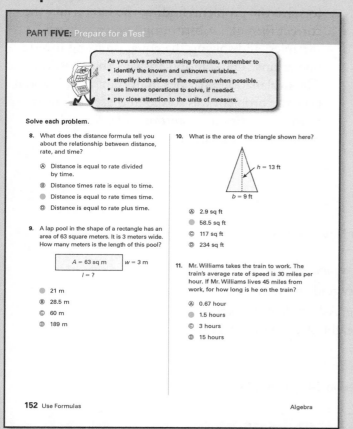

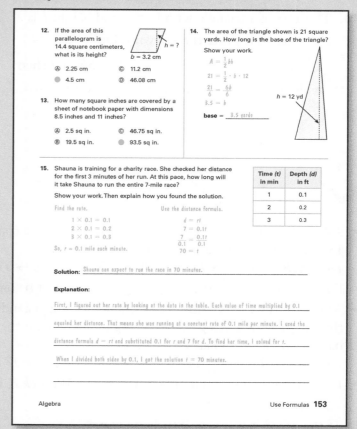

AT A GLANCE

Students practice problems involving formulas that might appear on a mathematics test.

STEP BY STEP

PAGES 152–153

- Tell students that they will practice answering questions that involve writing and solving equations.

- Point out the tips at the top of page 152. Explain to students that these tips will help them answer the problems correctly.

- You may wish to have students review the hints for avoiding mistakes on page 149 as well.

- Tell students to complete problems 8–15 on pages 152 and 153. Encourage students to check their answers. When they've solved an equation, they can substitute the value for the variable back into the equation to see if the expressions on both sides of the equal sign are equivalent.

- Discuss the correct responses as a class.

Answers and Explanations

8. Ⓒ The distance formula is $d = rt$, or, in words, *distance equals rate times time.*

9. Ⓐ The area of a rectangle with base b and height h is $A = bh$. Substitute the known values to get $63 = b \cdot 3$, or $63 = 3b$. Divide both sides by 3 to find $b = 21$ meters.

10. Ⓑ The area of a triangle with base b and height h is $A = \frac{1}{2}bh$. Substitute the known values to get $A = \frac{1}{2} \cdot 9 \cdot 13$. Multiply to find $A = 58.5$ sq ft.

11. Ⓑ The distance formula is $d = rt$. Substitute the known values to get $45 = 30t$. Divide both sides by 30 to find $t = 1.5$ hours.

12. Ⓑ The area of a parallelogram with base b and height h is $A = bh$. Substitute the known values to get $14.4 = 3.2h$. Divide both sides by 3.2 to find $h = 4.5$ cm.

13. Ⓓ The area of a rectangle with base b and height h is $A = bh$. Substitute the known values to get $A = 8.5 \cdot 11$. Multiply to find $A = 93.5$ sq in.

(continued on page 152)

(continued from page 151)

14. The area of a triangle with base b and height h is $A = \frac{1}{2}bh$. Substitute the known values to get $21 = \frac{1}{2} \cdot b \cdot 12$. Simplify to get $21 = 6b$, and then divide both sides by 6 to find $b = 3.5$ yards.

15. See the sample answer. It shows all the steps taken to solve the problem: finding the rate; using the correct formula; substituting known values variables; and solving the equation using inverse operations. The solution answers the question. The explanation provides important details about how the problem was solved and uses the math terms *rate*, *distance*, *constant rate*, *formula*, *substitute*, and *solution*.

✔ ASSESSMENT AND REMEDIATION

- Ask students to show the steps to find the height of a triangle whose base is 15 centimeters and area is 30 square centimeters.
  $(A = \frac{1}{2}bh \rightarrow 30 = \frac{1}{2} \cdot 15 \cdot h \rightarrow 30 = 7.5h \rightarrow 4 = h \rightarrow$ *The height is 4 centimeters.*)
- For students who are still struggling, use the chart below to guide remediation.
- After providing remediation, check students' understanding. Ask students to explain their steps while solving the following problem: Find the height of a rectangle whose base is 9.5 inches and area is 123.5 inches.
  $(A = bh \rightarrow 123.5 = 9.5h \rightarrow 13 = h \rightarrow$ *The height is 13 inches.*)
- If a student is still having difficulty, use *STAMS Book F*, Lesson 14, pages 134–143.

If the error is . . .	Students may . . .	To remediate . . .
using the wrong formula, and possibly finding an answer of 2 centimeters	not relate variables to measurements of a figure, or understand how the formula relates to the figure.	Allow students to create formula cards. On each of three index cards, have them draw a picture and write the name of a shape (triangle, rectangle, parallelogram) on one side, and write the corresponding area formula on the other side.
multiplying by a fraction incorrectly (i.e., finding $\frac{1}{2} \cdot 15 = 30$)	not understand the meaning of multiplying by $\frac{1}{2}$.	Explain that $\frac{1}{2} \cdot 15$ is the same as $15 \cdot \frac{1}{2}$, which means 15 halves. Draw 15 half-circles on the board. Then have students count the number of wholes. $(7\frac{1}{2})$ Explain that it takes two halves to make one whole, so the product of $15 \cdot \frac{1}{2}$ must be less than 15.
not using a formula at all, and just multiplying 15 by 30	not recognize how formulas help to organize information and guide the solution.	Reiterate the importance of writing the formula to represent the situation first, substituting the known values, and solving for the variable to arrive at the answer. In future courses, the formulas will get more complicated. Explain that this lesson is laying the foundation for procedures needed in further work with algebra and geometry.

⭐ ADDITIONAL ACTIVITY

For students who have mastered the skills in this lesson, see **Challenge Activity** (page 153).

ADDITIONAL ACTIVITIES

Hands-on Activity
Discover the relationship between distance, rate, and time.

Materials: stopwatch and 10-meter length marked off

Create a three-column table on the board with headings distance (m), rate (m/s), and time (s).

Have a student walk the 10-meter stretch at a slow pace as you time it in seconds from start to finish. Record distance and time in the table. Ask, "If (name) walked 10 meters in (time) seconds, how can you find the rate in meters per second?" (Divide 10 meters by the time, which is simplifying the fraction.) Perform the calculation and record the result in the table.

Ask another student to walk the 10 meters at a slightly faster pace. Before the walk, ask students, "Do you think it will take more time or less time to walk the same distance at a faster speed?" Note the predictions. Record the results in the table, calculating the rate in the same way as before.

Repeat this process two more times, with students moving faster each time. Help students conclude that for the same distance, as speed increases, time decreases.

Reteaching Activity
Conceptually establish area formulas.

Materials: grid paper, scissors

Direct students to draw a rectangle on centimeter grid paper with base 5 centimeters and height 4 centimeters. Have them find the area by counting the square centimeters in the rectangle. Establish that the 20 square centimeters are from 5 columns of 4, or $5 \cdot 4$, thus the formula $A = bh$.

Next have students draw a diagonal through the rectangle, and then cut along the diagonal. Ask them to place the triangles atop each other, noticing that each represents half of the original rectangle. Note that the base and height are the same as the rectangle, so the formula is $A = \frac{1}{2}bh$.

Vocabulary Activity
Make a crossword puzzle to reinforce terms.

Materials: grid paper

Have each student use the vocabulary words to make a puzzle where the words share common letters.

To help students check that their puzzles are complete, read a definition and have them check that they have used the corresponding word in their puzzle. Have them finish the puzzles with numbers for each vertical and horizontal word and numbered, written definitions. Finally, have pairs exchange and complete each other's puzzles.

Real-World Connection
Calculate Olympic speeds.

Look up some Olympic data and have students use it to calculate rates using the distance formula. For example, the Jamaican men won the 400-meter relay in the 2008 Olympics by setting a new world record of 37.1 seconds. What was their average speed? Students can assume the runners ran at the same rate. ($d = rt$; $400 = r \cdot 37.1$; r 10.8 m/s)

School-Home Connection
Inform families about using formulas.

Give each student a copy of the reproducible School-Home Connection for Lesson 15 (page 146) to share with the family. The activity in the letter has the family use formulas to solve problems, and then check answers for reasonableness.

Challenge Activity
Find the area of a trapezoid.

Sketch a trapezoid on the board with height 6 centimeters and bases 18 centimeters and 15 centimeters. Give students the formula for the area of a trapezoid: $A = \frac{1}{2}h(b_1 + b_2)$. Have students work with a partner to use the formula to find the area. (99 square centimeters)

LESSON OBJECTIVES

Students will:

- Use a formula to find the volume of a rectangular prism.
- Solve an equation to find the missing dimension of a rectangular prism.

PREREQUISITES

Students should be able to:

- Multiply three factors.
- Solve simple one-step equations.
- Understand area.

RELATED *STAMS*® LESSONS

- **Book E – Lesson 15**

  Understand Volume shows students in further detail why the volume formula works.

- **Book F – Lesson 14**

  Solve Equations Using Inverse Operations show students how to use inverse operations to solve one-step equations.

- **Book F – Lesson 15**

  Use Formulas has students practice using various types of formulas.

VOCABULARY

PAGE 154

- **volume:** the amount of space that fills a solid figure
- **cubic unit:** a unit of measure that is a 1-by-1-by-1 cube—for example, a cube with each side 1 cm is 1 cm³
- **rectangular prism:** a solid figure with six rectangular faces
- **dimensions:** the length, width, and height of such solid figures as rectangular prisms (also the length and width of such plane figures as rectangles)
- **formula:** an equation that shows the relationship between two or more quantities

MATH BACKGROUND

Volume is the amount of space inside a three-dimensional figure. It is measured in cubic units. For example, a cubic centimeter (cm³) is a cube that is 1 cm wide, 1 cm long, and 1 cm high. The volume V of a rectangular prism is given by the formula $V = Bh = (l \times w) \times h$, where B is the area of the rectangular base, h is the height of the prism, l is the length of the prism, and w is the width of the prism. If you had a prism with a length of 3 centimeters, a width of 2 centimeters, and a height of 4 centimeters, you could fit 24 cubic centimeters in the prism, meaning 4 layers with 6 cubes in each layer.

Interactive Whiteboard

Visualize Volume of Rectangular Prisms

Go to the *Interactive Whiteboard Lessons* to bring Parts One and Two to life. Use features such as sliding screens with problem answers to facilitate students' understanding of finding the volume of rectangular prisms, and missing dimensions.

Modeled Instruction

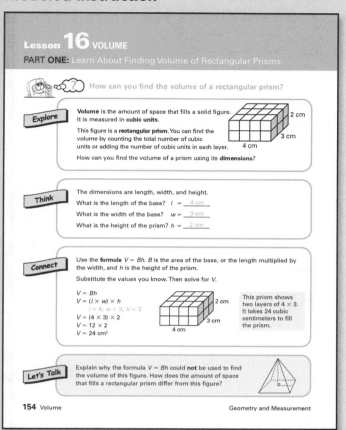

Guided Instruction

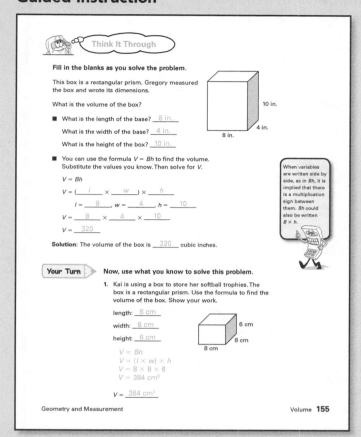

AT A GLANCE

Students activate their background knowledge about rectangular prisms and volume and then learn that the formula $V = Bh$ (or $V = (l \times w) \times h$) can be used to find the volume of a rectangular prism.

STEP BY STEP

PAGE 154

- Introduce the **Question** at the top of the page.
- Have students read about volume and study the rectangular prism in **Explore**.
- Read **Think** with students. Emphasize that the rectangular prism has three dimensions: length, width, and height.
- Discuss **Connect** with students. Help students see the connection between the dimensions of the rectangular prism and the formula for volume.

ELL Support: The variables are based on the English words *volume*, *base*, *length*, *width*, and *height*. Adjust the variables to correspond to students' native languages.

- Organize students in pairs or groups for **Let's Talk** and monitor their discussions.
- Be sure students understand that a pyramid is different from a prism because it is narrower at the top than at the bottom. Pyramids are not made up of equally-sized layers.

PAGE 155

- Read the **Think It Through** problem with students.
- Guide students to see that the volume can be found by multiplying length by width by height.

Tip: Draw other rectangular prisms on the board with the length, width, and height labeled. Have students find the volume of each using the formula.

- Monitor students as they complete **Your Turn**. Then discuss the correct answer.

Error Alert: Students may find only 8×6 because the length and the width have the same measure.

 ### ADDITIONAL ACTIVITY

See **Hands-on Activity** (page 161).

Modeled Instruction

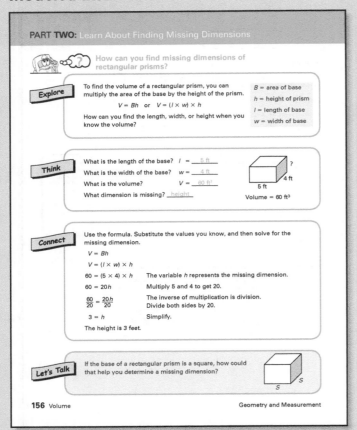

Guided Instruction

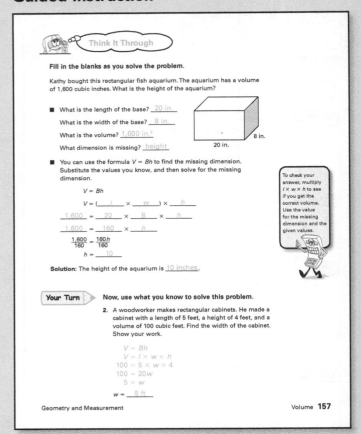

AT A GLANCE

Students learn that the volume formula can be used to find an unknown dimension of a rectangular prism.

STEP BY STEP

Page 156

- Introduce the **Question** at the top of the page.
- Read **Explore** with students. Reinforce that the formula for the volume of a rectangular prism is Volume $= Bh = (l \times w) \times h$.
- Read **Think** with students. Pause so students can read aloud the given measurements and the unknown dimension in orange.
- Tell students to study the formula and solution in **Connect**. Test their understanding by asking how they know which variable to solve for. Have students explain the steps to solve for the variable.
- Be sure students understand how to substitute the given information into the volume formula and then solve the one-variable equation using multiplication and division.

Tip: Have students substitute all the dimensions into the formula for volume and simplify to confirm that a height of 3 feet produces a volume of 60 cubic feet.

- Organize students in pairs or groups for **Let's Talk** and monitor their discussions.
- Students should understand that the length and width would be the same because the base is a square.

Page 157

- Read the **Think It Through** problem with students.
- Guide students as they solve the problem. Pause for students to fill in missing information. Then discuss each response.
- Monitor students as they complete **Your Turn**. Then discuss the correct answer.

Error Alert: Students who found an incorrect width may have made an error when substituting into the formula or when isolating the variable.

 ADDITIONAL ACTIVITY

See **Reteaching Activity** (page 161).

Modeled Practice

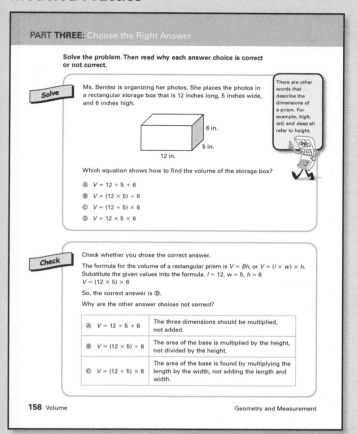

Guided Practice

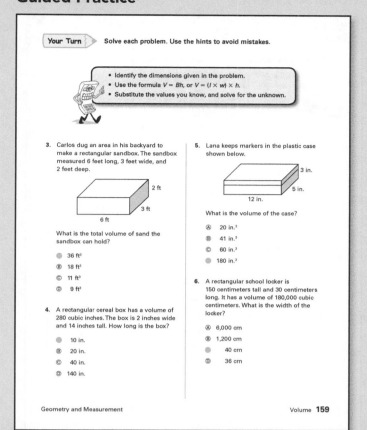

AT A GLANCE
Students reinforce their understanding of volume of rectangular prisms through solving a multiple-choice problem and analyzing correct and incorrect answer choices.

STEP BY STEP

PAGE 158
- Tell students that this page models finding the correct answer to a multiple-choice problem.
- Have students read the problem in **Solve** and choose the best answer. Remind students to check their math.
- Examine **Check** with students. Discuss the correct and incorrect choices.

PAGE 159
- Monitor students as they complete **Your Turn**.
- Organize students in pairs or small groups and have them discuss why each answer choice is correct or not correct and what errors may have been made.
- Review the answers with the class.

 ADDITIONAL ACTIVITY

See **Vocabulary Activity** (page 161).

Answer Analysis
3. ● $V = 6 \times 3 \times 2 = 36$
   Ⓑ Found the area of the base (6×3)
   Ⓒ Added the dimensions instead of multiplying
   Ⓓ Multiplied 6×3, and then divided by 2

4. ● $280 = l \times 2 \times 14; \ l = 280 \div 28; \ l = 10$
   Ⓑ Divided the volume by the height
   Ⓒ Divided the height by the width; then divided the volume by that quotient
   Ⓓ Divided the volume by the width

5. Ⓐ Added the dimensions instead of multiplying
   Ⓑ Multiplied length times height, and then added width ($12 \times 3) + 5$
   Ⓒ Found the area of the base (12×5)
   ● $V = 12 \times 5 \times 3 = 180$

6. Ⓐ Divided the volume only by the length
   Ⓑ Divided the volume only by the height
   ● $180,000 = 30 \times w \times 150;$
      $w = 180,000 \div 4,500 = 40$
   Ⓓ Divided the height by the length; then divided 180 by that quotient

Modeled Practice

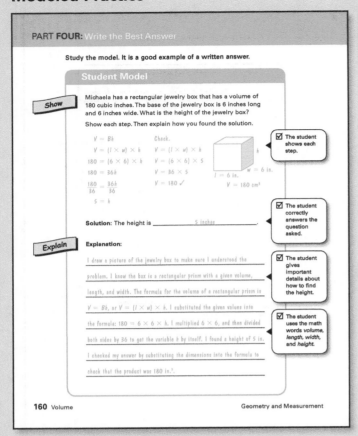

Guided Practice

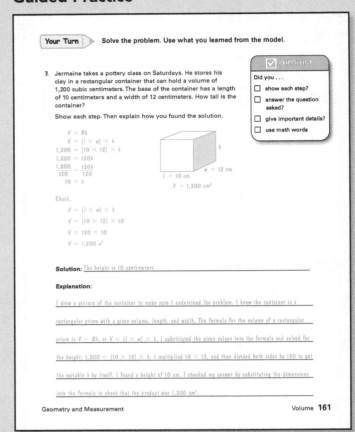

AT A GLANCE

Students study a model answer to an extended-response problem.

STEP BY STEP

Page 160

- Tell students that this page models building the solution to a problem one step at a time and writing to explain the solution.

- Have students read the problem in **Show**. Discuss how the formula and each mathematical step lead to the solution.

  Tip: Discuss the visual of the jewelry box. Suggest that students draw the figure when it is not given and label it to help them visualize the problem.

- Read **Explain** with students. Have students circle the math words in the explanation.

- Direct students' attention to the notes in the right margin. Tell students that this model would receive a high score for the reasons described in these notes.

Page 161

- Monitor students as they complete **Your Turn**.

- Encourage students to follow the **Checklist** to write the best answer.

- Have students discuss their work with a partner. Then discuss the correct answer as a class.

Answer and Explanation

7. See the sample answer. This answer shows all of the steps taken to solve the problem, including drawing a sketch, writing the volume formula and solving the equation for the unknown. The solution answers the question. The explanation provides important details about how the problem was solved and uses the math words *rectangular prism*, *volume*, *length*, *width*, *formula*, and *height*. The solution is recorded with the correct unit label.

 ADDITIONAL ACTIVITY

See **Real-World Connection** (page 161).

 ADDITIONAL ACTIVITY

See **School-Home Connection** (page 161).

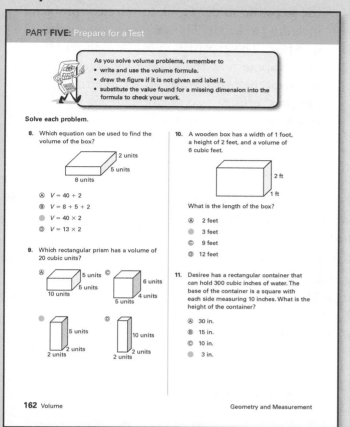

PART FIVE: Prepare for a Test

As you solve volume problems, remember to
• write and use the volume formula.
• draw the figure if it is not given and label it.
• substitute the value found for a missing dimension into the formula to check your work.

Solve each problem.

8. Which equation can be used to find the volume of the box?

2 units
5 units
8 units

Ⓐ $V = 40 + 2$
Ⓑ $V = 8 + 5 + 2$
● $V = 40 \times 2$
Ⓓ $V = 13 \times 2$

9. Which rectangular prism has a volume of 20 cubic units?

Ⓐ 5 units / 5 units / 10 units
Ⓒ 6 units / 4 units / 5 units
● 5 units / 2 units / 2 units
Ⓓ 10 units / 2 units / 2 units

10. A wooden box has a width of 1 foot, a height of 2 feet, and a volume of 6 cubic feet.

2 ft
1 ft

What is the length of the box?

Ⓐ 2 feet
● 3 feet
Ⓒ 9 feet
Ⓓ 12 feet

11. Desiree has a rectangular container that can hold 300 cubic inches of water. The base of the container is a square with each side measuring 10 inches. What is the height of the container?

Ⓐ 30 in.
Ⓑ 15 in.
Ⓒ 10 in.
● 3 in.

---

12. Mandy's grandfather built a rectangular bird feeder. It measures 4 inches long, 3 inches wide, and 6 inches tall. What is the total volume of bird seed the feeder can hold?

Ⓐ 8 in.³
Ⓒ 42 in.³
Ⓑ 13 in.³
● 72 in.³

13. Mrs. Franklin bought a storage box for her patio. The box measures 6 feet long and 3 feet wide and has a volume of 36 cubic feet. What is the height of the storage box?

Ⓐ 18 feet
Ⓒ 4 feet
Ⓑ 6 feet
● 2 feet

14. Kenneth is a carpenter. He enjoys building toy boxes. He made his cousin a toy box that is 24 inches long, 12 inches wide, and 12 inches high.

What is the volume of the toy box?

$V = Bh$
$V = l \times w \times h$
$V = 24 \times 12 \times 12$
$V = 3,456$ in.³

$V = \underline{\ 3,456\ in.^3\ }$

15. Ivan used a volume of 30 cubic centimeters of water to make a rectangular block of ice. The ice block has a length of 5 centimeters and a width of 3 centimeters. What is the height of the ice block?

Show each step. Then explain how you found the solution.

$V = Bh$
$V = (l \times w) \times h$
$30 = (5 \times 3) \times h$
$30 = 15h$
$\dfrac{30}{2} = \dfrac{15h}{15}$
$2 = h$

Check.
$V = (l \times w) \times h$
$V = (5 \times 3) \times 2$
$V = 15 \times 2$
$V = 30 \checkmark$

h
$w = 3\ cm$
$l = 5\ cm$
$V = 30\ cm^3$

Solution: _The height is 2 centimeters._

Explanation:

I drew a picture of the ice block to make sure I understood the problem. To find the height of the ice block, I substituted the given values into the formula for the volume of a rectangular prism.

$V = Bh$, $V = (l \times w) \times h$, to get $30 = (5 \times 3) \times h$. I multiplied 5×3, and then divided both sides by 15 to get the variable h by itself. I found a height of 2 cm. I checked my answer by substituting the dimensions into the formula and checking if the product was 30 cm³.

AT A GLANCE

Students practice using the volume formula for rectangular prisms to solve problems that might appear on a mathematics test.

STEP BY STEP

PAGES 162–163

• Tell students that they will practice solving problems that involve the volume of rectangular prisms.

• Point out the tips at the top of page 162. Explain to students that these tips will help them answer the problems correctly.

• You may wish to have students review the hints for avoiding mistakes on page 159 as well.

• Tell students to complete problems 8–15 on pages 162 and 163. Encourage students to check their answers.

• Discuss the correct responses as a class.

Answers and Explanations

8. Ⓒ The volume formula is $V = Bh$. B is the length multiplied by the width ($8 \times 5 = 40$). So, the volume is 40×2.

9. Ⓑ $20 = Bh = (l \times w) \times h$. So, the rectangular prism with a length of 2 units, a width of 2 units, and a height of 5 units will have a volume of 20 cubic units.

10. Ⓑ Use the volume formula, and solve for l. $6 = Bh = (l \times 1) \times 2$; $6 = 2l$; $l = 3$.

11. Ⓓ The base is a square, so the length and width have the same measure, 10 inches. The area of the base (B) is 10×10, or 100. Use the volume formula, and solve for h. $300 = 100h$; $h = 3$

12. Ⓓ The volume formula is $V = Bh = (l \times w) \times h$. So, the volume is $4 \times 3 \times 6 = 72$.

13. Ⓓ Use the volume formula, and solve for h. $36 = Bh = (6 \times 3) \times h$; $36 = 18h$; $h = 2$.

(continued on page 160)

(continued from page 159)

14. Use the volume formula, $V = Bh = (l \times w) \times h$. Substitute given values and solve for V.
    $V = (24 \times 12) \times 12 = 3{,}456$ cubic inches.

15. See the sample answer. This answer shows all of the steps the student took to solve the problem, including a sketch. The solution answers the question. The explanation provides important details about how the student solved the problem and uses the math words *height*, *substitute*, *formula*, *volume*, and *rectangular prism*. The answer is labeled with the correct units.

ASSESSMENT AND REMEDIATION

- Ask students to find the height of a rectangular prism with a volume of 24 cubic units, a length of 3 units, and a width of 2 units. (*h = 4 units*)
- For students who are still struggling, use the chart below to guide remediation.
- After providing remediation, check students' understanding. Ask students to explain their thinking while finding the height of a rectangular prism with a volume of 36 cubic cm, a length of 4 cm, and a width of 3 cm. (*h = 3 cm*)
- If a student is still having difficulty, use *STAMS Book F*, Lessons 14 and 15, pages 134–153.

If the error is . . .	Students may . . .	To remediate . . .
144 units	have substituted incorrectly into the volume formula, *or*	Encourage students to list the given values along with their corresponding variable. Then, write the volume formula and substitute a value for each variable.
	multiplied the given values, $24 \times 3 \times 2$.	Clarify that 24 cubic units is the volume and that $V = Bh = (l \times w) \times h$. Demonstrate substituting for each variable and solving for h, the height.
8 units	have made a basic math error, *or*	Review multiplication and division basic facts.
	have divided the volume by the length instead of by the product of the length and width.	Show the volume formula. Review with students the concepts on page 156. Have students practice isolating the variable using division.
12 units	have divided the volume by the width instead of by the product of the length and width.	Show the volume formula. Review with students the concepts on page 156. Have students practice isolating the variable using division.

ADDITIONAL ACTIVITY

For students who have mastered the skills in this lesson, see **Challenge Activity** (page 161).

ADDITIONAL ACTIVITIES

Hands-on Activity
Use connecting cubes to model volume.

Materials: 30 connecting cubes per group

Organize students in small groups and distribute connecting cubes. Have students make 6 towers of 5 cubes each. Then, have them place the towers together to make a rectangular prism.

Have students examine their rectangular prism. Ask, "What is the length? What is the width? What is the height? How many cubes did you use to make the rectangular prism?"

Record the dimensions on the board. Write the volume formula $V = Bh = (l \times w) \times h$. Fill in the values for each variable and show that multiplying the dimensions yields the total number of cubes used.

Repeat with other rectangular prism models.

Reteaching Activity
Use a model to find a missing dimension.

Materials: connecting cubes

Distribute connecting cubes to each student. Tell students to use 24 cubes to model a rectangular prism with a length of 4 units and a width of 3 units.

Ask students, "What is the volume of the rectangular prism you modeled?" *(24 cubic units)*

Write the volume formula on the board. Ask, "How can you use the formula to find the height?" *(Fill in the known values and solve for h.)* Demonstrate solving for h.

$$V = Bh$$
$$V = (l \times w) \times h$$
$$24 = (4 \times 3) \times h$$
$$24 = 12h$$
$$2 = h$$

Have students count the cubes to find the height of their model and verify the answer.

Vocabulary Activity
Play "Quiz Show" to reinforce terms.

Materials: index cards, markers

Divide students into two groups and provide each group with index cards and markers. As you read a vocabulary term aloud, the first contestant in each group writes a definition or draws a picture for the term. The two contestants raise their hands as soon as they have a response ready. The one with the first correct response earns a point for her team. Repeat with a new vocabulary term for each pair of contestants.

Real-World Connection
Use the volume formula with real-word rectangular prisms.

Materials: rectangular prisms, rulers

Display everyday examples of rectangular prisms, such as cereal boxes, tissue boxes, juice boxes, and storage containers. Then have students measure the length, width, and height of each and apply the volume formula to find the volume.

School-Home Connection
Inform families about volume of rectangular prisms.

Give each student a copy of the reproducible School-Home Connection for Lesson 16 (page 193) to share with the family. The activity in the letter has the family find volumes of rectangular prisms found in the home.

Challenge Activity
Write volume word problems.

Have students write volume word problems. Remind students that the problem should involve finding the volume or a missing dimension (length, width, or height) given the volume. Students may include a drawing with their problem. After students have written their problem, have them exchange it with a partner to solve.

 Dear Family,

This week your child is studying how to multiply whole numbers by fractions. Remember, multiplication is the same as repeated addition.

$\frac{1}{5} + \frac{1}{5} + \frac{1}{5}$ means 3 groups of $\frac{1}{5}$. This is the same as $3 \times \frac{1}{5}$.

Add: $\frac{1}{5} + \frac{1}{5} + \frac{1}{5} = \frac{3}{5}$ OR   Multiply: $3 \times \frac{1}{5} = \frac{3}{5}$

Any whole number can be written as a fraction. $6 = \frac{6}{1}$

Your child is also learning to multiply whole numbers by fractions with these three steps.

Step 1:	Multiply the numerators (the top numbers in the fractions).	$\frac{6}{1} \times \frac{2}{3} = \underline{\textbf{12}}$
Step 2:	Multiply the denominators (the bottom numbers in the fractions).	$\frac{6}{1} \times \frac{2}{3} = \frac{12}{3}$
Step 3:	If possible, simplify by dividing the numerator and denominator by the greatest common factor.	$\frac{12}{3} = \frac{\cancel{12}^{4}}{\cancel{3}_{1}} = \frac{4}{1} = \textbf{4}$
	The product of $\frac{6}{1} \times \frac{2}{3} = 4$.	

Both are divided by 3.

Invite your child to share what he or she knows about multiplying whole numbers by fractions by doing the following activity together.

Sincerely,

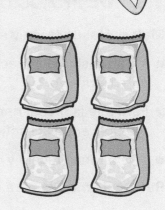

MULTIPLYING FRACTIONS ACTIVITY

Materials: a bowl and the ingredients shown in the recipe

■ Look at the recipe for snack mix below.

■ Rewrite the recipe so that it will make four times as much by multiplying the amount of each ingredient by 4.

■ Make the recipe and enjoy!

Recipe for Snack Mix

$\frac{1}{4}$ cup pretzels $\frac{3}{4}$ cup nuts of your choice

$\frac{1}{2}$ cup raisins $\frac{1}{3}$ cup chocolate chips (optional)

$\frac{2}{3}$ cup dried fruit

STAMS® Series, Book F

Estimada familia:

Esta semana su hijo(a) aprenderá a multiplicar números enteros por fracciones. Recuerden, l multiplicación es lo mismo que la suma repetida.

$\frac{1}{5} + \frac{1}{5} + \frac{1}{5}$ significa 3 grupos de $\frac{1}{5}$. Es lo mismo que $3 \times \frac{1}{5}$.

Suma: $\frac{1}{5} + \frac{1}{5} + \frac{1}{5} = \frac{3}{5}$ O   Multiplica: $3 \times \frac{1}{5} = \frac{3}{5}$

Su hijo(a) también aprenderá a multiplicar números enteros por fracciones con estos tres pasos.

Cualquier número entero se puede escribir como fracción. $6 = \frac{6}{1}$

Paso 1:	Multiplica los numeradores (los números de arriba de las fracciones).	$\frac{6}{1} \times \frac{2}{3} = \frac{\mathbf{12}}{}$
Paso 2:	Multiplica los denominadores (los números de abajo de las fracciones).	$\frac{6}{1} \times \frac{2}{3} = \frac{12}{\mathbf{3}}$
Paso 3:	Si es posible, simplifica dividiendo el numerador y el denominador entre el máximo común divisor.	$\frac{12}{3} = \frac{\overset{4}{\cancel{12}}}{\underset{1}{\cancel{3}}} = \frac{4}{1} = \mathbf{4}$
	El producto de $\frac{6}{1} \times \frac{2}{3} = 4$.	

Los dos se dividen entre 3.

Invite a su hijo(a) a compartir lo que sabe sobre cómo multiplicar números naturales por fracciones cuando completen juntos la siguiente actividad.

Atentamente,

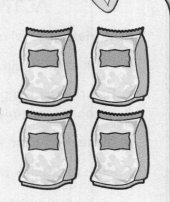

ACTIVIDAD DE MULTIPLICACIÓN DE FRACCIONES

Materiales: un tazón y los ingredientes de la receta

■ Miren la siguiente receta para preparar una mezcla para refrigerio.

■ Para que la receta rinda cuatro veces más, vuelvan a escribirla multiplicando la cantidad de cada ingrediente por 4.

■ ¡Preparen la receta y disfruten!

Receta de mezcla para refrigerio

$\frac{1}{4}$ de taza de pretzels $\frac{3}{4}$ de taza de frutos secos de su elección

$\frac{1}{2}$ taza de pasas $\frac{1}{3}$ de taza de chispas de chocolate (opcional)

$\frac{2}{3}$ de taza de fruta seca

 Dear Family,

This week your child is learning how to multiply fractions and mixed numbers by other fractions. To find the product of two fractions, just multiply the numerators and multiply the denominators.

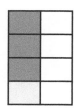 $\frac{1}{2}$ of the total parts are shaded.

$\frac{3}{4}$ of those parts are double-shaded.

So, $\frac{3}{4}$ of $\frac{1}{2}$ is $\frac{3}{8}$ of the whole, and $\frac{3}{4} \times \frac{1}{2} = \frac{3}{8}$.

Two fractions can be multiplied using these steps. For example, find $6\frac{1}{2} \times \frac{2}{3}$.

Step 1:	Cross-simplify if possible. (Divide a numerator and denominator by the same factor.)	$\frac{\overset{13}{\cancel{2}}}{\underset{1}{\cancel{2}}} \times \frac{\overset{1}{\cancel{2}}}{3} =$
Step 2:	Multiply the numerators, the top numbers in the fractions.	$\frac{13}{1} \times \frac{1}{3} = \frac{13}{}$
Step 3:	Multiply the denominators, the bottom numbers in the fractions.	$\frac{13}{1} \times \frac{1}{3} = \frac{13}{3}$
Step 4:	If possible, simplify your answer.	$\frac{13}{3} = 4\frac{1}{3}$

Mixed Number to Improper Fraction:
$6 \times 2 + 1 = 13$
$6\frac{1}{2} = \frac{13}{2}$

So $6\frac{1}{2} \times \frac{2}{3} = 4\frac{1}{3}$.

Invite your child to share what he or she knows about multiplying fractions and mixed numbers by doing the following activity together.

Sincerely,

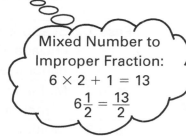

MULTIPLYING FRACTIONS AND MIXED NUMBERS ACTIVITY

Materials: a large pitcher and the ingredients in the recipe

Rewrite the recipe for party punch so that it will be more suitable for your family. Just multiply the amount of each ingredient by $\frac{1}{4}$. Make the recipe and enjoy!

Recipe for Cranberry Cooler Party Punch

12 cups cranberry juice $2\frac{1}{2}$ cups orange juice

$8\frac{1}{2}$ cups grape juice $1\frac{1}{4}$ cups lemon juice

$2\frac{3}{4}$ cups crushed pineapple

STAMS® Series, Book F

 **Estimada familia:**

Esta semana su hijo(a) aprenderá a multiplicar fracciones y números mixtos por otras fracciones. Para hallar el producto de dos fracciones, se multiplican los numeradores y los denominadores.

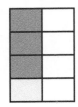

$\frac{1}{2}$ del total de las partes tiene sombreado claro.

$\frac{3}{4}$ de esas partes tienen sombreado oscuro.

Por lo tanto, $\frac{3}{4}$ de $\frac{1}{2}$ es $\frac{3}{8}$ del entero y $\frac{3}{4} \times \frac{1}{2} = \frac{3}{8}$.

Puedes multiplicar dos fracciones siguiendo estos pasos.
Por ejemplo, halla $6\frac{1}{2} \times \frac{2}{3}$.

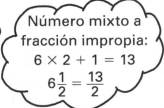

Número mixto a fracción impropia:
$6 \times 2 + 1 = 13$
$6\frac{1}{2} = \frac{13}{2}$

Paso 1:	Si es posible, simplifica de forma cruzada. (Divide un numerador y un denominador entre el mismo factor).	$\frac{\overset{}{\underset{1}{\cancel{13}{2}}}} \times \frac{\cancel{2}}{3} =$
Paso 2:	Multiplica los numeradores, los números de arriba en la fracción.	$\frac{\mathbf{13}}{1} \times \frac{1}{3} = \frac{\mathbf{13}}{}$
Paso 3:	Multiplica los denominadores, los números de abajo en la fracción.	$\frac{13}{\mathbf{1}} \times \frac{1}{3} = \frac{13}{\mathbf{3}}$
Paso 4:	Si es posible, simplifica tu respuesta.	$\frac{13}{3} = 4\frac{1}{3}$

Por lo tanto, $6\frac{1}{2} \times \frac{2}{3} = 4\frac{1}{3}$.

Invite a su hijo(a) a compartir lo que sabe sobre la multiplicación de fracciones y números mixtos cuando completen juntos la siguiente actividad.

Atentamente,

ACTIVIDAD DE MULTIPLICACIÓN DE FRACCIONES Y NÚMEROS MIXTOS

Materiales: una jarra grande y los ingredientes de la receta

Vuelvan a escribir la receta para que el refresco sea suficiente para toda la familia. Multipliquen cada ingrediente por $\frac{1}{4}$. Preparen la receta y, ¡a disfrutar!

Receta para preparar refresco de arándanos

12 tazas de jugo de arándanos $2\frac{1}{2}$ tazas de jugo de naranja

$8\frac{1}{2}$ tazas de jugo de uva $1\frac{1}{4}$ tazas de jugo de limón

$2\frac{3}{4}$ tazas de piña picada

 **Dear Family,**

This week your child is learning how to divide whole numbers by fractions.

The model shows $2 \div \frac{2}{5} = 5$.

Each meter of ribbon is divided into 5 equal parts. There are 5 groups of 2 equal parts in all.

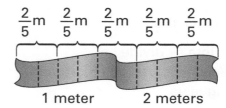

$\frac{2}{5}$m $\frac{2}{5}$m $\frac{2}{5}$m $\frac{2}{5}$m $\frac{2}{5}$m

1 meter   2 meters

The following three steps are used to find how many groups of $\frac{2}{5}$ are in 2.

Step 1:	Rewrite the division problem as a multiplication problem using the reciprocal of the second fraction.	$\frac{2}{1} \div \frac{2}{5} \rightarrow \frac{2}{1} \times \frac{5}{2}$
Step 2:	Multiply the numerators, and then multiply the denominators.	$\frac{2}{1} \times \frac{5}{2} = \frac{10}{2}$
Step 3:	If possible, simplify your answer.	$\frac{10}{2} = 5$

$\frac{5}{2}$ is the reciprocal of $\frac{2}{5}$.

So $2 \div \frac{2}{5} = 5$.

Invite your child to share what he or she knows about dividing whole numbers by fractions by doing the following activity together.

Sincerely,

DIVIDING WHOLE NUMBERS BY FRACTIONS ACTIVITY

Materials: a yard stick, tape measure, or ruler

■ Figure out how many tiles are needed to make a border along a wall.

■ Each tile measures $\frac{1}{3}$ foot, and the wall is 6 feet long. Calculate the answer to this problem: $6 \div \frac{1}{3}$.

■ Suppose you are going to use the tiles to make a border along a wall in your house. First, measure to find the length of the wall in feet. Then, divide that number by $\frac{1}{3}$.

Esta semana su hijo(a) aprenderá a dividir números enteros entre fracciones.

Este modelo muestra $2 \div \frac{2}{5} = 5$.

Canetro de cinta se divide en 5 partes iguales. En total hay 5 grupos de 2 partes iguales.

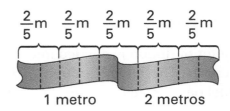

$\frac{2}{5}$m $\quad$ $\frac{2}{5}$m $\quad$ $\frac{2}{5}$m $\quad$ $\frac{2}{5}$m $\quad$ $\frac{2}{5}$m

1 metro $\qquad$ 2 metros

Los tres pasos siguientes se usan para hallar cuántos grupos de $\frac{2}{5}$ hay en 2.

Paso 1: Vuelve a escribir el problema de división como uno de multiplicación usando el recíproco de la segunda fracción.	$\frac{2}{1} \div \frac{2}{5} \rightarrow \frac{2}{1} \times \frac{5}{2}$
Paso 2: Multiplica los numeradores y después los denominadores.	$\frac{2}{1} \times \frac{5}{2} = \frac{10}{2}$
Paso 3: Si es posible, simplifica tu respuesta.	$\frac{10}{2} = 5$

$\frac{5}{2}$ es el recíproco de $\frac{2}{5}$.

Por lo tanto, $2 \div \frac{2}{5} = 5$.

Invite a su hijo(a) a compartir lo que sabe sobre la división de números enteros entre fracciones cuando completen juntos la siguiente actividad.

Atentamente,

ACTIVIDAD DE DIVISIÓN DE NÚMEROS ENTEROS ENTRE FRACCIONES

Materiales: regla de una yarda, cinta para medir o regla de escritorio

■ Calculen cuántos azulejos se necesitan para poner un borde de adorno a lo largo de una pared.

■ Cada azulejo mide $\frac{1}{3}$ de pie, y la pared mide 6 pies de largo. Calculen la respuesta de este problema: $6 \div \frac{1}{3}$.

■ Imaginen que usarán los azulejos para poner un borde de adorno a lo largo de una pared de su casa. Primero, midan la longitud en pies de la pared. Luego, dividan ese número entre $\frac{1}{3}$.

 **Dear Family,**

This week your child is studying how to divide fractions by fractions. Remember, dividing by a number is the same as multiplying by the reciprocal of the number.

Divide: $\frac{7}{8} \div \frac{3}{4}$

1. Rewrite the division problem as a multiplication problem using the reciprocal of $\frac{3}{4}$.	$\frac{7}{8} \div \frac{3}{4} = \frac{7}{8} \times \frac{4}{3}$	$\frac{4}{3}$ is the reciprocal of $\frac{3}{4}$.
2. Cross simplify, if possible. (Divide a numerator-denominator pair by a common factor.)	$\frac{7}{\overset{}{\underset{2}{8}}} \times \frac{\overset{1}{4}}{3}$	8 and 4 are divided by 4.
3. Multiply the numerators and multiply the denominators.	$\frac{7}{2} \times \frac{1}{3} = \frac{7}{6}$	$\frac{7}{6} = \frac{6}{6} + \frac{1}{6} = 1 + \frac{1}{6}$
4. Simplify if possible.	$\frac{7}{6} = 1\frac{1}{6}$	
	So, $\frac{7}{8} \div \frac{3}{4} = 1\frac{1}{6}$.	

Invite your child to share what he or she knows about dividing fractions by fractions by doing the following activity together.

Sincerely,

DIVIDING FRACTIONS BY FRACTIONS ACTIVITY

■ Figure out how many bean seeds can be planted.
  You have $\frac{7}{8}$ gallon of potting soil. You need $\frac{1}{32}$ gallon for each bean seed. How many $\frac{1}{32}$s are in $\frac{7}{8}$?

■ Calculate the answer by solving this problem: $\frac{7}{8} \div \frac{1}{32}$.

■ When you cook, garden, or do crafts, you often have to divide fractions. Take turns making up and solving two problems of your own.

STAMS® Series, Book F

Estimada familia:

Esta semana su hijo(a) aprenderá a dividir fracciones entre fracciones. Recordemos que dividir entre un número es lo mismo que multiplicar por el recíproco del número.

Divide: $\frac{7}{8} \div \frac{3}{4}$

1. Vuelve a escribir el problema de división como uno de multiplicación usando el recíproco de $\frac{3}{4}$.	$\frac{7}{8} \div \frac{3}{4} = \frac{7}{8} \times \frac{4}{3}$
2. Simplifica de forma cruzada si es posible. (Divide un numerador y un denominador entre un factor común).	$\frac{7}{\underset{2}{8}} \times \frac{\overset{1}{4}}{3}$
3. Multiplica los numeradores y multiplica los denominadores.	$\frac{7}{2} \times \frac{1}{3} = \frac{7}{6}$
4. Simplifica si es posible.	$\frac{7}{6} = 1\frac{1}{6}$
	Por lo tanto, $\frac{7}{8} \div \frac{3}{4} = 1\frac{1}{6}$.

$\frac{4}{3}$ es el recíproco de $\frac{3}{4}$.

8 y 4 se dividen entre 4.

$\frac{7}{6} = \frac{6}{6} + \frac{1}{6} = 1 + \frac{1}{6}$

Invite a su hijo(a) a compartir lo que sabe sobre cómo dividir fracciones entre fracciones cuando completen juntos la siguiente actividad.

Atentamente,

ACTIVIDAD DE DIVISIÓN DE FRACCIONES ENTRE FRACCIONES

■ Calculen cuántas semillas de frijol se pueden plantar.
Tienen $\frac{7}{8}$ de galón de abono. Necesitan $\frac{1}{32}$ de galón para cada semilla de frijol. ¿Cuántos $\frac{1}{32}$ hay en $\frac{7}{8}$?

■ Resuelvan este problema para calcular la respuesta: $\frac{7}{8} \div \frac{1}{32}$.

■ Cuando cocinan, trabajan en el jardín o hacen manualidades, a menudo deben dividir fracciones. Túrnense para inventar y resolver dos problemas propios.

 Dear Family,

This week your child is learning how to multiply and divide decimal numbers by powers of 10. Powers of 10 are 10, 100, 1,000, 10,000 and so forth.

This chart shows how to *multiply* 3.29 by 10, 100, and 1,000.

3.29 × 10 = 32.9	Move the decimal point **1** place to the *right*.
3.29 × 100 = 329	Move the decimal point **2** places to the *right*.
3.29 × 1,000 = 3,290	Move the decimal point **3** places to the *right*.

This chart shows how to *divide* 3.29 by 10, 100, and 1,000.

3.29 ÷ 10 = 0.329	Move the decimal point **1** place to the *left*.
3.29 ÷ 100 = 0.0329	Move the decimal point **2** places to the *left*.
3.29 ÷ 1,000 = 0.00329	Move the decimal point **3** places to the *left*.

For both multiplying and dividing, the decimal point moves right or left a number of spaces equal to the number of zeros in the power of 10. Fill in any blank spaces with zeros.

Invite your child to share what he or she knows about multiplying and dividing by 10, 100, and 1,000 by doing the following activity together.

Sincerely,

MULTIPLYING AND DIVIDING DECIMALS ACTIVITY

Materials: six cards, one for each direction: Multiply by 10, Multiply by 100, Multiply by 1,000, Divide by 10, Divide by 100, Divide by 1,000

- Make sure cards are turned facedown. Take turns. The first person takes a card, reads it out loud, and says any decimal number. Example: "Multiply by 100" and "1.39."

- The second person gives the answer (139), and then takes a turn by picking up a card and making up another number. Example: "Divide by 10" and "23.16."

- The first person gives the answer (2.316), and play continues until all six cards have been used.

- At the end of the game, the players with the greatest answer, the least answer, and the answer closest to zero each win one point.

- When in doubt, check with a calculator!

Estimada familia:

Esta semana su hijo(a) aprenderá a multiplicar y dividir números decimales entre potencias de 10. Las potencias de 10 son 10, 100, 1,000, 10,000 y así sucesivamente.

La tabla muestra cómo *multiplicar* 3.29 por 10, 100 y 1,000.

3.29 × 10 = 32.9	Mueve el punto decimal **1** posición a la *derecha*.
3.29 × 100 = 329	Mueve el punto decimal **2** posiciones a la *derecha*.
3.29 × 1,000 = 3,290	Mueve el punto decimal **3** posiciones a la *derecha*.

La tabla muestra cómo *dividir* 3.29 entre 10, 100 y 1,000.

3.29 ÷ 10 = 0.329	Mueve el punto decimal **1** posición a la *izquierda*.
3.29 ÷ 100 = 0.0329	Mueve el punto decimal **2** posiciones a la *izquierda*.
3.29 ÷ 1,000 = 0.00329	Mueve el punto decimal **3** posiciones a la *izquierda*.

Para multiplicar y para dividir, debes mover el punto decimal, a la derecha o a la izquierda, la misma cantidad de espacios que la cantidad de ceros que hay en la potencia de 10. Completa los espacios en blanco con ceros.

Invite a su hijo(a) a compartir lo que sabe sobre la multiplicación y la división entre 10, 100 y 1,000 cuando completen juntos la siguiente actividad.

Atentamente,

ACTIVIDAD DE MULTIPLICACIÓN Y DIVISIÓN DE DECIMALES

Materiales: seis tarjetas, una para cada operación: Multiplicar por 10, Multiplicar por 100, Multiplicar por 1,000, Dividir entre 10, Dividir entre 100, Dividir entre 1,000

■ Coloquen las tarjetas boca abajo. Túrnense. El primer jugador saca una tarjeta, la lee en voz alta y dice un número decimal. Ejemplo: "Multiplicar por 100" y "1.39."

■ El segundo jugador dice la respuesta (139) y luego saca una tarjeta e inventa otro número. Ejemplo: "Dividir entre 10" y "23.16."

■ El primer jugador dice la respuesta (2.316), y el juego continúa hasta que se hayan usado las seis tarjetas.

■ Al final del juego, ganan un punto cada uno los jugadores que tienen la respuesta mayor, la respuesta menor y la respuesta más cercana a cero.

■ Si tienen dudas, ¡comprueben las respuestas con la calculadora!

 Dear Family,

This week your child is learning how to multiply decimals and to use estimation to check that the answer makes sense.

For example, to estimate 18.7 × 51:

Round any decimal numbers to the nearest whole number.	18.7 → 19
Round numbers to the nearest 10 if this will make it easier to multiply.	19 → 20 51 → 50
Multiply the rounded numbers using mental math.	20 × 50 = 1,000

The estimate for the product of 18.7 × 51 is 1,000.

Your child is also learning to find the exact product of two decimal numbers and then use estimation to place the decimal point.

For example, to find 1.7 × 0.84:

Estimate the answer.	1.7 × 0.84 2 × 1 ≈ 2

Multiply as you would with whole numbers:
    Find 4 × 17.
    Write a zero as a placeholder. Find 8 × 17.
    Add the two products.
	1.7
	× 0.84
	——
	68
	+ 136**0**
	——
	1428

Use the estimate to help place the decimal point.	Because 1.7 × 0.84 is about 2, the product is 1.428.

Invite your child to share what he or she knows about multiplying decimals by doing the following activity.

Sincerely,

MULTIPLYING DECIMALS ACTIVITY

Materials: calculator, grocery items

- On a piece of paper, one person writes down two decimal numbers. With a calculator, multiply the two numbers without the decimal points.

- The other person estimates the product of the two numbers written on the piece of paper, and then explains where the decimal point should be placed in the product shown on the calculator.

- Switch places and repeat the exercise.

- Find a package of soup cans, bottles of juice, or other items that come in a package (i.e., more than 1 can). Multiply to find the weight of the package. Remember that estimating first will help you place the decimal point.

STAMS® Series, Book F

 **Estimada familia:**

Esta semana su hijo(a) aprenderá a multiplicar decimales y a estimar para comprobar que la respuesta tiene sentido.

Por ejemplo, para estimar 18.7×51:

Redondea 18.7 al número entero más cercano.	$18.7 \rightarrow 19$
Redondea a la decena más cercana si te es más fácil.	$19 \rightarrow 20 \quad 51 \rightarrow 50$
Multiplica mentalmente los números redondeados.	$20 \times 50 = 1{,}000$

La estimación del producto de 18.7×51 es 1,000.

Su hijo(a) también aprenderá a hallar el producto exacto de dos números decimales y a estimar para saber dónde colocar el punto decimal.

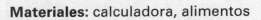 Por ejemplo, para hallar 1.7×0.84:

Estima la respuesta.	$1.7 \times 0.84 \rightarrow 2 \times 1 \approx 2$

Multiplica como si fueran números enteros:
   Halla 4×17.
   Escribe un cero como marcador de posición.
   Halla 8×17. Suma los dos productos.
	$\begin{array}{r} 1.7 \\ \times\, 0.84 \\ \hline 68 \\ +\, 136\mathbf{0} \\ \hline 1428 \end{array}$

Usa la estimación para colocar el punto decimal.	Como 1.7×0.84 es aproximadamente 2, el producto es 1.428.

Invite a su hijo(a) a compartir lo que sabe sobre la multiplicación de decimales cuando completen juntos la siguiente actividad.

Atentamente,

ACTIVIDAD DE MULTIPLICACIÓN DE DECIMALES

Materiales: calculadora, alimentos

- Uno de los participantes escribe dos números decimales en una hoja. Luego multiplica los dos números con la calculadora, sin los puntos decimales.

- El otro participante estima el producto de esos dos números y explica dónde debería colocarse el punto decimal en el producto que dio la calculadora.

- Intercambien los roles y repitan el ejercicio.

- Busquen una caja de latas de sopa o de cualquier otro alimento que venga en paquetes de varios productos. Multipliquen para hallar el peso de la caja. Recuerden que estimar primero los ayudará a saber dónde colocar el punto decimal.

Dear Family,

This week your child is studying how to divide decimals by whole numbers. First, your child will learn how to estimate the answer to a division problem, also known as the quotient.

To divide 87.45 by 11, first think, "87.45 is close to 88." 88 ÷ 11 = 8, so the quotient of 87.45 ÷ 11 is about 8.

Your child will also learn to use long division to find the exact quotient.

```
      7.95
11)87.45      First, ignore the decimal point.
  −77↓        There are 7 elevens in 87. Write 7 in the quotient. Multiply 7 by 11.
   104        Write 77 under 87. Subtract. Bring down the 4 tenths.
   −99↓       There are 9 elevens in 104. Write 9 in the quotient. Multiply 9 by 11.
     55       Write 99 under 104. Subtract. Bring down the 5 hundredths.
    −55       There are 5 elevens in 55. Write 5 in the quotient. Multiply 5 by 11.
      0       Write 55 under 55. Subtract. The difference is 0.
```

Then, put a decimal point in the quotient straight above the decimal point in 87.45. Check: 7.95 is close to the estimate of 8.

Invite your child to share what he or she knows about dividing decimals by whole numbers by doing the following activity together.

Sincerely,

DIVIDING DECIMALS BY WHOLE NUMBERS ACTIVITY

- Think of something you spent money on for the whole family, such as the grocery bill, tickets to the movies, or a board game.

- Divide the cost by the number of people in the family. This will describe the average cost for each family member.

- A book of puzzles cost $11.76.
  There are 4 people in the family.
  So, find the quotient of 11.76 ÷ 4.

- Be sure that the answer makes sense by estimating.
  For example, 29.4 is not a reasonable answer for the example above.

```
    2.94
4)11.76
 −8↓
   37
  −36↓
    16
   −16
     0
```

STAMS® Series, Book F

Estimada familia:

Esta semana su hijo(a) aprenderá a dividir decimales entre números enteros. Primero, aprenderá a estimar la respuesta de un problema de división, también conocida como cociente.

Para dividir 87.45 entre 11, primero piensa, "87.45 es cercano a 88".
88 ÷ 11 = 8; por lo tanto, el cociente de 87.45 ÷ 11 es aproximadamente 8.

Su hijo(a) también aprenderá a usar la división larga para hallar el cociente exacto.

```
      7.95
  11)87.45      Primero, ignora el punto decimal.
    − 77↓       Hay 7 onces en 87. Escribe 7 en el cociente. Multiplica 7 por 11.
      104       Escribe 77 debajo de 87. Resta. Baja los 4 décimos.
    − 99↓       Hay 9 onces en 104. Escribe 9 en el cociente. Multiplica 9 por 11.
       55       Escribe 99 debajo de 104. Resta. Baja los 5 centésimos.
     − 55       Hay 5 onces en 55. Escribe 5 en el cociente. Multiplica 5 por 11.
        0       Escribe 55 debajo de 55. Resta. La diferencia es 0.
```

Luego, coloca un punto decimal en el cociente justo arriba del punto decimal en 87.45. Comprueba: 7.95 es cercano a la estimación de 8.

Invite a su hijo(a) a compartir lo que sabe sobre cómo dividir decimales entre números enteros cuando completen juntos la siguiente actividad.

Atentamente,

ACTIVIDAD DE DIVISIÓN DE DECIMALES ENTRE NÚMEROS ENTEROS

■ Piensen en algo para toda la familia en lo que gastaron dinero, como la cuenta de la tienda de comestibles, los boletos del cine o un juego de mesa.

■ Dividan el costo entre el número de personas de la familia. Esto representará el costo promedio de cada miembro de la familia.

■ Una revista de crucigramas cuesta $11.76.
Hay 4 personas en la familia.
Por lo tanto, hallen el cociente de 11.76 ÷ 4.

■ Estimen para asegurarse de que la respuesta tiene sentido. Por ejemplo, 29.4 no es una respuesta razonable para el ejemplo de arriba.

```
      2.94
   4)11.76
    − 8↓
      37
    − 36↓
       16
     − 16
        0
```

Serie STAMS®, Libro F

 Dear Family,

This week your child is studying how to use estimation and long division to divide decimals by decimals.

For example, find 68.04 ÷ 2.1.
To estimate, round the decimal numbers to nearest whole number and then find compatible numbers.

The quotient will be approximately 35.

$$68.04 \rightarrow 68 \rightarrow 70 \qquad 2.1 \rightarrow 2 \qquad 70 \div 2 = 35$$

To use long division, express the divisor as a whole number. Multiply both the divisor and dividend by a power of 10.

$$2.1 \times 10 = 21 \qquad\qquad 68.04 \times 10 = 680.4$$

```
        32.4
   21)680.4
    − 63
       50
     − 42
        8 4
      − 8 4
          0
```

First, ignore the decimal point.
There are three 21s in 68. 3 × 21 = 63.
Subtract 63 from 68. Bring down the 0.
There are two 21s in 50. 2 × 21 = 42.
Subtract 42 from 50. Bring down the 4.
There are four 21s in 84. 4 × 21 = 84.
Subtract 84 from 84. The difference is 0.

Then, put a decimal point in the quotient straight above the decimal point in 680.4. Check: 32.4 is close to the estimate of 35.

Invite your child to share what he or she knows about dividing by decimals by doing the following activity together.

Sincerely,

DIVIDING BY DECIMALS ACTIVITY

Materials: store fliers and/or newspaper ads

■ Suppose you have saved $47.31 and suppose a package of your favorite snack is on sale for only $2.49 each.

■ Divide 47.31 by 2.49 to figure out how many packages you could buy. (47.31 ÷ 2.49 = 19, or 4731 ÷ 249 = 19)

■ Together look through store fliers or other advertisements to choose an item you would like to buy more than one of. Think about how much money you might have and determine how many items you can buy.

 Estimada familia:

Esta semana su hijo(a) aprenderá a usar la estimación y la división larga para dividir decimales entre decimales.

Por ejemplo, halla 68.04 ÷ 2.1.

Para estimar, redondea los números decimales al número entero más cercano y luego halla los números compatibles.

El cociente será aproximadamente 35.

$$68.04 \rightarrow 68 \rightarrow 70 \qquad 2.1 \rightarrow 2 \qquad 70 \div 2 = 35$$

Para usar la división larga, expresa el divisor como un número entero.
Multiplica el divisor y el dividendo por una potencia de 10.

$$2.1 \times 10 = 21 \qquad\qquad 68.04 \times 10 = 680.4$$

```
        32.4
   21)680.4
     − 63↓
        50 |
      − 42↓
        8 4
      − 8 4
          0
```

Primero, ignora el punto decimal.
Hay tres 21 en 68. 3 × 21 = 63.
Resta 63 de 68. Baja el 0.
Hay dos 21 en 50. 2 × 21 = 42.
Resta 42 de 50. Baja el 4.
Hay cuatro 21 en 84. 4 × 21 = 84.
Resta 84 de 84. La diferencia es 0.

Luego, coloca un punto decimal en el cociente justo encima del punto decimal en 680.4. Comprueba: 32.4 es cercano a la estimación de 35.

Invite a su hijo(a) a compartir lo que sabe sobre cómo dividir entre decimales cuando completen juntos la siguiente actividad.

Atentamente,

ACTIVIDAD DE DIVISIÓN ENTRE DECIMALES

Materiales: folletos de tiendas y/o anuncios de periódicos

■ Imaginen que ahorraron $47.31 y que uno de sus refrigerios favoritos está en oferta a solo $2.49 por paquete.

■ Dividan 47.31 entre 2.49 para calcular cuántos paquetes podrían comprar. (47.31 ÷ 2.49 = 19, ó 4731 ÷ 249 = 19)

■ Busquen folletos de tiendas o anuncios de periódicos para escoger un artículo del que les gustaría comprar más de una unidad. Piensen en cuánto dinero tienen y determinen cuántos artículos pueden comprar.

 Dear Family,

This week your child is studying what ratios are and how to write them. A ratio compares two quantities or numbers. The chart shows ratios for a group of 3 boys and 2 girls expressed three ways for each.

Part to Part	Part to Whole	Whole to Part
Boys to Girls $\frac{3}{2}$ 3 to 2 3:2	Boys to All Children $\frac{3}{5}$ 3 to 5 3:5	All Children to Boys $\frac{5}{3}$ 5 to 3 5:3
Girls to Boys $\frac{2}{3}$ 2 to 3 2:3	Girls to All Children $\frac{2}{5}$ 2 to 5 2:5	All Children to Girls $\frac{5}{2}$ 5 to 2 5:2

Your child is also learning how to find equivalent ratios, or ratios that are equal to each other. To find an equivalent ratio, multiply or divide both parts of the ratio by the same number.

Multiply both quantities by 3. $\frac{8}{10} \times \frac{3}{3} = \frac{24}{30}$

Divide both quantities by 2. $\frac{8}{10} \div \frac{2}{2} = \frac{4}{5}$

So $\frac{8}{10}$, $\frac{24}{30}$, and $\frac{4}{5}$ are all equivalent ratios.

Invite your child to share what he or she knows about ratios by doing the following activity together.

Sincerely,

EQUIVALENT RATIO ACTIVITY

Materials: Brown paper bags cut apart to make a large sheet of paper or other large sheets of paper, markers or crayons

- Make homemade book covers. Together decide on a design to use such as stripes of color or rows of colored shapes such as hearts or stars.

- Choose a ratio for one person to draw with his or her design. For example, a pattern of 3 red stripes and 5 blue stripes would represent a ratio of 3:5.

- The other person will make the same pattern with an equivalent ratio; for example, 9 red stripes and 15 blue stripes.

- Discuss other ratios that represent your pattern. For example, how does 3 to 8 describe the stripes pattern?

Estimada familia:

Esta semana su hijo(a) aprenderá qué son las razones y cómo se escriben. Una razón compara dos cantidades o números. La tabla muestra, expresadas de tres maneras, razones correspondientes a un grupo de 3 varones y 2 niñas en total.

Parte a parte	Parte a entero	Entero a parte
Varones a niñas	Varones al grupo	Grupo a varones
$\frac{3}{2}$ 3 a 2 3:2	$\frac{3}{5}$ 3 a 5 3:5	$\frac{5}{3}$ 5 a 3 5:3
Niñas a varones	Niñas al grupo	Grupo a niñas
$\frac{2}{3}$ 2 a 3 2:3	$\frac{2}{5}$ 2 a 5 2:5	$\frac{5}{2}$ 5 a 2 5:2

Su hijo(a) también aprenderá a hallar razones equivalentes o razones que son iguales entre sí. Para hallar una razón equivalente, multiplica o divide las dos partes de la razón entre el mismo número.

Multiplica las dos cantidades por 3. $\frac{8}{10} \times \frac{3}{3} = \frac{24}{30}$

Divide las dos cantidades entre 2. $\frac{8}{10} \div \frac{2}{2} = \frac{4}{5}$

Por lo tanto, $\frac{8}{10}$, $\frac{24}{30}$ y $\frac{4}{5}$ son todas razones equivalentes.

Invite a su hijo(a) a compartir lo que sabe sobre las razones cuando completen juntos la siguiente actividad.

Atentamente,

ACTIVIDAD DE RAZONES EQUIVALENTES

Materiales: hojas grandes de papel o bolsas de papel cortadas para formar una hoja grande, marcadores y crayones

■ Creen sus propias cubiertas de libros. Decidan juntos el diseño, como franjas de colores o filas de figuras, como corazones o estrellas, de distintos colores.

■ Elijan una razón para que una persona use en su diseño. Por ejemplo, un patrón de 3 franjas rojas y 5 franjas azules representará una razón de 3:5.

■ La otra persona hará el mismo patrón con una razón equivalente; por ejemplo, 9 franjas rojas y 15 franjas azules.

■ Comenten otras razones que representan su patrón. Por ejemplo, ¿cómo describe el patrón de franjas la razón 3 a 8?

 Dear Family,

This week your child is studying percents. A percent is a ratio that compares a number to 100. Remember, a ratio is used to compare any two numbers.

Your child is learning to write a ratio as a percent.

- If the denominator of the ratio is 100, write the numerator and a percent sign.

$$\frac{40}{100} = 40\%$$

- If the denominator of the ratio is *not* 100, first write an equivalent ratio with a denominator of 100.

$$\frac{6}{10} \rightarrow \frac{6 \times 10}{10 \times 10} = \frac{60}{100} = 60\%$$

OR

- First, use division to write the ratio as a decimal. Then, multiply the decimal answer by 100 and write the percent symbol.

$$\begin{array}{r} 0.16 \\ 25\overline{)4.00} \\ -\underline{2\,5}\downarrow \\ 1\,50 \\ -\underline{1\,50} \\ 0 \end{array}$$

$$0.16 \times 100 = 16 \rightarrow 16\%$$

Invite your child to share what he or she knows about percents by doing the following activity together.

Sincerely,

PERCENT ACTIVITY

Materials: catalogs or sale fliers

- You can use percents to compare costs of items on sale.

- **EXAMPLE:** Suppose you see two shirts you like in different catalogs. In the *Buy it Cheap* catalog, the shirt is listed at $20 dollars with $3 off. In the *Good Buys* catalog, the shirt is listed at $22 with $5 off.

- Figure out the percent off for each catalog price. To do that, find the percent for $\frac{3}{20}$ and $\frac{5}{22}$.

- Together look through some catalogs or fliers and choose a couple of items that are on sale. Figure out the percent you would be saving.

STAMS® Series, Book F

 Estimada familia:

Esta semana su hijo(a) estudiará los porcentajes. Un porcentaje es una razón que compara un número con 100. Las razones sirven para comparar dos números cualesquiera.

Su hijo(a) aprenderá a escribir una razón como un porcentaje.

■ Si el denominador de la razón es 100, escribe el numerador y un símbolo de porcentaje.

$$\frac{40}{100} = 40\%$$

■ Si el denominador de la razón *no* es 100, primero escribe una razón equivalente con un denominador de 100.

$$\frac{6}{10} \rightarrow \frac{6 \times 10}{10 \times 10} = \frac{60}{100} = 60\%$$

O

■ Primero, usa la división para escribir la razón como un decimal. Luego, multiplica la respuesta decimal por 100 y escribe el símbolo de porcentaje.

$$\begin{array}{r} 0.16 \\ 25\overline{)4.00} \\ -\,2\,5\downarrow \\ \hline 1\,50 \\ -\,1\,50 \\ \hline \end{array}$$

$$0.16 \times 100 = 16 \rightarrow 16\%$$

Invite a su hijo(a) a compartir lo que sabe sobre los porcentajes cuando completen juntos la siguiente actividad.

Atentamente,

ACTIVIDAD DE PORCENTAJES

Materiales: catálogos o folletos de artículos

■ Pueden usar porcentajes para comparar el costo de artículos en oferta.

■ **EJEMPLO:** Imaginen que ven dos camisetas que les gustan en distintos catálogos.
En el catálogo de *Compre barato*, la camiseta cuesta $20 dólares con un descuento de $3.
En el catálogo de *Buenas ofertas*, la camiseta cuesta $22 con un descuento de $5.

■ Calculen el porcentaje de descuento del precio de cada catálogo.
Para eso, hallen el porcentaje de $\frac{3}{20}$ y $\frac{5}{22}$.

■ Busquen catálogos o folletos y escojan un par de artículos en oferta.
Calculen el porcentaje que ahorrarán.

©Curriculum Associates, LLC   Serie STAMS®, Libro F

 Dear Family,

This week your child is studying unit rates. One way to think about unit rate is *how much for one*.

Name	Meaning	Example
ratio	comparison of two quantities measured in same unit	3:20 – inch to inch
rate	comparison of two quantities measured in different units	150:3 – miles to hours
unit rate	rate with denominator of 1	27:1 – miles to gallons

Your child will use multiplication and division to solve rate problems, including finding a unit rate. For example, you can find the pay rate for 1 hour if you know that the amount paid for 20 hours is 180 dollars.

Write a ratio: $\dfrac{180 \text{ dollars}}{20 \text{ hours}}$.

Write an equivalent ratio: $\dfrac{x \text{ dollars}}{1 \text{ hour}}$.

Set the ratios equal to each other: $\dfrac{180 \text{ dollars}}{20 \text{ hours}} = \dfrac{x \text{ dollars}}{1 \text{ hour}}$.

Solve the proportion the same way you find an equivalent fraction.

$$\div\, 20$$
$$\frac{180}{20} = \frac{9}{1}$$
$$\div\, 20$$

A proportion shows two equal ratios.

The pay rate for 1 hour is \$9.
The unit rate is \$9.

Invite your child to share what he or she knows about unit rates by doing the following activity together.

Sincerely,

UNIT RATES ACTIVITY

Materials: grocery store fliers or a trip to the grocery store

■ One way to understand unit rates is to think about unit prices. The unit price is posted on the shelf under most items at the grocery store.

■ **EXAMPLE:** A 75 ounce bottle of detergent costs \$8.99, so divide 8.99 by 75 to determine the unit price—\$0.1199. Now, figure out the unit price of a 50 ounce bottle of detergent that sells for \$3.50. You will find that this 50 ounce bottle is the better buy.

■ You can compare prices and determine the best buy by looking at grocery store fliers. Together, look at a flier and figure out the unit prices of some items you normally buy. Write down the answers and compare them to what is on the shelves at the grocery store during your next trip there.

Estimada familia:

Esta semana su hijo(a) aprenderá sobre las tasas unitarias. Una manera de pensar en una tasa unitaria es *cuánto vale uno*.

Nombre	Significado	Ejemplo
razón	comparación de dos cantidades medidas en la misma unidad	3:20 – pulgada a pulgada
tasa	comparación de dos cantidades medidas en unidades diferentes	150:3 – millas a horas
tasa unitaria	tasa con denominador 1	27:1 – millas a galones

Su hijo(a) usará la multiplicación y la división para resolver problemas con tasas, como hallar una tasa unitaria. Por ejemplo, se puede hallar la tarifa por 1 hora si se sabe que la cantidad que se paga por 20 horas es 180 dólares.

Escribe una razón: $\dfrac{180 \text{ dólares}}{20 \text{ horas}}$.   Escribe una razón equivalente: $\dfrac{x \text{ dólares}}{1 \text{ hora}}$.

Escribe las razones como una igualdad: $\dfrac{180 \text{ dólares}}{20 \text{ horas}} = \dfrac{x \text{ dólares}}{1 \text{ hora}}$.

> Una proporción muestra dos razones iguales.

Resuelve la proporción de la misma manera en que hallas una fracción equivalente.

$$\overset{\div\ 20}{\underset{\div\ 20}{\dfrac{180}{20} = \dfrac{9}{1}}}$$

La tarifa por 1 hora es $9.
La tasa unitaria es $9.

Invite a su hijo(a) a compartir lo que sabe sobre las tasas unitarias cuando completen juntos la siguiente actividad.

Atentamente,

ACTIVIDAD DE TASAS UNITARIAS

Materiales: folletos del mercado o visita al mercado

■ Una manera de entender las tasas unitarias es pensar en los precios por unidad. El precio por unidad está anotado debajo de la mayoría de los artículos en el mercado.

■ **EJEMPLO:** Una botella de detergente de 75 onzas cuesta $8.99; por lo tanto, dividan 8.99 entre 75 para determinar el precio por unidad: $0.1199. Ahora, calculen el precio por unidad de una botella de detergente de 50 onzas que cuesta $3.50. Verán que esta botella de 50 onzas es más barata.

■ Pueden comparar precios y determinar qué artículo es más barato si miran los folletos del mercado. Juntos, miren un folleto y calculen los precios por unidad de algunos artículos que compran habitualmente. Escriban las respuestas y compárenlas con los precios del mercado en su próxima visita.

 Dear Family,

This week your child is studying ratios in tables of data. Each pair of values in the table can be represented by the same ratio.

Missing values in a table can be found by writing and solving proportions. You can also show how the values in a table are related by writing an equation.

People (p)	Tents (t)
8	2
12	3
20	5
32	?

Find the missing value. Use a proportion:

$$\frac{8}{2} \overset{\times 4}{\underset{\times 4}{=}} \frac{32}{t}$$

So, $t = 8$ tents.

OR Write an equation. Look for a pattern:

$$2 = 8 \div 4$$
$$3 = 12 \div 4$$
$$5 = 20 \div 4$$
$$t = p \div 4$$

Invite your child to share what he or she knows about ratios in tables by doing the following activity together.

Sincerely,

RATIOS IN DATA TABLES ACTIVITY

- Copy the table at the right.

- Together, think of possible descriptions for the data in the table, such as wheels on a tricycle.

- Find the missing value and write an equation for this table. (missing value: 24; equation: $b = 3 \times a$)

a	b
1	3
2	6
5	15
8	

- Now take turns. One person creates a table, and the other makes up a description, finds a missing value, and writes an equation.

STAMS® Series, Book F

 Estimada familia:

Esta semana su hijo(a) estudiará las razones que hay en tablas de datos. Cada par de valores de la tabla puede representarse con la misma razón.

Puedes hallar los valores que faltan en una tabla si escribes y resuelves proporciones. También puedes mostrar cómo se relacionan los valores de la tabla mediante una ecuación.

Personas (p)	Tiendas (t)
8	2
12	3
20	5
32	?

Halla el valor que falta. O Escribe una ecuación.
Usa una proporción: Busca un patrón:

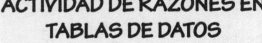

$$\frac{8}{2} \overset{\times 4}{\underset{\times 4}{=}} \frac{32}{t}$$

$2 = 8 \div 4$
$3 = 12 \div 4$
$5 = 20 \div 4$
$t = p \div 4$

Por lo tanto, $t = 8$ tiendas.

Invite a su hijo(a) a compartir lo que sabe sobre las razones en tablas cuando completen juntos la siguiente actividad.

Atentamente,

ACTIVIDAD DE RAZONES EN TABLAS DE DATOS

- Copien la tabla de la derecha.

- Piensen en cosas que pueden describir los datos de la tabla, como las ruedas en un triciclo.

- Hallen el valor que falta y escriban una ecuación para esta tabla. (missing value: 24; equation: $b = 3 \times a$)

- Ahora túrnense. Una persona hace una tabla y la otra inventa una descripción, halla el valor que falta y escribe una ecuación.

a	b
1	3
2	6
5	15
8	

Conexión de la escuela a casa: Lección 12

 Dear Family,

This week your child is learning to use number sense to solve equations. An *equation* is a mathematical statement that shows that two expressions are equal. Any quantity in an expression that is unknown can be represented by a variable, usually a letter like *x*, *y*, or *m*.

> Mrs. Omni paid $20.36 for groceries, leaving $123.85 in her wallet. How much money was in her wallet before she paid for the groceries?

Use the following steps to solve the given problem.

Step 1: Identify the unknown.
Let *m* be the amount of money in her wallet before the purchase.

Step 2: Write a subtraction equation.
money before purchase − cost of groceries = remaining money
$m - 20.36 = 123.85$

Step 3: Solve the equation by working backward.
Add.
So, $m = 144.21$.

$$\begin{array}{r} \overset{1\ 1}{123.85} \\ +\ \ 20.36 \\ \hline 144.21 \end{array}$$

Step 4: Check your answer.
Substitute the value of *m* into the equation to check.
$m - 20.36 = 123.85 \rightarrow 144.21 - 20.36 = 123.85$ ✓

Invite your child to share what he or she knows about using number sense to solve equations by doing the following activity together.

Sincerely,

SOLVING EQUATIONS ACTIVITY

■ Work together to write equations and solve the problems below.
  • Count the money each of you has in your wallet. Figure out how much you will need to get or give away to have exactly $10.00.
  • Measure your heights in inches. How many inches would you have to add or subtract to be the same height?
  • Count the number of eating utensils (forks, spoons, etc) in the house. Figure out how many utensils the family could use each day, if there are 7 days to use the utensils.

■ Make up some other problems about your family. Write equations and use number sense to solve them.

 Estimada familia:

Esta semana su hijo(a) aprenderá a usar el sentido numérico para resolver ecuaciones. Una *ecuación* es un enunciado matemático que muestra que dos expresiones son iguales. Toda cantidad en una expresión que es una incógnita se puede representar con una variable, generalmente una letra como *x*, *y* o *m*.

> La señora Omni pagó $20.36 por unos alimentos y dejó $123.85 en su billetera. ¿Cuánto dinero había en su billetera antes de que pagara los alimentos?

Sigue los siguientes pasos para resolver el problema dado.

Paso 1: Identifica la incógnita.

Sea *d* la cantidad de dinero que había en la billetera antes de la compra.

Paso 2: Escribe una ecuación de resta.

dinero antes de la compra − costo de los alimentos = dinero restante

$d - 20.36 = 123.85$

Paso 3: Resuelve la ecuación trabajando desde el final hasta el principio.
Suma. Por lo tanto, $d = 144.21$.

$$\begin{array}{r} \overset{1\ 1}{123.85} \\ +\ \ 20.36 \\ \hline 144.21 \end{array}$$

Paso 4: Comprueba tu respuesta.

Para comprobar, sustituye el valor de *d* en la ecuación.

$d - 20.36 = 123.85 \rightarrow 144.21 - 20.36 = 123.85$ ✓

Invite a su hijo(a) a compartir lo que sabe sobre cómo usar el sentido numérico para resolver ecuaciones cuando completen juntos la siguiente actividad.

Atentamente,

ACTIVIDAD DE RESOLVER ECUACIONES

■ Trabajen juntos para escribir ecuaciones y resolver estos problemas:

• Cuenten el dinero que tiene cada uno en su cartera. Calculen cuánto necesitarán obtener o regalar para tener exactamente $10.00.

• Midan su altura en pulgadas. ¿Cuántas pulgadas tendrían que sumar o restar para tener la misma altura?

• Cuenten el número de utensilios para comer (tenedores, cucharas, etc.) que hay en la casa. Calculen cuántos utensilios podría usar la familia cada día si hay 7 días para usarlos.

■ Inventen otros problemas sobre su familia. Escriban ecuaciones y usen el sentido numérico para resolverlas.

 Dear Family,

This week your child is learning to solve equations using inverse operations. *Inverse operations* are opposite operations, where one undoes what the other does.

- Addition (+) and subtraction (−) are inverse operations.
- Multiplication (×, ·) and division (÷) are inverse operations.

The table below shows how to use inverse operations to solve equations.

		What number added to 4 equals 20?	The quotient of a number and 12 is 2. Find the number.
1.	Determine what is being done to the variable.	$x + 4 = 20$ 4 is being added to x.	$\frac{n}{12} = 2$ n is being divided by 12.
2.	Perform the inverse operation on both sides of the equation.	$x + 4 - 4 = 20 - 4$ Use − to undo +.	$12 \cdot \frac{n}{12} = 12 \cdot 2$ Use × to undo ÷.
3.	Simplify each side of the equation.	$x = 16$ The solution is 16.	$n = 24$ The solution is 24.

Invite your child to share what he or she knows about using inverse operations to solve equations by doing the following activity together.

Sincerely,

SOLVING EQUATIONS ACTIVITY

- Work together to write equations and solve the problems below.
  - What number added to your age equals your father's age?
  - You should get at least 63 hours of sleep each week. What number multiplied by 7 equals 63? Is that the number of hours you sleep each night?
  - You want to put 5 crackers for each family member on a cheese tray. How many crackers will you need in all?

- Make up some other problems about your family. Write equations and use inverse operations to solve them.

 Estimada familia:

Esta semana su hijo(a) aprenderá a resolver ecuaciones usando operaciones inversas. Las *operaciones inversas* son operaciones opuestas en las que una deshace lo que la otra hace.

■ La suma (+) y la resta (−) son operaciones inversas.
■ La multiplicación (×, ·) y la división (÷) son operaciones inversas.

La siguiente tabla muestra cómo resolver ecuaciones mediante operaciones inversas.

	¿Qué número sumado a 4 es igual a 20?	El cociente de un número y 12 es 2. Halla el número.
1. Determina lo que se está haciendo a la variable.	$x + 4 = 20$ Se suma 4 a x.	$\frac{n}{12} = 2$ n se divide entre 12.
2. Haz la operación inversa en ambos lados de la ecuación.	$x + 4 - \mathbf{4} = 20 - \mathbf{4}$ Usa − para deshacer +.	$\mathbf{12} \cdot \frac{n}{12} = \mathbf{12} \cdot 2$ Usa × para deshacer ÷.
3. Simplifica cada lado de la ecuación.	$x = 16$ La solución es 16.	$n = 24$ La solución es 24.

Invite a su hijo(a) a compartir lo que sabe sobre cómo resolver ecuaciones mediante operaciones inversas cuando completen juntos la siguiente actividad.

Atentamente,

ACTIVIDAD DE RESOLVER ECUACIONES

■ Trabajen juntos para escribir ecuaciones y resolver los siguientes problemas.
  • ¿Qué número sumado a tu edad es igual a la edad de tu padre?
  • Deberías dormir 63 horas por semana como mínimo. ¿Qué número multiplicado por 7 es igual a 63? ¿Es ese el número de horas que duermes cada noche?
  • Quieres poner en una bandeja 5 galletas saladas para cada miembro de la familia. ¿Cuántas galletas saladas necesitarás en total?

■ Inventen otros problemas sobre su familia. Escriban ecuaciones y resuélvanlas mediante operaciones inversas.

 Dear Family,

This week your child is learning to use formulas. Formulas are equations that show relationships between quantities that are always true.

First, your child solved problems involving distance (*d*) using the formula $d = rt$, where *r* is rate and *t* is time. Then, he or she used other formulas to find missing dimensions of figures.

The table below shows how to use formulas to solve problems.

Problem A: What is the rate of the car if it was driven 150 miles in 3 hours?

Problem B: How wide is a rectangular floor with an area of 135 square feet and a length of 15 feet?

	Problem A	Problem B
1. Write the formula. Substitute the values you know.	$d = rt$ $150 = r \cdot 3$	$A = lw$ $135 = 15 \cdot w$
2. Solve for the variable. Perform the inverse operation on both sides of the equation.	$\dfrac{150}{3} = \dfrac{r \cdot 3}{3}$	$\dfrac{135}{15} = \dfrac{15w}{15}$
	\multicolumn{2}{c}{Use ÷ to undo ×.}	
3. Simplify each side of the equation.	$50 = r$ The rate is 50 miles per hour.	$9 = w$ The width is 9 feet.

Invite your child to share what he or she knows about using formulas by doing the following activity together.

Sincerely,

USING FORMULAS ACTIVITY

■ Play *I Can ...*

■ Use the scenarios below or make up your own. Answer the question and then decide if the statement made is realistic.
 • I can run 500 feet in 30 seconds. What is my rate, or speed?
 • I can make a rectangle by folding a sheet of paper in half. It has an area of 46.75 square inches and has a height of 5.5 inches. What is the length of the rectangle?

Estimada familia:

Esta semana su hijo(a) aprenderá a usar fórmulas. Las fórmulas son ecuaciones que muestran relaciones entre cantidades que siempre son verdaderas.

Primero, su hijo(a) resolvió problemas sobre distancias (d) con la fórmula $d = rt$, donde r es la velocidad y t es el tiempo. Luego, él o ella usó otras fórmulas para hallar dimensiones que faltaban en figuras.

La siguiente tabla muestra cómo usar fórmulas para resolver problemas.

Problema A: ¿Cuál es la velocidad del auto si se condujo a 150 millas durante 3 horas?

Problema B: ¿Cuál es el ancho de un piso rectangular con un área de 135 pies cuadrados y una longitud de 15 pies?

	Problema A	Problema B
1. Escribe la fórmula. Sustituye los valores que conoces.	$d = rt$ $150 = r \cdot 3$	$A = lw$ $135 = 15 \cdot w$
2. Resuelve la variable. Haz la operación inversa en ambos lados de la ecuación.	$\dfrac{150}{3} = \dfrac{r \cdot 3}{3}$	$\dfrac{135}{15} = \dfrac{15w}{15}$
	Usa ÷ para deshacer ×.	
3. Simplifica cada lado de la ecuación.	$50 = r$ La velocidad es 50 millas por hora.	$9 = w$ El ancho es 9 pies.

Invite a su hijo(a) a compartir lo que sabe sobre el uso de fórmulas cuando completen juntos la siguiente actividad.

Atentamente,

ACTIVIDAD DE USAR FÓRMULAS

■ Jueguen a *Yo puedo* …

■ Usen las siguientes situaciones o inventen algunas. Respondan la pregunta luego y decidan si la respuesta que formularon es realista.
- Yo puedo correr 500 pies en 30 segundos. ¿Cuál es mi velocidad?
- Yo puedo hacer una rectángulo doblando un trozo de papel a la mitad. Tiene un área de 46.75 pulgadas cuadradas y una altura de 5.5 pulgadas. ¿Cuál es la longitud del rectángulo?

Dear Family,

This week your child is learning about the volume of rectangular prisms. A *rectangular prism* is a solid figure with six rectangular faces. *Volume* is the amount of space that fills a solid figure and is measured in cubic units.

First, your child found the volume of a rectangular prism when the dimensions length, width, and height were given.

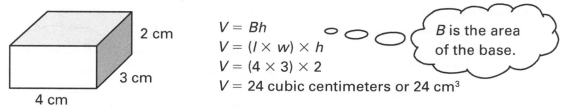

$V = Bh$
$V = (l \times w) \times h$
$V = (4 \times 3) \times 2$
$V = 24$ cubic centimeters or 24 cm³

B is the area of the base.

Then, your child learned how to find a missing dimension when the volume and other two dimensions were given.

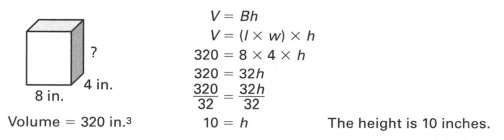

Volume = 320 in.³

$V = Bh$
$V = (l \times w) \times h$
$320 = 8 \times 4 \times h$
$320 = 32h$
$\dfrac{320}{32} = \dfrac{32h}{32}$
$10 = h$ The height is 10 inches.

Invite your child to share what he or she knows about finding the volume of rectangular prisms by completing the following activity together.

Sincerely,

VOLUME OF RECTANGULAR PRISMS ACTIVITY

Materials: ruler or yardstick

Play *Guess My Prism*.

■ Look around the house for something that is a rectangular prism or shaped like one. Don't let the other player know what it is.

■ Measure the prism's dimensions. Round the measurements to the nearest whole inch (or foot), and then use the formula to calculate the volume.

■ Write down the prism's volume and two of its dimensions. Let the other person calculate the missing dimension and then guess the prism.

Esta semana su hijo(a) estudiará el volumen de los prismas rectangulares. Un *prisma rectangular* es una figura sólida con seis caras rectangulares. El *volumen* es la cantidad de espacio que ocupa una figura sólida y se mide en unidades cúbicas.

Primero, su hijo(a) halló el volumen de un prisma rectangular dadas las dimensiones de la longitud, el ancho y la altura.

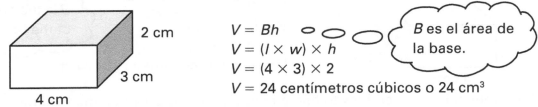

$V = Bh$

$V = (l \times w) \times h$

$V = (4 \times 3) \times 2$

$V = 24$ centímetros cúbicos o 24 cm³

B es el área de la base.

Luego, aprendió a hallar una dimensión que falta dados el volumen y otras dos dimensiones.

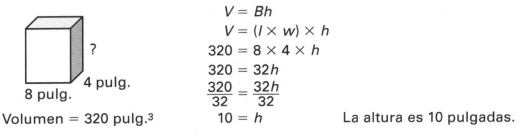

? 4 pulg.

8 pulg.

Volumen = 320 pulg.³

$V = Bh$

$V = (l \times w) \times h$

$320 = 8 \times 4 \times h$

$320 = 32h$

$\dfrac{320}{32} = \dfrac{32h}{32}$

$10 = h$ La altura es 10 pulgadas.

Invite a su hijo(a) a compartir lo que sabe sobre cómo hallar el volumen de un prisma rectangular cuando completen juntos la siguiente actividad.

Atentamente,

ACTIVIDAD DEL VOLUMEN DE PRISMAS RECTANGULARES

Materiales: regla de escritorio o regla de una yarda

Jueguen a *¿Cuál es mi prisma?*

- Busquen una cosa de la casa que sea un prisma rectangular o que tenga esa forma. No permitan que el otro jugador sepa qué es.

- Midan las dimensiones del prisma. Redondeen las medidas a la pulgada entera más cercana (o al pie más cercano) y usen la fórmula para calcular el volumen.

- Anoten el volumen del prisma y dos de sus dimensiones. La otra persona deberá calcular la dimensión que falta y luego adivinar cuál es el prisma.

ADDITIONAL LESSON PLANS

Number and Operations

Integers *(Can be used at any time)*

Data Analysis and Probability

Statistics *(Can be used after Lesson 7)*

ADDITIONAL SCHOOL-HOME CONNECTIONS *(Reproducibles)*

Integers

LESSON OBJECTIVES

Students will:

- Use integers to describe real-life situations.
- Understand and determine absolute value of an integer.
- Compare and order integers with and without a number line.

PREREQUISITES

Students should be able to:

- Compare and order whole numbers.
- Locate whole numbers on a number line.

VOCABULARY

PAGE 166

- **whole numbers:** the set of numbers 0, 1, 2, 3, …
- **integers:** the set of whole numbers and their opposites. …, $^-3$, $^-2$, $^-1$, 0, 1, 2, 3, …
- **opposites:** numbers that are the same distance from 0 on a number line, such as 3 and $^-3$
- **positive integers:** integers to the right of zero on the number line. They are shown using a positive sign (+) or no sign.
- **negative integers:** integers to the left of zero on the number line. They are shown using a negative sign (−).
- **absolute value:** the distance of a number from zero on the number line

PAGE 168

- **compare:** to determine if one number is greater than, less than, or equal to another number
- **order:** to arrange three or more numbers in order from least to greatest or greatest to least

MATH BACKGROUND

In this lesson, students will be introduced to the class of numbers called integers, which includes 0, the counting numbers 1, 2, 3, 4, … and the opposites of the counting numbers, $^-1$, $^-2$, $^-3$, $^-4$, and so on. Ordering negative numbers can be confusing, but students can usually understand that 25 degrees below zero is colder than 2 degrees below zero, so context is key in this lesson. When using signed numbers to represent temperatures or elevations above or below sea level, students may find a vertical number line to be helpful.

The absolute value of a number x, written $|x|$, is the distance the number is from 0 on a number line. Because absolute value is a distance, $|x| \geq 0$; that is, the absolute value of a number is always *nonnegative*.

Interactive Whiteboard
Visualize Integers

Go to the *Interactive Whiteboard Lessons* to bring Parts One and Two to life. Use features such as manipulable number lines to deepen students' understanding of integers.

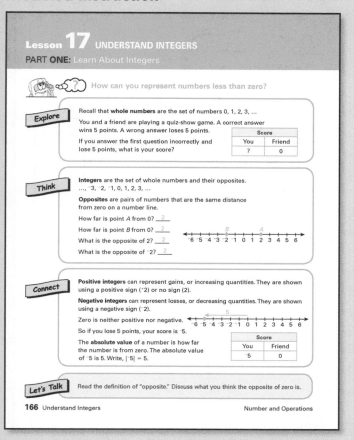

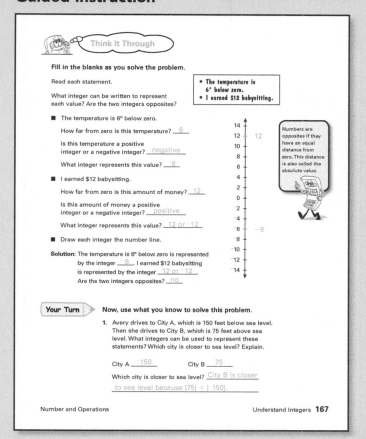

AT A GLANCE

Students activate their background knowledge about whole numbers and then learn that integers consist of whole numbers and their opposites.

STEP BY STEP

PAGE 166

- Introduce the **Question** at the top of the page.

- Have students study the game described in **Explore** and discuss the difference between a gain and a loss.

- Read **Think** with students. Emphasize that opposites describe the location of the number relative to zero.

- Discuss **Connect** with students. Help students see that zero separates the positive and negative numbers on a number line. Positive numbers are to the right, and negative numbers are like a mirror image to the left.

Tip: When writing positive numbers on the board, write them both with and without the positive sign. This helps students connect that numbers written without symbols are positive.

- Organize students in pairs or groups for **Let's Talk** and monitor their discussions.

- Point out that there is only one zero, so the opposite of 0 is 0.

PAGE 167

- Read the **Think It Through** problem with students.

- Guide students as they solve the problem. Help them think about whether each situation describes something below zero or above zero.

- Help students see that the vertical number line relates to both thermometer readings and elevation.

ELL Support: Use hand motions to help students understand that positive numbers are to the right of (or above) zero and negative numbers are to the left of (or below) zero.

- Monitor students as they complete **Your Turn**. Then discuss the correct answer.

Error Alert: Suggest to students that they think of sea level as 0 on the number line.

 ADDITIONAL ACTIVITY

See **Hands-on Activity** (page 203).

Modeled Instruction

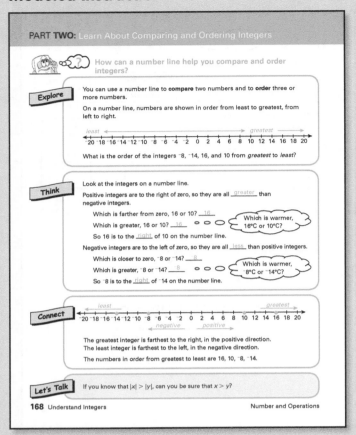

Guided Instruction

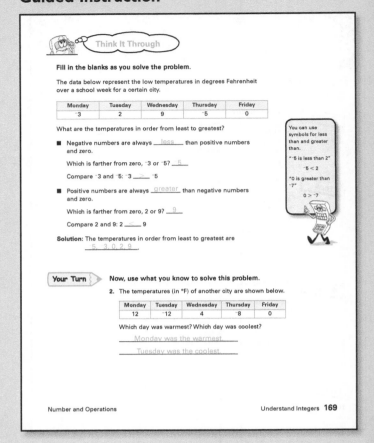

AT A GLANCE
. . . .

Students learn to compare and order integers with and without a number line.

STEP BY STEP
. . . .

Page 168

- Introduce the **Question** at the top of the page.
- Read **Explore** with students. Reinforce that numbers to the left are less than numbers to the right on a number line.

> ELL Support: Write words "greater" and "greatest" on the board along with "less" and "least." Point out that each set has a very similar meaning.

- Read **Think** with students. Pause so students can read aloud the numbers and words in blue.
- Tell students to study the number line in **Connect**. Test their understanding by having them place their finger on different integers as you call them out.

- Organize students in pairs or groups for **Let's Talk** and monitor their discussions.
- Be sure students understand that the greater number is not always farther from zero. For example, 2 is greater than ⁻8 yet ⁻8 is farther from zero.

Page 169

- Read the **Think It Through** problem with students.
- Guide students as they solve the problem. Pause for students to fill in missing information. Then discuss each response.

> Tip: Have students create a number line from ⁻10 to ⁺10 to help them place and order integers.

- Monitor students as they complete **Your Turn**. Then discuss the correct answer.

> Error Alert: Students may think that zero is the least number. Remind them that negative numbers are less than zero.

 ### ADDITIONAL ACTIVITY
. . . .

See **Reteaching Activity** (page 203).

Modeled Practice

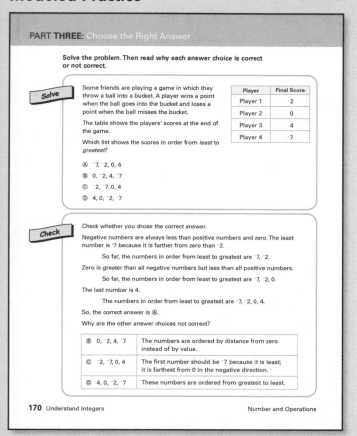

Guided Practice

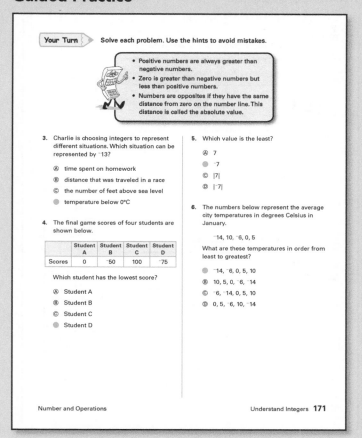

AT A GLANCE

Students reinforce their understanding of integers through solving a multiple-choice problem and analyzing correct and incorrect answer choices.

STEP BY STEP

PAGE 170

- Tell students that this page models finding the correct answer to a multiple-choice problem.
- Have students read the problem in **Solve** and choose the best answer. Remind students to check their math.
- Examine **Check** with students. Discuss the correct and incorrect choices.

PAGE 171

- Monitor students as they complete **Your Turn**.
- Organize students in pairs or small groups and have them discuss why each answer choice is correct or not and what errors may have been made.
- Review the answers with the class.

ADDITIONAL ACTIVITY

See **Vocabulary Activity** (page 203).

Answer Analysis

3. Ⓐ Thought time spent can be less than zero
   Ⓑ Thought distance ran can be less than zero
   Ⓒ Thought above sea level can be less than zero
   ● Temperatures below 0°C are negative.

4. Ⓐ Thought that zero is always the least amount
   Ⓑ Chose a negative number only
   Ⓒ Chose the greatest amount rather than the least
   ● The least amount is the negative number farthest from zero.

5. Ⓐ Chose the greatest value instead of least
   ● This is least because all other values are 7.
   Ⓒ Thought absolute value sign means opposite
   Ⓓ Chose a number containing a negative sign

6. ● The least number is the farthest left.
   Ⓑ Ordered from greatest to least
   Ⓒ Reversed negative numbers
   Ⓓ Thought zero is the least number

Modeled Practice

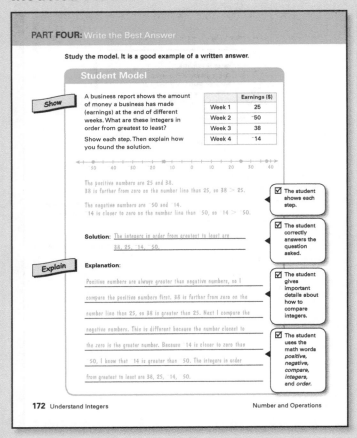

Guided Practice

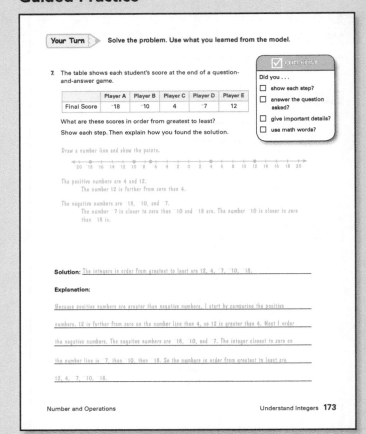

AT A GLANCE
· ·

Students study a model answer to an extended-response problem.

STEP BY STEP
· ·

PAGE 172

- Tell students that this page models building the solution to a problem one step at a time and writing to explain the solution.

- Have students read the problem in **Show**. Discuss how the comparison of positive and negative numbers separately leads to the solution.

> Tip: Explain that a number line is not necessary to order numbers if the distance from zero is considered, but that a number line can be very helpful for checking and explaining your thinking.

- Read **Explain** with students. Have students circle the math words in the explanation.

- Direct students' attention to the notes in the right margin. Tell students that this model would receive a high score for the reasons described in these notes.

PAGE 173

- Monitor students as they complete **Your Turn**.

- Encourage students to follow the **Checklist** to write the best answer.

- Have students discuss their work with a partner. Then discuss the correct answer as a class.

Answer and Explanation

7. See the sample answer. This answer shows all of the steps taken to solve the problem, including a step-by-step comparison. The solution answers the question. The explanation provides important details about how the problem was solved and uses the math words *positive*, *negative*, *compare*, *number line*, *order*, *greatest*, *least*, and *integer*.

 ADDITIONAL ACTIVITY
· ·
See **Real-World Connection** (page 203).

 ADDITIONAL ACTIVITY
· ·
See **School-Home Connection** (page 203).

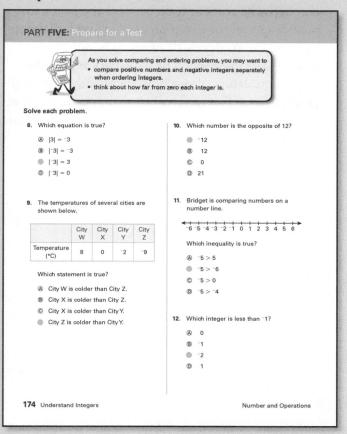

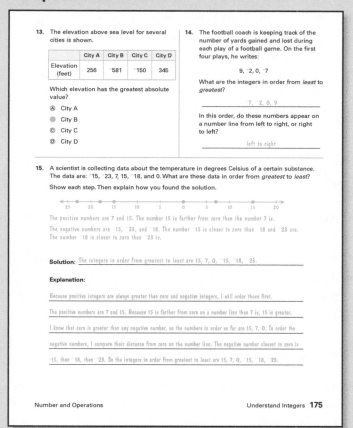

AT A GLANCE

Students practice comparing and ordering integers to solve problems that might appear on a mathematics test.

STEP BY STEP

PAGES 174–175

- Tell students that they will practice writing, ordering, and comparing integers.
- Point out the tips at the top of page 174. Explain to students that these tips will help them answer the problems correctly.
- You may wish to have students review the hints for avoiding mistakes on page 171 as well.
- Tell students to complete problems 8–15 on pages 174 and 175. Encourage students to check their answers.
- Discuss the correct responses as a class.

Answers and Explanations

8. Ⓒ The absolute value is the distance from zero on the number line.

9. Ⓓ When comparing negative temperatures, the coldest temperature is the negative number that is farthest from zero on the number line.

10. Ⓐ A number and its opposite are the same distance from zero on the number line.

11. Ⓑ Because ⁻5 is closer to zero on the number line, it is greater than ⁻6.

12. Ⓒ Because ⁻2 is farther from zero on the number line, it is less than ⁻1.

13. Ⓑ The number with the greatest absolute value is the number farthest from zero in either the positive or negative direction.

(continued on page 202)

(continued from page 201)

14. Because the least numbers are needed first, the first step can involve comparing the negative numbers. The integer ⁻7 is farther from 0 in the negative direction on the number line, so it is less than ⁻2. The number 0 is between the negative and positive numbers.

15. See the sample answer. This answer shows all of the steps the student took to solve the problem, including a step-by-step procedure and a diagram to show the student's thinking. The solution answers the question. The explanation provides important details about how the student solved the problem and uses the math words *positive integers*, *negative integers*, *order*, *number line*, *greatest*, *least*, and *compare*.

 ASSESSMENT AND REMEDIATION

- Ask students to order the numbers ⁻29, ⁻14, 35, ⁻40, and 0 from least to greatest.
  (⁻40, ⁻29, ⁻14, 0, 35)
- For students who are still struggling, use the chart below to guide remediation.
- After providing remediation, check students' understanding. Ask students to explain their thinking for ordering the integers 0, ⁻57, 29, ⁻32, and ⁻2 from least to greatest.
  (⁻57, ⁻32, ⁻2, 0, 29)

If the error is . . .	Students may . . .	To remediate . . .
the negative integers are in reverse order	not be using distance from zero to determine order, *or*	Help students to understand that ⁻40 is less than ⁻29 by having them imagine a giant number line or a staircase going below ground where each step is numbered with negative numbers that tell how far below the zero level it is. Ask "Where would step ⁻250 be?" Encourage them to think of what numbers such as ⁻1,000 or ⁻6,500 might mean.
	be confusing the placement of numbers on a number line.	Have students check each answer by sketching a number line and then placing the numbers correctly.
zero is not ordered correctly	not understand that zero is NOT the least number possible, *or*	Show students a thermometer and have them find 0°. Then ask what happens when the temperature falls below 0°.
	not be familiar with the location of zero on the number line.	Place a number line in the classroom that can be referred to by the student. Call out different integers (including zero) and have the student place their hand on the number at the correct position.
the numbers are in order without regard to sign	not recognize the meaning of the symbol in front of the number.	Encourage students to use a colored pencil or other method to highlight the sign in front of the number. When ordering numbers, have students separate positive numbers from negative numbers before beginning to compare.

 ADDITIONAL ACTIVITY

For students who have mastered the skills in this lesson, see **Challenge Activity** (page 203).

ADDITIONAL ACTIVITIES

 Hands-on Activity
Use individual integers to create number line.

Materials: integers on cards or separate pieces of paper

Have students write the integers ⁻10 through ⁺10 on separate cards or pieces of paper. (There will be 21 cards including zero.) Have each student draw a card randomly and then place it in number-line order on the floor or other flat surface. (Use more or fewer integers as class size dictates.)

Give directions to individual students such as:

- Stand by the opposite of 3.
- Show me an integer whose absolute value is 5. (Point out that 5 and ⁻5 are possible.)
- Choose a number less than ⁻4.
- Show why ⁻4 is less than ⁻2. (Have students walk the distance to show ⁻4 is farther from zero.)

 Reteaching Activity
Use number lines to compare integers.

Materials: blank number lines

Organize students in pairs and provide each pair with a blank number line. Provide pairs with a positive number and a negative number and have them create a number line using those integers and all integers in between. For example, students might create a number line from ⁻20 to 4.

Next, have students practice locating numbers as different integers are called out. Have students work with a partner so that one student will have a finger on ⁻8 and the other student will have a finger on ⁻2. Then ask which integer is greater, which is farther from zero, what are the opposites, and so forth.

 Vocabulary Activity
Play "Quiz Show" to reinforce terms.

Materials: index cards, markers

Divide students into two groups and provide each group with index cards and markers. As you read a vocabulary term aloud, the first contestant in each group writes a definition or draws a picture for the term. The two contestants raise their hands as soon as they have a response ready. The one with the first correct response earns a point for her team. Repeat with a new vocabulary term for each pair of contestants.

 Real-World Connection
Identify everyday examples of integers.

Brainstorm with students or allow them to search the Internet, newspaper, magazines, or other media to find examples of integers in real life. Point out that often a negative number will be described in words rather than using a negative symbol. For example, the business lost $100,000 last quarter. The temperature dropped to 25° below zero.

 School-Home Connection
Inform families about integer concepts.

Give each student a copy of the reproducible School-Home Connection for Lesson 17 (page 213) to share with the family. The activity in the letter has the family represent situations with integers.

 Challenge Activity
Compare and order integers quickly.

Have students create cards with integers from ⁻10 to ⁺10. Have students choose four or five cards and then race to put them in order from least to greatest. Students can race against each other or against the clock. Increase the challenge by having students include positive and negative decimal numbers such as ⁻2.3 and ⁻3.2.

Statistics

LESSON OBJECTIVES

Students will:

• Understand and calculate mean, median, and range.

• Determine and describe how an outlier can affect the mean and median.

PREREQUISITES

Students should be able to:

• Add and subtract whole numbers and decimal numbers.

• Divide whole numbers and decimal numbers by whole numbers.

• Order whole numbers and decimal numbers.

RELATED *STAMS*® LESSON

• Book F – Lesson 7

Divide Decimals by Whole Numbers has students use estimation and place value understanding to divide decimals by whole numbers.

VOCABULARY

PAGE 176

• **data:** factual information, often numbers that describe something

• **measure (of data):** a basis or standard of comparison (Note: Mean and median are often called *measures of central tendency*. Range is a measure of spread.)

• **mean:** the sum of the values divided by the number of values

• **median:** the middle value in an ordered list if the number of values is odd; the mean of the two middle values if the number of values is even

• **range:** the difference between the greatest value and the least value

PAGE 178

• **outlier:** a data value that is much greater or much less than most of the other values in the data set

MATH BACKGROUND

Students can use mean, median, and range to summarize or describe a set of data. Mean and median are measures of center and range is a measure of spread.

Suppose seven students have these quiz scores: 20, 70, 80, 82, 90, 90, 100. The mean (also called *average*) is $\frac{532}{7} = 76$; it is the total shared equally. The median is the middle number when the numbers are in order, 82. The range is $100 - 20 = 80$. A large range indicates a large difference between the highest and lowest scores. Most scores are between 70 and 100. 20 is called an outlier because it is not close to the other scores.

Interactive Whiteboard
Visualize Mean, Median, and Range

Go to the *Interactive Whiteboard Lessons* to bring Parts One and Two to life. Use features such as clonable data and manipulable formulas to deepen students' understanding of mean, median, and range.

Modeled Instruction

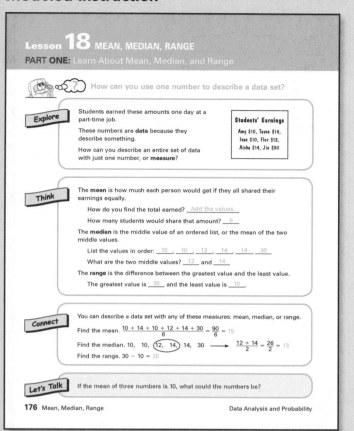

Lesson 18 MEAN, MEDIAN, RANGE

PART ONE: Learn About Mean, Median, and Range

How can you use one number to describe a data set?

Explore

Students earned these amounts one day at a part-time job.

These numbers are **data** because they describe something.

How can you describe an entire set of data with just one number, or **measure**?

Students' Earnings
Amy $10, Tavon $14,
Ivan $10, Flor $12,
Aisha $14, Jin $30

Think

The **mean** is how much each person would get if they all shared their earnings equally.

How do you find the total earned? __Add the values.__

How many students would share that amount? __6__

The **median** is the middle value of an ordered list, or the mean of the two middle values.

List the values in order: __10__, __10__, __12__, __14__, __14__, __30__

What are the two middle values? __12__ and __14__

The **range** is the difference between the greatest value and the least value.

The greatest value is __30__ and the least value is __10__.

Connect

You can describe a data set with any of these measures: mean, median, or range.

Find the mean. $\frac{10 + 14 + 10 + 12 + 14 + 30}{6} = \frac{90}{6} = 15$

Find the median. 10, 10, (12, 14,) 14, 30 → $\frac{12 + 14}{2} = \frac{26}{2} = 13$

Find the range. 30 − 10 = 20

Let's Talk

If the mean of three numbers is 10, what could the numbers be?

176 Mean, Median, Range   Data Analysis and Probability

Guided Instruction

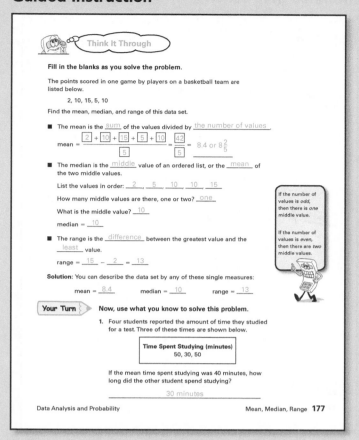

Think It Through

Fill in the blanks as you solve the problem.

The points scored in one game by players on a basketball team are listed below.

2, 10, 15, 5, 10

Find the mean, median, and range of this data set.

■ The mean is the __sum__ of the values divided by __the number of values__.

mean = $\frac{2 + 10 + 15 + 5 + 10}{5} = \frac{42}{5} = 8.4$ or $8\frac{2}{5}$

■ The median is the __middle__ value of an ordered list, or the __mean__ of the two middle values.

List the values in order: __2__, __5__, __10__, __10__, __15__

How many middle values are there, one or two? __one__

What is the middle value? __10__

median = __10__

■ The range is the __difference__ between the greatest value and the __least__ value.

range = __15__ − __2__ = __13__

Solution: You can describe the data set by any of these single measures:

mean = __8.4__   median = __10__   range = __13__

If the number of values is *odd*, then there is *one* middle value.

If the number of values is *even*, then there are *two* middle values.

Your Turn   Now, use what you know to solve this problem.

1. Four students reported the amount of time they studied for a test. Three of these times are shown below.

Time Spent Studying (minutes)
50, 30, 50

If the mean time spent studying was 40 minutes, how long did the other student spend studying?

__30 minutes__

Data Analysis and Probability   Mean, Median, Range 177

AT A GLANCE

Students activate their background knowledge about data and then learn that mean and median can each be used as a single number to describe a data set.

STEP BY STEP

PAGE 176

- Introduce the **Question** at the top of the page.
- Have students read **Explore**.
- Read **Think** with students. By reading the definitions of mean, median, and range, students are preparing to find these values in **Connect**.

ELL Support: Discuss some of the everyday meanings of *mean*, such as "nasty" and "intend." Clarify the definition in math as presented in Think.

- Discuss **Connect** with students. Explain that the mean is the total shared equally, the median is greater than about half the data values and less than about half, and the range describes the spread.

Tip: Draw an arrow to show the median.

10   10   12 ↑ 14   14   30
median = 13

- Organize students in pairs or groups for **Let's Talk** and monitor their discussions.
- Help students see that if three amounts shared equally is 10, then the total amount shared is 30. Any three numbers that add to 30 will have a mean of 10.

PAGE 177

- Read the **Think It Through** problem with students.
- Guide students as they solve the problem. Point out that in this problem the median is the single data value in the middle of the ordered list.
- Monitor students as they complete **Your Turn**. Then discuss the correct answer.

Error Alert: If students need help getting started, have them first find the total study time.

 ADDITIONAL ACTIVITY

See **Hands-on Activity** (page 211).

Modeled Instruction

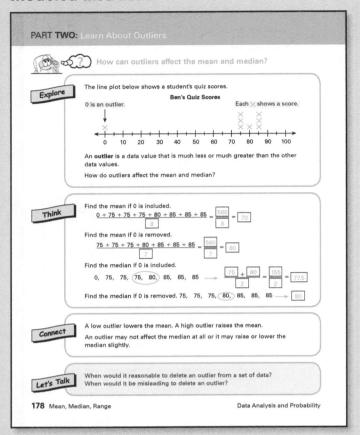

Guided Instruction

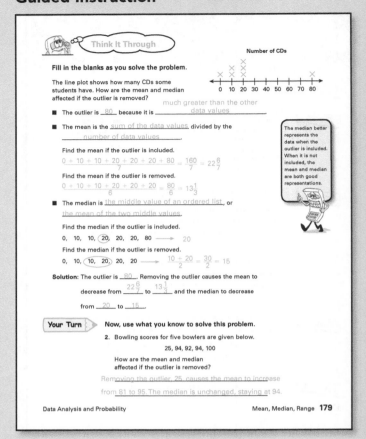

AT A GLANCE

Students learn that when an outlier is removed from a data set, the mean changes and the median sometimes changes.

STEP BY STEP

PAGE 178

- Introduce the **Question** at the top of the page.

ELL Support: Explain that the word *affect* in this lesson means "change." The mean or median are affected if they are changed.

- Read **Explore** with students. Reinforce that 0 is an outlier because it is much less than 75, 80, and 85, which are clustered together.
- Read **Think** with students. Emphasize that when a data point is deleted, the divisor changes.
- In **Connect**, point out that when the outlier was included, the mean was a value outside the cluster of data. Removing the outlier brought the mean into the middle of the cluster. In both cases, the median was within the cluster.

- Organize students in pairs or groups for **Let's Talk** and monitor their discussions.
- Help students realize that it is misleading to omit any point from a data set unless it was an error or if you state that outliers have been removed.

PAGE 179

- Read the **Think It Through** problem with students.
- Guide students as they solve the problem. Pause for students to fill in missing information. Then discuss each response. Emphasize that the median in this problem is affected by removing the outlier.
- Monitor students as they complete **Your Turn**. Then discuss the correct answer.

Error Alert: Students who wrote that the median increases may not have ordered the data first.

 ADDITIONAL ACTIVITY

See **Reteaching Activity** (page 211).

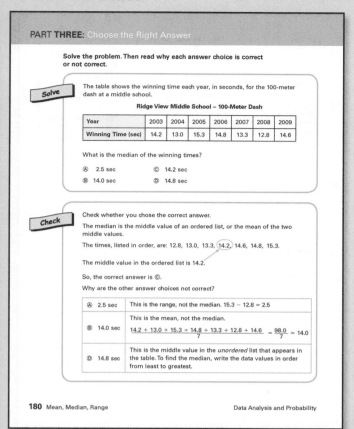

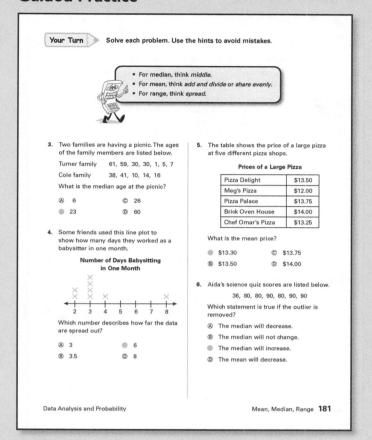

AT A GLANCE

Students reinforce their understanding of measures and outliers through solving multiple-choice problems and analyzing correct and incorrect answer choices.

STEP BY STEP

PAGE 180

- Tell students that this page models finding the correct answer to a multiple-choice problem.

- Have students read the problem in **Solve** and choose the best answer. Remind students to check their math.

- Examine **Check** with students. Discuss the correct and incorrect choices.

PAGE 181

- Monitor students as they complete **Your Turn**.

- Organize students in pairs or small groups and have them discuss why each answer choice is correct or not and what errors may have been made.

- Review the answers with the class.

ADDITIONAL ACTIVITY

See **Vocabulary Activity** (page 211).

Answer Analysis

3. Ⓐ Found mean of middle values in unordered list
   ● This is the mean of the two middle values in the ordered list.
   Ⓒ Found the mean; $\frac{312}{12} = 26$
   Ⓓ Found the range; $61 - 1 = 60$

4. Ⓐ Found the median
   Ⓑ Found the mean; $\frac{28}{8} = 3.5$
   ● This is the difference between the greatest value and the least value; $8 - 2 = 6$.
   Ⓓ Chose the outlier

5. ● This is the sum of the values divided by the number of values; $\frac{\$66.50}{5} = \$13.30$.
   Ⓑ Found the median
   Ⓒ Found the middle value in unordered list
   Ⓓ Chose the greatest value

6. Ⓐ Found the median in the unordered list.
   Ⓑ Thinks third value of 6 values is middle value
   ● The median increases from 80 to 85.
   Ⓓ Forgot to divide by 6, not 7

Modeled Practice

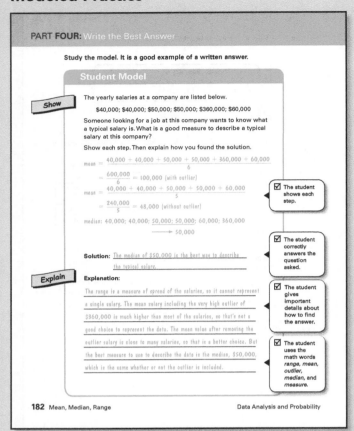

Study the model. It is a good example of a written answer.

Student Model

Show

The yearly salaries at a company are listed below.

$40,000; $40,000; $50,000; $50,000; $360,000; $60,000

Someone looking for a job at this company wants to know what a typical salary is. What is a good measure to describe a typical salary at this company?

Show each step. Then explain how you found the solution.

$$mean = \frac{40,000 + 40,000 + 50,000 + 50,000 + 360,000 + 60,000}{6}$$

$$= \frac{600,000}{6} = 100,000 \text{ (with outlier)}$$

$$mean = \frac{40,000 + 40,000 + 50,000 + 50,000 + 60,000}{5}$$

$$= \frac{240,000}{5} = 48,000 \text{ (without outlier)}$$

median: 40,000; 40,000; 50,000; 50,000; 60,000; 360,000

$\longrightarrow$ 50,000

☑ The student shows each step.

Solution: The median of $50,000 is the best way to describe the typical salary.

☑ The student correctly answers the question asked.

Explain

Explanation:

The range is a measure of spread of the salaries, so it cannot represent a single salary. The mean salary including the very high outlier of $360,000 is much higher than most of the salaries, so that's not a good choice to represent the data. The mean value after removing the outlier salary is close to many salaries, so that is a better choice. But the best measure to use to describe the data is the median, $50,000, which is the same whether or not the outlier is included.

☑ The student gives important details about how to find the answer.

☑ The student uses the math words *range, mean, outlier, median,* and *measure.*

Guided Practice

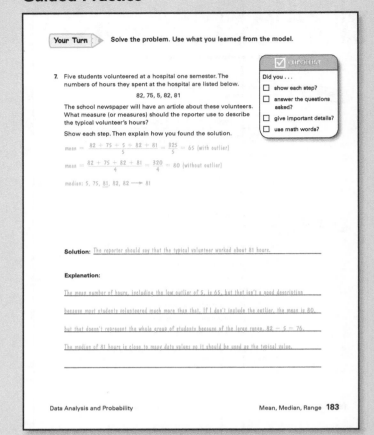

Your Turn Solve the problem. Use what you learned from the model.

7. Five students volunteered at a hospital one semester. The numbers of hours they spent at the hospital are listed below.

82, 75, 5, 82, 81

The school newspaper will have an article about these volunteers. What measure (or measures) should the reporter use to describe the typical volunteer's hours?

Show each step. Then explain how you found the solution.

☑ CHECKLIST

Did you . . .

☐ show each step?

☐ answer the questions asked?

☐ give important details?

☐ use math words?

$$mean = \frac{82 + 75 + 5 + 82 + 81}{5} = \frac{325}{5} = 65 \text{ (with outlier)}$$

$$mean = \frac{82 + 75 + 82 + 81}{4} = \frac{320}{4} = 80 \text{ (without outlier)}$$

median: 5, 75, 81, 82, 82 $\longrightarrow$ 81

Solution: The reporter should say that the typical volunteer worked about 81 hours.

Explanation:

The mean number of hours, including the low outlier of 5, is 65, but that isn't a good description because most students volunteered much more than that. If I don't include the outlier, the mean is 80, but that doesn't represent the whole group of students because of the large range, 82 − 5 = 76. The median of 81 hours is close to many data values so it should be used as the typical value.

AT A GLANCE

Students study a model answer to an extended-response problem.

STEP BY STEP

PAGE 182

- Tell students that this page models building the solution to a problem one step at a time and writing to explain the solution.

- Have students read the problem in **Show**. Have students identify the outlier. ($360,000)

Tip: Explain that a measure is representative of a salary at the company if it is close to the salary of a typical employee at the company.

- Read **Explain** with students. Be sure students understand that range cannot represent a salary because it is the difference between two salaries.

- Direct students' attention to the notes in the right margin. Tell students that this model would receive a high score for the reasons described in these notes.

PAGE 183

- Monitor students as they complete **Your Turn**.
- Encourage students to follow the **Checklist** to write the best answer.
- Have students discuss their work with a partner. Then discuss the correct answer as a class.

Answer and Explanation

7. See the sample answer. (Students may also be able to justify using the mean of 80.) This answer shows all of the steps taken to solve the problem, including finding the mean when the outlier is included and when the outlier is removed. The solution answers the question. The explanation provides important details about choosing the appropriate measure and uses the math words *mean, outlier, range,* and *median.*

 ADDITIONAL ACTIVITY

See **Real-World Connection** (page 211).

 ADDITIONAL ACTIVITY

See **School-Home Connection** (page 211).

Independent Practice

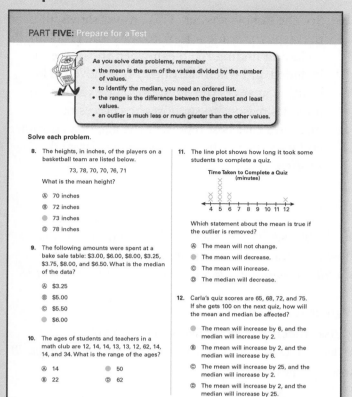

As you solve data problems, remember
- the mean is the sum of the values divided by the number of values.
- to identify the median, you need an ordered list.
- the range is the difference between the greatest and least values.
- an outlier is much less or much greater than the other values.

Solve each problem.

8. The heights, in inches, of the players on a basketball team are listed below.

   73, 78, 70, 70, 76, 71

   What is the mean height?

   Ⓐ 70 inches
   Ⓑ 72 inches
   Ⓒ 73 inches
   Ⓓ 78 inches

9. The following amounts were spent at a bake sale table: $3.00, $6.00, $8.00, $3.25, $3.75, $8.00, and $6.50. What is the median of the data?

   Ⓐ $3.25
   Ⓑ $5.00
   Ⓒ $5.50
   Ⓓ $6.00

10. The ages of students and teachers in a math club are 12, 14, 14, 13, 13, 12, 62, 14, 14, and 34. What is the range of the ages?

    Ⓐ 14   Ⓒ 50
    Ⓑ 22   Ⓓ 62

11. The line plot shows how long it took some students to complete a quiz.

    Time Taken to Complete a Quiz (minutes)

    (line plot marked from 4 to 12)

    Which statement about the mean is true if the outlier is removed?

    Ⓐ The mean will not change.
    Ⓑ The mean will decrease.
    Ⓒ The mean will increase.
    Ⓓ The median will decrease.

12. Carla's quiz scores are 65, 68, 72, and 75. If she gets 100 on the next quiz, how will the mean and median be affected?

    Ⓐ The mean will increase by 6, and the median will increase by 2.
    Ⓑ The mean will increase by 2, and the median will increase by 6.
    Ⓒ The mean will increase by 25, and the median will increase by 2.
    Ⓓ The mean will increase by 2, and the median will increase by 25.

Independent Practice

13. The mean time five students spent on chores in one week is 2.25 hours. The data below shows how much time four of the students spent.

    Time Spent on Chores (hours)
    Terrell 2.75, Fina 1.50, Dan ?, Nate 3.25, Trina 2.50

    How much time did Dan spend on chores?

    Ⓐ 1.25 hours
    Ⓑ 1.50 hours
    Ⓒ 2.25 hours
    Ⓓ 2.50 hours

14. Find the mean and median of the data.

    Numbers of Players on Teams

Softball	18	Basketball	23
Baseball	16	Track	21
Tennis	12	Wrestling	9

    $$mean = \frac{18 + 16 + 12 + 23 + 21 + 9}{6} = \frac{99}{6} = 16.5$$

    mean number on a team: __16.5__

    median: 9, 12, 16, 18, 21, 23 → 17

    median number on a team: __17__

15. The owner of a video game store wants to know the age of a typical customer so he can plan special events. The ages of the 7 customers in the store one morning are listed below.

    14, 12, 12, 14, 62, 14, 12

    What measure (or measures) would you use to describe to the owner the age of a typical customer?

    Show each step. Then explain how you found the solution.

    $$mean = \frac{14 + 12 + 12 + 14 + 62 + 14 + 12}{7} = \frac{140}{7} = 20 \text{ (with outlier)}$$

    $$mean = \frac{14 + 12 + 12 + 14 + 14 + 12}{6} = \frac{78}{6} = 13 \text{ (without outlier)}$$

    median: 12, 12, 12, 14, 14, 14, 62 → 14

    Solution: I would use the median and tell the owner that a typical customer is about 14 years old.

    Explanation:
    The mean age including the outlier age of 62 years old is 20 years old. If I don't include the outlier, the mean is 13, but that doesn't really represent the whole group. The median of 14 years old is close to many data values so it should be used as the typical value.

AT A GLANCE

Students solve problems involving mean, median, range, and outliers that might appear on a mathematics test.

STEP BY STEP

Pages 184–185

- Tell students that they will practice solving problems involving mean, median, range, and outliers.

- Point out the tips at the top of page 184. Explain to students that these tips will help them answer the problems correctly.

- You may wish to have students review the hints for avoiding mistakes on page 181 as well.

- Tell students to complete problems 8–15 on pages 184 and 185. Encourage students to check their answers.

- Discuss the correct responses as a class.

Answers and Explanations

8. Ⓒ The mean is the sum of the data values divided by the number of data values:
   $$\frac{73 + 78 + 70 + 70 + 76 + 71}{6} = \frac{438}{6} = 73.$$

9. Ⓓ The median is the middle value in the ordered list;
   3.00, 3.25, 3.75, 6.00, 6.50, 8.00, 8.00 → 6.00.

10. Ⓒ The range is the difference between the greatest value and the least value: $62 - 12 = 50$.

11. Ⓑ The mean with the outlier included is $\frac{57}{10} = 5.7$. The mean with the outlier 12 removed is $\frac{45}{9} = 5$. So the mean will decrease.

12. Ⓐ The mean will increase by 6, from $\frac{280}{4} = 70$ to $\frac{380}{5} = 76$. The median will increase by 2, from 70 to 72.

13. Ⓐ The mean is $\frac{2.75 + 1.50 + x + 3.25 + 2.50}{5}$ $x = 1.25$. Dan spent 1.25 hours doing chores.

(continued on page 210)

(continued from page 209)

14. The mean is the sum of the data values divided by the number of data values: $\frac{99}{6} = 16.5$. The median is the mean of the two middle values in the ordered list: 9, 12, <u>16, 18</u>, 21, 23 → $\frac{16 + 18}{2} = \frac{34}{2} = 17$.

15. See the sample answer. This answer shows all of the steps the student took to solve the problem, including finding the mean when the outlier is included and when the outlier is removed. The solution answers the question. The explanation provides reasons to support the choices of measures that best represent the age of a customer and uses the math words *mean, outlier,* and *median.*

✔ ASSESSMENT AND REMEDIATION

- Give students these movie ticket prices: $8.50, $7.00, $28.00, $8.00, $8.50. Ask them to find the mean, median, and range, showing their work. Then ask them to describe how the mean and median are affected if the outlier is removed. *(mean: $12.00; median: $8.50; range: $21.00; if the outlier is removed, the mean decreases by $4.00 and the median decreases by $0.25)*

- For students who are still struggling, use the chart below to guide remediation.

- After providing remediation, check students' understanding. Ask students to show their work and explain their thinking while finding the mean, median, and range for the data set 1, 3, 7, 8, 8, 9. *(mean: 6; median: 7.5, range: 8)*

- If a student is still having difficulty, use *STAMS Book F*, Lesson 7, pages 64–73.

If the error is . . .	Students may . . .	To remediate . . .
the mean is $8.50 and the median is $12.00 when the outlier is included	have confused mean and median.	Have the student develop his or her own creative way to remember the difference between the words mean and median by associating the words with something else. For example, remember that the median on the highway is the strip of grass or concrete that runs down the middle, so median is the middle number.
the mean is $6.40 after the outlier is removed; the student divided by 5.	not have recounted the number of values.	Have the student talk through a problem, explaining exactly what and why he or she is doing at each step. See if he or she can correct the oversight.
the median is $28.00 when the outlier is included; not writing the data values in order.	not understand the concept of order or middle.	Provide a concrete example or real-life scenario, such as children lining up by height and naming height of the one in the middle, or children lining up by age and naming the age of the one in the middle.
not knowing how to remove the outlier	not understand what an outlier is.	Provide a real-life scenario, such as trying to measure how heavy an average backpack is. Suppose 20 students have backpacks weighing 11 or 12 pounds and one kid has a 36-pound backpack. Who has got the unusual backpack? Is that real data, or is the student going away for the weekend?

☆ ADDITIONAL ACTIVITY

For students who have mastered the skills in this lesson, see **Challenge Activity** (page 211).

ADDITIONAL ACTIVITIES

 Hands-on Activity
Use counters to model median, range, and mean.

Materials: 30 counters per group

Organize students in small groups and distribute counters. Tell students to make stacks with these numbers of counters: 8, 5, 11, 2, and 4. Have them model the median, range, and mean as follows:

Say, "Arrange the stacks in order of height from least to greatest. The stack in the middle shows the median. What is the median?" (5)

Say, "Compare the shortest and tallest stacks to find the range. How many more counters are in the tallest stack?" (9) "That is the range."

Say, "Rearrange the counters to make all stacks the same height. How many are in each stack?" (6) "That is the mean. The mean is the number in each group when all the groups are equal."

 Reteaching Activity
Cross off numbers to find the median.

Have students write these numbers: 8, 3, 7, 6, 2. Tell them to rewrite the numbers in order from least to greatest, crossing them off the original list one at a time to keep track. Then have them cross off numbers in pairs, working "outside in" until they are left with the middle number, which is the median.

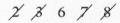

 Vocabulary Activity
Play "What Am I?" to reinforce terms.

Materials: index cards for each pair

Have students write the vocabulary words on index cards, mix up the cards, and place them face down in a stack. The first student picks a card and gives an example of the vocabulary word. For example, if a student picks *median*, she might write 2, 3, 5, 7, 11 and circle the 5. The other player tries to guess the word. Continue until all the cards have been used. Conclude the

activity by having student pairs work together to agree on the best example for each vocabulary word and draw or write that on the back of its card.

 Real-World Connection
Decide when average indicates *mean*.

Elicit real-world phrases that use the word *average*, such as *bowling average*, *average number of points per game*, *test average*, and *the average citizen*. Discuss with students which phrases indicate a mean and which do not, eliciting reasons.

Sample discussion results:

Bowling average: This is a mean; example:
$$\frac{120 + 90 + 105}{3} = \frac{315}{3} = 105.$$
The average citizen: This is not a mean; it refers to a "typical citizen."

 School-Home Connection
Inform families about mean, median, range, and outliers.

Give each student a copy of the reproducible School-Home Connection for Lesson 18 (page 215) to share with the family. The activity in the letter has the family calculate mean, median, and range of the weights of grocery items.

 Challenge Activity
Given median, mean, and range, create a data set.

Have students solve this problem:

Jim recorded the daily low temperature each day for five days. The median was 3°C, the mean was 4°C, and the range was 19°C. What might have been the five temperatures?
(Possible answer: ⁻5°C, 2°C, 3°C, 6°C, 14°C)

 Dear Family,

This week your child is learning about integers. Most of the numbers we use every day (1, 2, 3, 4, ...) are positive integers. The opposites of positive integers are called negative integers.

Positive Integers	Negative Integers
1, 67, 415	⁻1, ⁻67, ⁻415
greater than 0	less than 0
represent gains or increasing quantities, such as earnings or feet above sea level	represent losses or decreasing quantities, such as debts or feet below sea level

Zero is neither positive nor negative.

Your child also learned how to order integers based on a number's position on the number line.

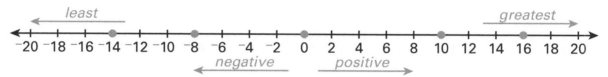

Least to greatest: ⁻14, ⁻8, 0, 10, 16

The absolute value of a number is how far the number is from zero.
Absolute value: $|{-8}| = 8$ $|10| = 10$

Invite your child to share what he or she knows about integers by doing the following activity together.

Sincerely,

INTEGER ACTIVITY

■ Work independently. Take five minutes and make a list of things that can be represented by positive numbers and assign a possible value.
  • Examples: today's temperature, 72°F; a stock market gain, 87 points; an amount put in a piggy bank, $10.

■ Take another five minutes and list things that can be represented by negative numbers and assign a possible value.
  • Examples: temperature on January 1, ⁻5°F; 12-yard loss in football, ⁻12 yards; drop in movie attendance, ⁻108,763 people.

■ Together take a look at your lists. For each value, write a number that is greater or a number that is less, and then describe what that number means.

Estimada familia:

Esta semana su hijo(a) aprenderá sobre los enteros. La mayoría de los números que usamos a diario (1, 2, 3, 4…) son enteros positivos. Los enteros negativos son los opuestos de los enteros positivos.

El cero no es ni positivo ni negativo.

Enteros positivos	Enteros negativos
1, 67, 415	⁻1, ⁻67, ⁻415
mayor que 0	menor que 0
representan una ganancia o una cantidad que aumenta, por ejemplo, un ingreso o un número de pies sobre el nivel del mar	representan una pérdida o una cantidad que disminuye, por ejemplo, una deuda o un número de pies por debajo del nivel del mar

Su hijo(a) también aprenderá a ordenar enteros según la posición que ocupan en la recta numérica.

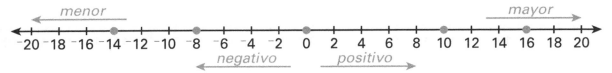

De menor a mayor: ⁻14, ⁻8, 0, 10, 16

El valor absoluto de un número es la distancia entre ese número y el cero.
Valor absoluto: |⁻8| = 8 |10| = 10

Invite a su hijo(a) a compartir lo que sabe sobre los enteros cuando completen juntos la siguiente actividad.

Atentamente,

ACTIVIDAD DE ENTEROS POSITIVOS Y NEGATIVOS

■ Trabajen de forma individual. Tómense cinco minutos para hacer una lista de cosas que pueden representarse con números positivos; piensen en un valor para esas cosas.
  • Ejemplos: la temperatura de hoy: 72°F; una ganancia en el mercado de valores: 87 puntos; dinero que se puso en una alcancía: $10.

■ Tómense otros cinco minutos para hacer una lista de cosas que pueden representarse con números negativos; piensen en un valor para esas cosas.
  • Ejemplos: la temperatura del 1.° de enero: ⁻5°F; un retroceso de 12 yardas en un partido de fútbol americano: ⁻12 yardas.

■ Miren juntos las listas. Escriban un número que sea menor o mayor que cada uno de los valores y luego describan qué significa ese número.

©Curriculum Associates, LLC   Serie STAMS®, Libro F

Dear Family,

This week your child is studying how to describe an entire set of numbers, or data, using the terms *mean*, *median*, *range*, and *outlier*.

- *Mean* is the average, or the sum of the all the values divided by the number of values in the set. The mean is often used as a description of what is typical but it can be misleading if data includes outliers (far-from-average numbers).

- *Median* is the middle value when the numbers are listed in order. The median is less often used but can be a better description of what is typical if the data include one or two outliers.

- *Range* is the difference between the greatest and least values in a set of data.

- *Outliers* are values that are far from all the other data and are clearly not typical.

Invite your child to share what he or she knows about describing data by completing the following activity together.

Sincerely,

MEAN, MEDIAN, AND RANGE ACTIVITY

- Find at least 8 grocery items that are packaged in boxes, such as cereal, rice, oatmeal, and raisins.

- Make a list of the weights of all the items.

- Find the mean, median, and range of the weights.

- Is there an outlier in your data? If so, how would removing it affect the mean, median, and range?

- Ask each other questions about the data. For example, *If we carried 5 average-weight boxes in one sack, how much would that weigh? If we included one outlier, such as a 17-pound bag of dog food, how much would the mean and median change?*

STAMS® Series, Book F

Estimada familia:

Esta semana su hijo(a) aprenderá a describir un conjunto completo de números o datos con los términos *media*, *mediana*, *rango* y *valor atípico*.

- La *media* es el promedio, es decir, la suma de todos los valores dividida entre el número de valores del conjunto. La media generalmente se usa como una descripción de lo que es típico, pero puede ser engañosa si en los datos hay valores atípicos (números alejados del promedio).

- La *mediana* es el valor del medio cuando los números están en orden. La mediana se usa con menos frecuencia, pero puede ser una mejor descripción de lo que es típico si en los datos hay uno o dos valores atípicos.

- El *rango* es la diferencia entre el valor más grande y el más chico de un conjunto de datos.

- Los *valores atípicos* son valores que están alejados de todos los demás datos y, claramente, no son típicos.

Invite a su hijo(a) a compartir lo que sabe sobre cómo describir datos cuando completen juntos la siguiente actividad.

Atentamente,

ACTIVIDAD DE MEDIA, MEDIANA Y RANGO

- Hallen por lo menos 8 alimentos que estén en cajas, como el cereal, el arroz, la avena y las pasas.

- Hagan una lista con el peso de todos los objetos.

- Hallen la media, la mediana y el rango de los pesos.

- ¿Hay algún valor atípico en esos datos? Si es así, ¿cómo cambiarían la media, la mediana y el rango si se sacara ese valor atípico?

- Háganse preguntas mutuas sobre los datos. Por ejemplo: *Si lleváramos 5 cajas de peso promedio dentro de una bolsa, ¿cuánto pesaría la bolsa? Si incluyéramos un valor atípico, como una bolsa de 17 libras de comida para perros, ¿cómo cambiarían la media y la mediana?*